Disciplining Interdisciplinarity

Integration and Implementation Sciences for
Researching Complex Real-World Problems

Disciplining Interdisciplinarity

Integration and Implementation Sciences for
Researching Complex Real-World Problems

Gabriele Bammer

With 24 Commentaries by

Simon Bronitt; L. David Brown; Marcel Bursztyn and Maria Beatriz Maury;
Lawrence Cram; Ian Elsum; Holly J. Falk-Krzesinski; Fasihuddin; Howard Gadlin and
L. Michelle Bennett; Budi Haryanto; Julie Thompson Klein; Ted Lefroy; Catherine Lyall;
M. Duane Nellis; Linda Neuhauser; Deborah O'Connell with Damien Farine,
Michael O'Connor and Michael Dunlop; Michael O'Rourke; Christian Pohl; Merritt Polk;
Alison Ritter; Alice Roughley; Michael Smithson; Daniel Walker; Michael Wesley;
Glenn Withers

Australian
National
University

E PRESS

Published by ANU E Press
The Australian National University
Canberra ACT 0200, Australia
Email: anuepress@anu.edu.au
This title is also available online at http://epress.anu.edu.au

National Library of Australia Cataloguing-in-Publication entry

Author: Bammer, Gabriele

Title: Disciplining interdisciplinarity : integration and
                     implementation sciences for researching
                     complex real-world problems / Gabriele
                     Bammer.

ISBN: 9781922144270 (pbk.) 9781922144287 (ebook)

Notes: Includes bibliographical references.

Subjects: Social sciences—Methodology.
                     Science—Methodology.
                     Applied sociology.
                     Social problems.

Dewey Number: 300.72

Cover design and layout by ANU E Press

Printed by Griffin Press

This edition © 2013 ANU E Press

Contents

Domain 2. Understanding and Managing Diverse Unknowns

**Domain 3. Providing Integrated Research Support for Policy
and Practice Change**

I2S As A Whole

Moving Forward

Commentaries

Guide to Commentaries by Author (alphabetical)

For Warren Bond and Norbert and Maria Bammer

Preface

The seed for this book was planted in the early 1970s, at an undergraduate seminar on new trends in biology, where my class was told that 'multidisciplinarity' was the way of the future. But where, I wondered, did multidisciplinarity have its academic home? My lecturers had already supported me in enrolling in joint science and arts degrees, but it turned out that I was the first at the university to do this and there was no-one else undertaking anything similar. Where could I find other students with the same interests and a faculty dedicated to multidisciplinary research and teaching that I could eventually join? My career is defined by that search. Along the way I tried different kinds of what came to be called 'interdisciplinary' and 'transdisciplinary' research, but none was quite right. I did not know what I was looking for; I just knew I had not found it.

Twenty years after starting my quest, I had the opportunity to try out my evolving ideas as the leader of an investigation into the feasibility of prescribing diamorphine (pharmaceutical heroin) to treat heroin dependence. By the end of what turned into a seven-year project, the methodology was widely praised and I was encouraged to apply it to a new problem. It took a while to figure out what to do next, but I decided that rather than work on another specific issue, I wanted to try to systematise the approach, much of which had been intuitive. That way it could be applied by others and maybe even underpin the intellectual home I had been seeking. I brought in ideas from a range of areas—including systems thinking, the study of unknowns and public policy—of which I was previously ignorant or only dimly aware. Twelve years later this book is the result.[1] It proposes a new research style (integrative applied research), a new discipline (Integration and Implementation Sciences or I2S) and a Big-Science-type project (the I2S Development Drive).

This book aims to enlist you in the further development of these ideas, as a contributor or a critic or both. The structure of the book is unusual as it combines a single-authored proposal (Chapters 1–34) with 24 commentaries (Chapters 35–59). Let me first say something about my proposal. It paints a big picture covering a broad sweep of territory. Reading it requires a large measure of goodwill.[2] My challenge has been to provide enough detail to engage you, without alienating you because of the inevitable imperfections. I do not ask you to set aside criticism and scepticism. The ideas must prove themselves. But in trying to cover so much terrain and in stripping out complexities to make the arguments straightforward, there are inevitably many gaps and errors.

---

1 I have published various versions of the ideas along the way, especially Bammer (2005). Since that paper I have reduced the links with information science and 'repackaged' the other ideas.
2 Checkland (1984, p. 11) introduced me to the notion of reader goodwill.

This preface documents the origins of my ideas and acknowledges the most important contributors. It will also help explain the grounding of my approach and some of the holes.[3]

In writing the proposal, I soon realised that the relevant material and range of experts are vast and that if I tried to be thorough in including them all, I would never finish. Instead I hit on the idea of a range of commentaries, which would start to highlight missing areas, along with points of debate about the proposal.[4] I was not asking the commentators—some I know well, others I have only met briefly—for endorsement, but for critical appraisal, and am delighted with how well their contributions have filled that role. Furthermore, the point of the commentaries was not to provide material for modifying my proposal. Instead, they begin a process of engaging a much larger set of proponents and critics to determine if the way forward presented is desirable and feasible. I hope that you will be inspired to join this endeavour and that you too will see gaps and areas of disagreement as opportunities to participate.

The Book's Origins and Acknowledgments

On this long journey I have benefited from much collegial support, as well as criticism, both of which have motivated improvements and sharpened ideas. In the brief acknowledgments that follow, I include people, funders and organisations pivotal in the formative experiences and provide short accounts of how I connected with each of the commentators.

Beginning

The undergraduate seminar that laid the foundations for my career occurred at the Flinders University of South Australia. I remember with appreciation a vibrant campus and smart, engaged lecturers who were trying new ways of presenting their subjects. In biology, for example, the traditional disciplines like botany and zoology were replaced with a unifying focus on the cell. I particularly valued being pushed to stop parroting and to think critically and creatively by the lecturers, tutors and demonstrators in biology, psychology and geography, as well as in first-year physics, chemistry and mathematics.

I moved to the University of Sydney to undertake my PhD and was given the opportunity to work at the intersection of pharmacology and psychology.

---

3   For example, I acknowledge that the lack of a strong theoretical base is a consistent criticism of my work. I agree that such a grounding is important, but it is not where my expertise lies.
4   All those invited were not able to contribute. A consequence is that some important areas are missing from the commentaries.

Although I eventually decided that that was not the kind of interdisciplinarity I wanted to pursue, I am grateful to Greg Chesher (my supervisor) and David Jackson, who provided guidance during those years.

The Australian National University and the 'Heroin Trial'

Most of my career has been spent at The Australian National University (ANU), where I have been employed in various capacities since 1979. The most important of those jobs was my appointment in 1989 to the National Centre for Epidemiology and Population Health (NCEPH), where I still work and which I currently head. Before describing that period, let me mention two earlier appointments at ANU that were also influential. One was with the (then) Human Sciences Program, where Ian Hughes, Rosemary Brissenden and David Dumaresq were innovative in interdisciplinary teaching. The program also introduced me to others interested in interdisciplinarity, notably Brian Martin who helped me appreciate that knowledge is socially constructed. During that period I made the switch away from research using animal models of human behaviour to studying humans directly.

The second key position was with the Research School of Social Sciences where I was employed in the Director's office to investigate a new disorder (RSI or repetition strain injury, as it was called at that time) resulting from the introduction of computers into offices. That gave me a first taste of examining a problem from various disciplinary perspectives, although this was not team based but largely relied on me finding and employing a range of different methods. Thanks go to Sue Wilson and the committee she chaired, which oversaw the research, as well as to Ilse Blignault who was also investigating the disorder and became a collaborator. It was my first experience of working with stakeholders and I am grateful to many individuals, especially a number of affected ANU employees and people associated with the RSI and Overuse Injury Association of the ACT and other groups, who provided numerous valuable lessons.

Much of my research from 1991 to 1997 involved investigating the feasibility of prescribing diamorphine to dependent heroin users (the 'heroin trial'). I will always be grateful to Bob Douglas, NCEPH's inaugural director, for giving me the opportunity to implement my ideas about interdisciplinary research, providing a lively environment in which to work, and teaching me about taking risks. The project was a collaborative venture with the Australian Institute of Criminology and I also want to acknowledge the Institute's three directors over that period: Duncan Chappell, Grant Wardlaw and Adam Graycar. I ran the project by establishing numerous small teams that worked in parallel and in different ways. For example, some were grouped around a disciplinary expert investigating a discipline-based question, others brought together drug users, police or treatment service providers to think through an aspect of a trial that might affect their lives or work, still others mixed disciplines and stakeholders to examine different angles for a particular issue. I do not have strong views about drug dependence and this allowed me to take a disinterested stance and to work with opponents as well as supporters of diamorphine prescription, as well as to take a comprehensive view of what could potentially go wrong in a trial.

At various key points during the research, I was responsible for drawing together the results from the different teams and I formulated the final recommendations, although Bob Douglas and the relevant Australian Institute of Criminology director provided oversight and support. There were scores of collaborators, some of whom provided insights into their disciplines, others into their lives as drug users, police or treatment providers. The names of those involved are acknowledged in various publications emanating from that time, especially the major reports.[5] I also got to better understand the workings of the media, as they were intensely interested in the feasibility research throughout. And, finally, the process involved long and sometimes very intense periods of interacting with government policy makers.[6]

Collaborations continued with some people on subsequent projects and I particularly acknowledge Phyll Dance, Bev Sibthorpe, David Legge, Robyn Attewell and Sue Wilson, as well as Michael Moore who was the politician who sparked the feasibility research. As the following account will show, David McDonald, with whom I also first worked on the feasibility research, has been a consistent and valued collaborator.

Research and Other Activities after the 'Heroin Trial'

As I started working through ideas that might help me understand the intuitive processes used in the diamorphine trial feasibility investigation, I continued to do more conventional research. Even so, in most of it I was able to further develop aspects of what became integrative applied research and Integration and Implementation Sciences (I2S). Let me briefly acknowledge the key people, projects and funders here, in roughly chronological order.

Margaret Hamilton, who had been on the diamorphine trial feasibility study advisory board, invited me to work with some of her staff at Turning Point in Melbourne investigating other new pharmacotherapies for heroin dependence and then enlisted me to help her design what was to become the Drug Policy Modelling Program.

---

5   These can be found at <http://nceph.anu.edu.au/research/publications> and <http://digitalcollections. anu.edu.au> (both accessed 19 September 2012).

6   In the end, the Government decided not to support our final recommendation, which was to conduct a small pilot study, followed by larger trials if the results warranted such progression.

Alison Ritter (one of the commentators), who heads the Drug Policy Modelling Program funded by the Colonial Foundation Trust, was a supportive and reflective collaborator. I was able to conduct a number of influential projects through the program, especially a symposium on uncertainty, a reading group on the research–policy interface, work for a book on dialogue methods and a project on common metrics, about which there is more below. Later I also describe spin-off projects involving the other Drug Policy Modelling Program chief investigators: Paul Dietze, Pascal Perez and Lorraine Mazerolle.

The work of Michael Smithson (another commentator) on unknowns provided the stimulus and basis for one of the major components of I2S (see Domain 2, Chapters 10–16), and I have valued working with him on these significant ideas. We ran the symposium on uncertainty together and the participants (named in the book *Uncertainty and Risk: Multidisciplinary perspectives*) provided many significant insights.

Lyndall Strazdins, David McDonald, Peter Deane, Helen Berry and Lorrae van Kerkhoff, together with Alison Ritter and myself, formed the reading group on the research–policy interface. That line of work was continued through the Australian Research Alliance on Children and Youth and a partnership with Ann Sanson and Annette Michaux, where we ran a series of workshops and produced an edited book.

David McDonald, assisted by Peter Deane, led the work on the book *Research Integration Using Dialogue Methods* and the common metrics project. The former was co-funded by Land & Water Australia and the finished product was launched by Ted Lefroy (one of the commentators). Lyn Stephens joined us on a follow-up project.

Alice Roughley (a commentator), while at Land & Water Australia, co-organised (with Catherine Mobbs) a symposium on 'integration', at which they asked me to pull together the key findings. That was where I first presented the ideas that would become the core (five-question) framework, which were embellished and endorsed at the meeting. Alice later arranged for me to consult for the Desert Knowledge Cooperative Research Centre on their knowledge synthesis activities and subsequently joined NCEPH to lead a project about organisational and other barriers and facilitators to integrative applied research.

David Moore and Paul Dietze invited me to collaborate on a National Health and Medical Research Council funded project about psychostimulant use, where we brought on board Pascal Perez and Anne Dray to merge epidemiological and ethnographic insights using agent-based modelling.

Lorraine Mazerolle enlisted me to join her as a chief investigator on a successful bid to establish the Australian Research Council Centre of Excellence in Policing and Security and to head up a crosscutting integration and implementation program, which is still under way. Through that centre I got to know Michael Wesley (a commentator), who was one of the other chief investigators. (He also kindly launched the book *Uncertainty and Risk: Multidisciplinary perspectives*.) When Lorraine stepped down as Director, her place was taken by Simon Bronitt (another commentator), with whom I had first worked when he wrote a paper on criminal liability for the diamorphine trial feasibility research. Participation in the Centre of Excellence allowed me to continue various projects on unknowns with Michael Smithson, as well as enabling me to progress work on 'Executive Sessions' (see Chapter 20 for more explanation). David McDonald and I undertook a project with the chief investigators and other senior researchers about their experiences in influencing policy and practice. Jen Badham is currently taking the lead in writing a book about different modelling methods.

Michael Smithson, Alice Roughley, David McDonald, Jen Badham and Lorrae van Kerkhoff at various times contributed to teaching nascent I2S ideas to Australian integrative applied research leaders in short courses.

The Australian Council of Learned Academies hired me as a consultant to undertake a project entitled 'Strengthening Interdisciplinary Research: What it is, what it does, how it does it and how it is supported'. Not only did I benefit from stimulating discussions with the steering committee, but I also had the opportunity to interview some of Australia's leading figures in research policy and interdisciplinary research practice, among them Glenn Withers (a commentator).

Lawrence Cram (another commentator), as the (now former) ANU Deputy Vice-Chancellor (Research), has been a supportive and valued sounding-board for many years and also provided input into the symposium on uncertainty, as well as the Australian Council of Learned Academies project.

Over the years, I have watched the transformation of CSIRO with great interest and had many profitable interactions with the organisation's researchers and leaders, including especially Deborah O'Connell, Daniel Walker and Ian Elsum, who all provided commentaries.

International Influences

There were also many important international collaborations and activities, of which I mention only the most significant here. Participation in the inaugural Fulbright New Century Scholars program in 2001–02 was particularly influential. Valerie Brown, with whom I had had numerous discussions about 'interdisciplinarity' over the years, encouraged me to apply and Ilona Kickbusch, who led the program, was supportive, as were the other fellows. The novel aspect of this program was that the scholars were all working on the same problem (in our case global health) and we met as a group, as well as spending time at our placements.

The Fulbright program made it possible for me to spend six months at Harvard University's Kennedy School of Government, where I have subsequently held a research fellowship. I chose this as my primary affiliation because it was completely outside my comfort zone and I figured it was probably the toughest environment in which I could put myself. The time I spent there was exhilarating and my plan to write a version of this book then came to nothing, while I instead revelled in the intellectual delights the Kennedy School offered. Most importantly I learnt to think big. The courage to propose a new discipline and a Big-Science-type project (the I2S Development Drive) to establish it stem from that experience.

Mark Moore, then head of the Hauser Center for Nonprofit Organizations, made my placement possible. I benefited from numerous insights in our discussions, not only during the time I was located there, but also during subsequent visits. Mark provided valuable feedback on an early draft of this book. In addition, he and Frank Hartmann participated in many hours of interviews about the Executive Sessions they had organised and run (see Chapter 20). Caryn Anderson helped transcribe and analyse these, along with interviews with some participants and others involved in organising these events. Later, I was very pleased to transfer my research fellowship to the Program in Criminal Justice Policy and Management, as well as to participate as an observer in the Executive Session on Policing and Public Safety and to discuss the process with the facilitator, Christine Cole.

David Brown (a commentator) helped make my original stay at the Hauser Center productive through a collaboration on practice–research engagement (which also involved Srilatha Batliwala and Frances Kunreuther) and it remains a topic of ongoing discussion. Through the Hauser Center I met Sanjeev Khagram, who sparked my interest in the World Commission on Dams.

Bill Clark and Nancy Dickson, also at the Kennedy School, were generous in discussing my ideas while I was at Harvard and during later visits and introduced me to Marcel Bursztyn (a commentator) when he was a fellow with them.

From 2000 onwards I also tried to find out about systems thinking, interdisciplinarity, transdisciplinarity and related topics by attending as many conferences as I could, as well as visiting people whose work I had read or heard about. These experiences informed my view that the field was fragmented and marginalised. I also received various invitations for which I have been very grateful. (Again the acknowledgments below are listed in approximate chronological order.)

Allan Best, Scott Leischow and Pam Clark invited me to participate in the US National Cancer Institute funded project 'Initiative on the Study and Implementation of Systems', at which I met Bill Trochim, George Richardson and others. Bill Trochim coined the acronym 'I2S'. Through them I met Bobby Milstein who provided helpful feedback on the book.

Gerald Midgley and Wendy Gregory made me welcome when I visited them at the University of Hull and have continued to help orient me to the systems field. Gerald also provided constructive input on an early draft of the book.

Julie Thompson Klein (a commentator) is a doyen in the field of interdisciplinarity and is encouraging about everyone's contributions. We first met at an Association for Integrative Studies conference.

Gertrude Hirsch Hadorn and Christian Pohl (another commentator) hosted a six-week visiting fellowship at ETH-Zurich (Swiss Federal Institute of Technology, Zurich) funded by the Competence Centre Environment and Sustainability and administered by Nikolaus Gotsch. They facilitated a number of collaborative publications and invited me to present at a td-Net conference, where I met Catherine Lyall and Merritt Polk (both commentators), whom I subsequently visited in Edinburgh and Gothenberg, respectively.

Linda Neuhauser (a commentator) was very hospitable when I first turned up to find out more about her Health Research for Action Center at the University of California, Berkeley, as well as on later visits, and I enjoyed hosting her stay at ANU.

Michael O'Rourke (another commentator) invited me to the Enhancing Communication in Cross-Disciplinary Research conference, at which I met not only him, but also Duane Nellis, Howard Gadlin, Michelle Bennett and Holly Falk-Krzesinski (all commentators). Holly subsequently invited me to the Science of Team Science conference.

The Australian Agency for International Development (AusAID), through its Australian Leadership Awards Fellowships, has funded three programs for research leaders from the Asia-Pacific region on 'Bridging the Research–Policy Divide'. Fasihuddin and Budi Haryanto (both commentators) were two of the participants. Mahomed Patel, David McDonald, Ilse Blignault, Lorrae van Kerkhoff and Caryn Anderson were among those who helped run the programs, which were partly a spin-off from my involvement in the Global Environmental Change and Food Systems (GECAFS) project, where I worked with John Ingram, Polly Ericksen, Ajaya Dixit, Ahsan Uddin Ahmed and many others.

Writing the Book

I was extremely fortunate that between 2000 and 2011, my academic position at NCEPH allowed me to concentrate on producing this book. Since 2008 it has also been my major in-kind contribution to the work of the Australian Research Council Centre of Excellence in Policing and Security.

I am particularly grateful to the commentators for participating in this project and for the value their ideas have added.

Peter Deane has admirably filled the roles of research assistant and webmaster since 2002 and chased references as well as undertaking various other tasks for the book. Peter, Jen Badham, David McDonald, Damon Muller and Lyn Stephens participated in throwing around ideas from which the title and the final name for Domain 2 emerged. Jen assisted in crafting the name 'I2S Development Drive' and had other inputs, especially to the sections on modelling. Warren Bond drew the figures.

As well as being a long-term, valued NCEPH colleague, Dorothy Broom significantly helped clarify my ideas by editing the book, deftly exposing vagueness, crutch words and turgid prose. Of course, responsibility for all remaining woolly thinking, stilted expression and grammatical errors is mine alone.

Although I remain a slow adopter, Caryn Anderson introduced me to information science and has consistently pushed me to embrace the digital age. She and Peter Deane helped think through post-publication strategies for fostering ongoing development of I2S.

Two anonymous reviewers provided useful suggestions for improving the book, along with ideas that strayed into the territory of commentary. I made changes to implement improvements and have noted the commentary-like ideas as footnotes.

These are all-too-brief recognitions of my most salient debts. Naming everyone with whom I have been privileged to discuss the ideas underpinning this book becomes unwieldy, but I am grateful to you all.

You can follow, and contribute to, the further development of I2S at <http://i2s.anu.edu.au>

Setting the Scene

1. The Challenge and a New Approach

The question that motivates this book is: '*How can academic research enhance its contributions to addressing widespread poverty, global climate change, organised crime, escalating healthcare costs or the myriad other major problems facing human societies?*' I analyse the solution that has been most widely advocated—namely bringing together relevant disciplines through interdisciplinary teamwork. Indeed the 2004 US National Academies report *Facilitating Interdisciplinary Research*[1] declared that:

> Interdisciplinary thinking is rapidly becoming an integral feature of research as a result of four powerful 'drivers': the inherent complexity of nature and society, the desire to explore problems and questions that are not confined to a single discipline, the need to solve societal problems, and the power of new technologies.

The intent of such interdisciplinary investigations is to maintain the benefits of discipline-based research, while overcoming the limitations. In other words, it is to preserve each discipline's ability to contribute detailed (and sometimes groundbreaking) understanding of specific issues,[2] while moving beyond the restricted scope of individual disciplines, which can go just so far because each covers only some aspects of a complex problem.

I argue that, despite its promise and many excellent individual examples, most interdisciplinary research remains at the academic margins, largely because understanding about such investigations is fragmented. This results from failure to capture the wealth of available experience in a way that allows it to be transmitted and built on. Instead, relevant insights languish undocumented in people's heads or scattered in the published and grey literatures. As a consequence there is no substantial, well-established, internationally accepted methodology. There are no standard procedures for deciding, for example, which disciplines to include, what each discipline will contribute or how the different findings will be melded together. In the absence of comprehensive guidance, newcomers to this type of research still largely rely on intuition to invent for themselves a way to deal with the challenges of interdisciplinary partnership.

---

1 Committee on Facilitating Interdisciplinary Research et al. (2004, p. 40).

2 Howard Gardner (2006, p. 138), for example, avers that disciplines 'represent the most advanced and best ways to think about issues consequential to human beings'.

This book addresses that absence. I put forward a proposal for improving the methodological soundness of interdisciplinary research tackling complex social and environmental problems to allow this style of investigation to deliver more fully on its potential and to become firmly embedded in the research mainstream.

Of course, there have been attempts to standardise research that brings together different disciplinary insights; several are presented below and this book builds on their contributions. But my frustration is that they have lacked the necessary scale and traction, which is not surprising for pioneering efforts. This book is based on the premise that there is now enough useful experience and conceptual development to both warrant and permit rethinking what is meant by interdisciplinary research on major real-world problems and how to conduct it most effectively.

Previous groundbreaking work has been both theory and practice based. Small (mostly) groups of researchers have been building theories of interdisciplinarity[3] or of related approaches that include those variously referred to as multidisciplinarity, transdisciplinarity,[4] post-normal science,[5] systemic intervention,[6] integrated assessment,[7] sustainability science,[8] team science,[9] mode 2[10] and action research.[11,12] There tends to be little interaction among these groups, especially for comparative analyses and sharing of insights.

The practice-based advances stem from the work of many research teams. They tend to use 'interdisciplinary' and these other labels to describe their investigations, but employ the terms loosely rather than adhering to precise definitions developed by the theoreticians. Each team usually studies a succession of related problems, generally in one area such as environment or population health. Individual teams have often developed (and sometimes documented) one or more relevant concepts and methods, which they seek to apply to the problems they research. On the whole, there is little cross-fertilisation of the processes of interdisciplinarity between these groups and the teams tend to be isolated from each other. Even teams working in the same broad area (such as environmental problems) are generally not in the habit of sharing methodological

---

3 Frodeman et al. (2010); Klein (1990); Newell (1998); Repko (2008).
4 Bergman et al. (2010); Hirsch Hadorn et al. (2008); Pohl and Hirsch Hadorn (2007b); Scholz, R. W. (2011).
5 Funtowicz and Ravetz (1993).
6 Midgley (2000).
7 Van Asselt et al. (2001).
8 Clark (2007).
9 Falk-Krzesinski et al. (2011); Stokols et al. (2008).
10 Gibbons et al. (1994).
11 Reason and Bradbury (2001).
12 An anonymous reviewer and some of the commentators pointed out that management sciences, operations research, and complex systems science should also be added to these groups.

insights, and interactions are even rarer between groups investigating different topics, so researchers working on environmental problems hardly ever look for new theory or methods from those studying health issues, for instance.

There are also few connections between the theoreticians and the practitioners. Theoretical developments mostly have not benefited from the extensive range of practical insights. Further, many of the practitioners reinvent conceptual bases for their studies. My observation is that instead of progress built on fertile debate, there are growing pockets of dogma. Prescriptions include such dictums as

- ensuring that all research partners have equal status in order to neutralise power differences
- requiring close working relationships between researchers and those in a position to implement findings
- insisting on a common language and problem definition before starting any investigation.

But such instructions are only suitable in some circumstances.

The argument underpinning this book is that the development of interdisciplinary research on complex real-world problems is held back by the combination of fragmentation, unorganised diversity and dogma. The book therefore sets out to provide a framework that

- builds on the theoretical developments and relevant research experience in interdisciplinarity, multidisciplinarity, transdisciplinarity, post-normal science, systemic intervention, integrated assessment, sustainability science, team science, mode 2, action research and other initiatives
- enables substantial, widespread exchange of ideas and methods
- can be used to collect and evaluate the methodologies.

I begin by developing four arguments.

1. That a specific focus is required, especially since terms like interdisciplinarity have multiple meanings. This book subsequently concentrates on the type of research foreshadowed so far—namely research that involves experts from multiple, diverse disciplines working together on a complex real-world problem.

2. That there is no one 'best' way to conduct such research, but instead there are multiple options, each with advantages and disadvantages. Together they constitute a research style, which I call integrative applied research.

3. That a new discipline—Integration and Implementation Sciences (I2S)—provides an effective way of documenting and transmitting concepts and methods that underpin integrative applied research.

4. That there are thousands of research projects that can provide relevant material, especially concepts, methods and case examples, some on a small scale, some substantial. Because the pertinent material is scattered and often undocumented, compilation is resource intensive, making the natural evolution of I2S likely to take decades. Given that the complex problems facing society require urgent attention, the process could and should be accelerated through a new 'Big Science'-type project. By this I mean a project of the scale and dynamism of the Human Genome Project[13] or the Manhattan Project, which built the atomic bomb.[14] I refer to this as the I2S Development Drive.

In Chapter 2, I make the case that one of the most significant lessons to be learnt from the efforts that have gone into developing interdisciplinarity and related approaches[15] is that integrative applied research is about more than bringing together experts from multiple disciplines, and actually covers three domains

1. synthesising not only disciplinary but also stakeholder knowledge—in other words, pulling together what is known about the problem from both academic research and practical experience

2. understanding and managing diverse unknowns or, to put it another way, appreciating that everything about a complex problem cannot be known and that remaining unknowns must be taken into account in decision making and action

3. providing integrated research support for policy and practice change—that is, supplying policy makers and practitioners with a better understanding of the problem (both what is known and what is not known) in a way that supports them in making decisions and taking action.

I proceed further in Chapter 2 to present a specific framework for fleshing out these three domains, which is the core of I2S and which provides the focus for most of the rest of the book. I foreshadow how populating the framework is the basis for the 'Big Science'-type I2S Development Drive and a significant task for the future. The key purpose of the book is to make the case for I2S as a new discipline by describing its basic structure, and to kick-start a discussion about these ideas. That is the rationale for the last section of the book, which

---

13 Lambright (2002).
14 Rhodes (1986).
15 From now on I will mostly use this or similar terms to refer to interdisciplinarity, multidisciplinarity, transdisciplinarity, post-normal science, systemic intervention, integrated assessment, sustainability science, team science, mode 2, action research and similar initiatives—both the theoretical and the practical research.

comprises commissioned commentaries from colleagues who have been conducting 'interdisciplinary' research on complex real-world problems or who have leadership roles in research organisations which are keen to contribute more effectively to understanding and responding to society's major challenges.

Let us now return to the four opening arguments

- taking a specific focus
- defining a new research style
- developing a disciplinary underpinning
- responding to the scale and urgency of the task.

Taking a Specific Focus: Looking at one type of interdisciplinarity

One reason existing approaches have difficulty in achieving traction in the research mainstream is that the terms used to describe them have a range of meanings.[16] Let us look at the commonly used term 'interdisciplinarity', which can refer to

- research at the intersection of two disciplines, such as biology and chemistry or psychology and mathematics, which can spawn new disciplines (biochemistry and mathematical psychology, in the two cases given here); this can be large or small-scale and undertaken by individuals or teams
- research across the boundaries of several closely related disciplines like sociology, anthropology and psychology, which involves extensive 'borrowing'[17] of concepts and methods; this can also be large or small-scale and undertaken by individuals or teams
- fields and 'disciplines', like women's studies, population health, criminology and media studies, which draw on a range of disciplinary inputs; within any of these, different disciplines may work together closely or operate in parallel
- research on phenomena that occur across different disciplines, like patterning or hierarchy—for example, patterns occur in many aspects of the natural world and in social systems, from chemical structures at the microscopic level, arrays of stars, planets and other objects in the astronomical world to the movements of fish and birds, friendship networks and traffic flows[18]

---

16 I have recently developed this argument more fully in Bammer (2012).
17 Discussed in Klein (1990).
18 For example, see the topics at the following symposium: <http://www.radcliffe.edu/events/calendar_2010patterning.aspx> (accessed 2 December 2011).

- research that involves experts from various disciplines and stakeholders from relevant practice areas working on a common problem, such as cybercrime, obesity or erosion.[19]

While all are important, this book concentrates only on the last—namely research that involves experts from multiple disciplines and stakeholders investigating a common problem. The emphasis here is on complex real-world social and environmental problems.

My aim is, therefore, to focus on only one of the kinds of research that are covered by the term 'interdisciplinary' and to put the others aside. The intention is to allow a significant type of research to be recognised, given prominence and further developed.

Defining a New Research Style: Integrative applied research

One consequence of taking a specific focus is that it quickly becomes evident that there is no agreed precise, overarching term that describes *only* investigations involving several disciplinary experts and stakeholders investigating a shared problem. As I have foreshadowed, and will describe in more detail in Chapter 2, the research I am interested in also aims to deal more comprehensively with all the different kinds of remaining unknowns and combines an overview of unknowns along with appreciation of what is known about the problem to support policy and practice change.

As well as being referred to as interdisciplinary, such studies are commonly described by the names multidisciplinary, transdisciplinary and cross-disciplinary. But, as with interdisciplinary, these additional expressions have other meanings.[20] These multiple meanings get in the way of thinking clearly about the research of interest here. Furthermore, the type of research I am describing does not fully overlap with post-normal science, systemic intervention and the other related approaches, although useful concepts and methods can be drawn from them.

---

19 It is noteworthy that the Committee on Facilitating Interdisciplinary Research et al. (2004) covered all these approaches to interdisciplinarity except research on phenomena that occur in different disciplines, like patterning or hierarchy.

20 For example, multidisciplinarity and transdisciplinarity are also terms used to describe specific ways of conducting research. Put simply, in multidisciplinary research, each discipline defines and addresses the problem in its conventional way, following which the different disciplinary insights are presented side by side. In transdisciplinary research, disciplinary experts commence the research by actively working together (often with stakeholders and policy makers) to generate a shared understanding and way of tackling the problem, which then guide the investigation and the implementation of its findings.

I therefore argue for a new name that

a) refers only to research involving experts from several disciplines plus stakeholders working on a common complex real-world problem in a way that not only brings together their insights but also deals comprehensively with unknowns, all in order to support policy and practice change

b) is an overarching term that can accommodate a range of options for undertaking such research—for example, it can house various ways of combining disciplinary and stakeholder insights.

I propose 'integrative applied research'.[21]

The point about integrative applied research encompassing a range of methodological options is significant. It opens up the possibility of thinking about integrative applied research as a research style, analogous to quantitative research, empirical research, experimental research and theoretical research. Such a research style can be used to address many types of complex real-world problems—in other words, social problems like organised crime, environmental problems such as global climate change and healthcare problems including escalating costs.

In addition, it orients thinking to a search for more options rather than a hunt for a single 'best' methodology. Said another way, it recognises that different research problems and circumstances require different approaches. Further, each option will have particular advantages and disadvantages. For example, as I described earlier, it is often thought that a team of experts from different disciplines should develop a shared problem definition before commencing their investigation. But there are times when it is most appropriate for each discipline to characterise the problem as it sees fit, rather than compromising on an agreed joint definition. The advantage of starting from a common problem statement is that everyone is working to the same end, but the disadvantage is that achieving such agreement is time consuming and may reduce flexibility for considering new aspects of the problem that become evident as the research progresses. In the alternative, where each discipline works independently, the up-front 'transaction cost'[22] is avoided and flexibility is more likely to be maintained, but the disadvantage is that it may be hard to combine the different disciplinary perspectives.

The point here is not to find a prescription for undertaking integrative applied research, but to recognise and support multiple approaches.

---

21 Although applied research is often thought of as leading to the development of some technological innovation, I use it in a broader meaning to refer to research that can also lead to change in government or other policy and in various practices, such as the way services are delivered or technologies are embraced.

22 The transaction cost is the time a team needs to devote to the processes required to successfully work together. If, for example, a team wants to develop a shared understanding and approach to the problem, it needs to be prepared to devote considerable time to understanding how each discipline sees the problem, what methods it can bring to bear and how terms used by one discipline can have different meanings in another.

Developing a Disciplinary Underpinning: Integration and Implementation Sciences (I2S)

In the same way that the discipline of statistics supports different forms of quantitative research, it can be argued that integrative applied research also needs to be underpinned by a discipline. I propose that it is called Integration and Implementation Sciences or I2S.[23] The advantages that such a discipline confers are briefly discussed here. Considerable work is required to develop the discipline and this is explored in subsequent chapters.

A central function of I2S is to bring concepts[24] and methods relevant to undertaking integrative applied research into sharper relief and to allow them to be assessed and built on. I2S captures the considerable effort that various research teams have put into, for example, developing theory about problem definition, and techniques for bringing together different disciplinary insights and stakeholder perspectives.[25]

As well as supplying an effective way to collect and assess relevant concepts and methods, a discipline also provides a way to transmit them between research groups tackling major real-world challenges, even if they are working in very different areas. Statistics again provides a useful analogy. Statisticians work on myriad social and environmental problems, but when they make a methodological breakthrough, it is transmitted to and evaluated by others in the statistics discipline before being published in the statistics literature. A new statistical technique developed when researching a question on climate change is then much more readily available to statisticians working on issues in drug policy or international terrorism. The aim is for I2S to operate in the same way.[26]

In time, the I2S discipline will have major professional journals and conferences where ideas are exchanged, thus overcoming the current situation where cross-fertilisation and networking are restricted.[27] It will allow research teams tackling complex real-world problems to progress from having a very limited array of concepts and methods at their disposal, to being provided with a range of options from which they can choose.

---

23 It may seem bizarre to suggest the formation of yet another discipline, when the problem seems to be the inability of researchers to work across existing 'silos'; however, I argue that the challenge is to exploit, not to eliminate, the strengths of disciplines.

24 I use the word 'concept' to cover everything from a productive idea to a theory.

25 It counters the argument that integrative applied research is simply a matter of personal skill in facilitating or managing teamwork. Such skills are important, but there is much more involved.

26 Statistical insights are not evaluated by experts from other disciplines who happen to be interested in the problem the statistician is working on. In contrast, the review process for developments that could be classed as enhancing I2S is much more hit-and-miss, because there is no identifiable college of peers using the same methodology. It is common, therefore, for referees to be interested in the same problem, but to use different methods (usually from one or other discipline) in their own work.

27 This point is elaborated in Chapter 31.

Development of the I2S discipline naturally has ramifications for individual researchers. Currently those who are active in building expertise relevant to integrative applied research are hampered by the ad-hoc and constrained ability to engage with a broad range of concepts and techniques, as well as often being marginalised within the academic mainstream. Belonging to a vibrant, active discipline will not only improve their research, but also confer recognition and status. The aim is for I2S specialists to be seen as essential members of integrative applied research teams, in the same way that statisticians provide critical and respected input to teams tackling quantitative problems.

Integrative applied research teams will generally comprise investigators from relevant disciplines, including one or more I2S specialists. The role of the I2S specialists, like that of the other team members, is to provide the best available relevant information and methodology from their field. But in their case it will be about options for scoping and setting boundaries around the problem, for combining the various disciplinary expertises, for supporting policy change, and so on. The idea is not for the tasks related to integration and implementation to be left to the I2S specialists, but rather for specialists to work closely with the rest of the team to make the group aware of the activities that need to be undertaken and options for doing so. I describe the various dimensions of the role of I2S specialists in chapters to follow.[28]

Responding to the Scale and Urgency of the Task: The I2S Development Drive

Developing a new discipline is a major undertaking. The starting points are those foreshadowed earlier—namely the small amount of theoretically based research about transdisciplinarity, systemic intervention, integrated assessment and related initiatives, and the extensive existing research on complex environmental, health and other social problems, which its practitioners loosely describe as interdisciplinary, multidisciplinary, transdisciplinary or with some related term.[29] Both have devised concepts and methods relevant to I2S. The level of documentation is highly variable, as well as scattered. Nevertheless, if completed projects as well as current ones are included, I estimate that, around the world, there are thousands who could contribute pertinent material.[30]

---

28 Specifically in Chapters 9, 16, 23 and 30. An anonymous reviewer pointed out that 'we need I2S specialists both in the research/science and [the] implementation/practitioner arenas', and suggested that attention must also be given to 'practitioners, policy makers, and stakeholders'. I agree, but to keep the focus manageable, have restricted it to researchers for this book.

29 Examples include CSIRO's national research flagships (<http://www.csiro.au/partnerships/NRF.html>), the National Science Foundation's synthesis centres (<http://www.nsf.gov/news/news_summ.jsp?cntn_id=121229&org=NSF&from=news>) and Australia's Cooperative Research Centres (<https://www.crc.gov.au/Information/default.aspx>) (all accessed 5 December 2011).

30 Not all of these research groups are tackling *complex* problems, but the concepts and methods they have developed often have broader relevance. This was our experience when we compiled a book of dialogue methods for knowledge synthesis (see McDonald et al. 2009). Many of the cases describe relatively straightforward issues, but the methods can be used on complex problems too.

Building I2S requires gathering together and assessing not only the concepts and methods applicable to integrative applied research, but also case examples of how these theories and techniques have been applied to different real-world problems. Examining cases is highly instructive for understanding the strengths and weaknesses of various concepts and methods, as well as when their application is most appropriate.

The challenge then is to find, collate and evaluate relevant concepts, methods and case examples from thousands of research projects. Because much of the germane material is undocumented, reviewing the literature will cover only a portion of the terrain. Further, such reviews will be resource intensive because pertinent materials are widely scattered in the published and grey literatures and are often not described in a way that makes their relevance to I2S immediately apparent.[31] Getting access to undocumented information involves different demands, especially in locating those with information and determining ways to elicit their contributions. Because existing networks tend to be small and restricted, identifying key researchers is unlikely to be straightforward. Further, given that these researchers will already have heavy demands on their time, establishing ways to make their involvement in developing I2S manageable and rewarding will require creativity and resources.

The task of compilation is therefore formidable. It also requires evaluation of the concepts, methods and case examples to decide on their relative merits. Without a well-established I2S discipline, there is currently no extensive college of peers to draw on for undertaking such assessments. The process of compilation will, however, also identify those with experience in the concepts or methods of interest. The most skilled can then be enlisted in evaluation processes.

The urgency of many of the world's most challenging problems means that we cannot afford to wait for this new discipline to evolve in the normal academic way, which could take decades. Establishing I2S can be boosted by mounting a new Big-Science-type project, akin to the effort that decoded the human genome, producing an explosion of new understanding of diseases and their cures.[32] Such an effort, referred to here as the I2S Development Drive, would be charged with identifying relevant research projects and groups, obtaining

31   Again, this was our experience in compiling a book of dialogue methods for knowledge synthesis (see McDonald et al. 2009). Most of these methods were developed for purposes other than knowledge synthesis, but can readily be adapted.

32   This Big Science project, conducted between 1986 and 2001, provided the international scientific community with a solid foundation from which to tackle the genetic bases of disease. Decoding sections of the genome occurred in individual laboratories of 20 centres across six countries. Originally it was conceived as an even broader international undertaking. It is estimated that thousands of researchers were involved (see Collins et al. 2003; Lambright 2002; Sulston and Ferry 2002; Venter 2007). A brief description of the project using the I2S framework can be found in Bammer (2008). The original 'Big Science' project was the building of the atomic bomb during World War II, often referred to as the Manhattan Project (see Rhodes 1986).

and collecting a range of concepts, methods and case examples from available literatures and research team members, as well as developing a process for evaluating them in order to produce foundational texts for the I2S discipline.[33]

The Aims of this Book

This book has the following aims.

1. To propose a structure for building the discipline of Integration and Implementation Sciences (I2S). The key elements are outlined in Chapter 2 and then described more fully in four subsequent sections of the book. Ideas for how the discipline will operate are presented in the sixth section, 'Moving Forward'.

2. To plant the seed for the I2S Development Drive as a new Big-Science-type project to establish I2S.

3. To start a worldwide discussion about I2S and the I2S Development Drive, especially the potential value, limitations, domains and operation of I2S. The commentaries in Section 7 by distinguished researchers and leaders of research organisations set this discussion in motion.

It is worth emphasising that, although the book describes some relevant concepts, methods and case examples, the focus is on proposing a structure for the I2S discipline. Populating the structure with the full range of existing theories, techniques and illustrations is the task of the I2S Development Drive, which will build the functioning discipline. The rationale for the commentaries is to catalyse the essential debate about whether the idea of an I2S discipline has merit, the strengths and weaknesses of the proposed structure, and the necessity for, and potential value of, the I2S Development Drive.

---

33 In the chapters that follow, I describe specific tasks for the I2S Development Drive and these are summarised in Chapter 34.

2. Getting Specific: Three domains, a five-question framework and the overall approach

This chapter presents a preview of the disciplinary structure of I2S, which is developed in detail in Chapters 3 to 30. The starting point is the three domains that characterise integrative applied research and I2S: 1) synthesising disciplinary and stakeholder knowledge, 2) understanding and managing diverse unknowns, and 3) providing integrated research support for policy and practice change.

I then provide a series of definitions for terms used throughout the book. I have delayed presenting the definitions until now because it is only at this stage that all the terms have been introduced and fully explained.[1]

Returning to the main argument, a five-question framework for fleshing out each of the three domains is presented. The notion of an I2S disciplinary 'storehouse' is then introduced, along with discussion of how it will be filled with concepts, methods and case examples by the I2S Development Drive.

The last two parts of this chapter focus, first, on the structure of the book and, second, on the audiences and the function of the commentaries, reiterating and expanding on what I have set out beforehand.

Three Domains

I propose three foundational domains for integrative applied research and I2S. These were foreshadowed in Chapter 1, but are described in more detail here—namely

1. synthesising disciplinary and stakeholder knowledge

2. understanding and managing diverse unknowns

3. providing integrated research support for policy and practice change.

The basis for the first domain—synthesising disciplinary and stakeholder knowledge—is the widespread recognition[2] that improved appreciation of

---

1   To try to keep the argument clear, some terms were only partially explained in Chapter 1, with this description being embellished after other necessary concepts are introduced.
2   Especially in the approaches that have informed the development of integrative applied research—namely interdisciplinarity, multidisciplinarity, transdisciplinarity, post-normal science, systemic intervention, integrated assessment, sustainability science, team science, mode 2, action research and related initiatives.

complex real-world problems does not just involve combining knowledge from multiple disciplines, but also requires relevant stakeholder knowledge to be taken into account. Stakeholders are all those groups who have a practical grasp of the problem. It can be useful to think about them as: a) those affected by the problem, and b) those in a position to influence the problem. Relevant stakeholders will vary from case to case, but can include communities, occupational groups, socioeconomic groups, people affected by a disease, as well as business groups and politicians. To take a specific example, the World Commission on Dams worked with 'government agencies, project affected people and non-governmental organisations, people's movements, the dam construction industry, the export credit agencies and private investors, and the international development community'.[3] Stakeholder groups are rarely homogeneous, but are likely to contain a range of perspectives about the problem of interest. Common ways of capturing stakeholder knowledge are to undertake surveys of relevant groups, to conduct workshops with them and to invite representatives to be on research advisory committees.[4] This domain is described in detail in the next section, encompassing Chapters 3 to 9.

While there is broad agreement about the importance of bringing together disciplinary and stakeholder knowledge, the second domain—understanding and managing diverse unknowns—generally receives much less attention, although its significance has been highlighted by post-normal science,[5] as well as some research on environmental problems.[6] In integrative applied research, the focus on complex real-world problems means that new ways of understanding and managing unknowns have to be developed, rather than relying only on current standard approaches. As I describe in Chapter 10, a key issue for complex real-world problems is that unknowns cannot be eliminated and that imperfection is an inevitable result. I return to the theme of imperfection at various places in the book.

The approach taken here contrasts with most research traditions, which see unknowns only as the substrate that they convert to knowledge. In fact, the hallmark of good discipline-based research is to carve out a specific productive unknown to work on and to banish the rest from consideration. That is how progress is made; however, in integrative applied research, the problem-based focus has two consequences. One is that, from the perspective of understanding the problem, there may be critical gaps resulting from issues that do not come into the domain of a discipline or have been banished in the various disciplinary approaches. A path has to be found that brings consideration of these gaps

---

3   World Commission on Dams (2000, p. viii).
4   Some approaches, like action research, aim to include stakeholders as co-researchers, but this is more likely to work on a small scale, such as improving a particular health service.
5   Funtowicz and Ravetz (1993).
6   See, for example, Kasperson (2008).

into play, without drowning in the impossibility of dealing with all relevant unknowns. The other consequence is that different disciplinary and stakeholder approaches to the unknown need to be brought together to provide a rich understanding of different types of, and ways of dealing with, unknowns. This domain is much less well developed than the other two, but, as described in the third section of the book (Chapters 10–16), significant steps are being made to find ways forward.

Finally, there is now considerable interest in how research influences policy and practice change, with growing literatures on 'research translation', 'knowledge brokering', 'commercialisation', and so on. The third domain—providing integrated research support for policy and practice change—seeks to synthesise and build on these advances. Two major foci are significant. One is the emphasis on *integrated* research—in other words, not just dealing with what is known about a problem, but also providing a way to understand and respond to what is not known.[7] An important aim here is to assist with better decision making, which encompasses reducing, or at least being better prepared for, unintended consequences of policy or practice initiatives, which arise from ineffective understanding and management of unknowns. The second focus is research *support*. As described in the fourth section of the book (Chapters 17–23), which deals with this domain, research has a challenging role vis-a-vis policy and practice change: it is neither dominant nor subservient, and I seek to characterise this through the term 'support'. As described further in that section, it can be helpful to think about change as occurring in three major arenas: government, business and civil society. Research may set out to be useful on a narrow or a broad scale. For example, it may be confined to one part of one arena, seeking to inform one government policy (such as a policy on homelessness) or one set of practices (such as the way illicit drug users are dealt with in treatment services). Broad input can be offered across two or three arenas and, within them, several policy and practice areas. Research on global climate change provides a good example here, in that it seeks to influence government policy in a range of areas (transport, housing, industrial development, and so on), as well as reorienting business activities and changing consumer and community behaviours.

As I have foreshadowed, these three domains provide the primary structure for the book, with a section comprising seven chapters devoted to each of them, as well as a fifth section (Chapters 24–30) that looks at all three together. Before considering the domains in more detail, let me define the key terms that have now been introduced and will continue to be used throughout the book.

---

7   This moves beyond focusing only on the *evidence* base for policy and practice.

Definitions

I make a central distinction between 'synthesis' and 'integration'.[8] 'Synthesis' is used for the bringing together of disciplinary and stakeholder knowledge, as in the first domain of I2S. 'Integration' (and related terms) refers to the combination of the synthesised knowledge with a considered response to the remaining unknowns about the problem.

Thus

> **Integrated research support** is based on both what is known about the problem (resulting from the synthesis of disciplinary and stakeholder perspectives) and explicit recognition of what is not known about the problem (resulting from the consideration of diverse unknowns).

> **Integrative applied research** is a research style that deals with complex real-world problems by bringing together disciplinary and stakeholder knowledge and explicitly dealing with remaining unknowns, in order to use that integrated research to support policy and practice change. An **integrative applied research team** is composed of investigators from a range of disciplines, including one or more I2S specialists. Many, but not necessarily all, team members also have expertise in the complex real-world problem under consideration. The team explicitly interacts with stakeholders, policy makers and practitioners.

> **Integration and Implementation Sciences or I2S** is the discipline that underpins integrative applied research and which develops and applies concepts and methods for knowledge synthesis, understanding and managing diverse unknowns and providing integrated research support for policy and practice change.

In day-to-day English, synthesis, integrated, integrative and integration are variously interchangeable, but I have stuck to the specific uses defined throughout this book.

Similarly I use 'stakeholders', 'policy makers' and 'practitioners' in particular ways.

> **'Stakeholders'** is used in the first domain to cover all the non-academic groups who have a valuable perspective on the problem.

> **'Policy makers'** and **'practitioners'** are used in the third domain specifically to cover the groups who will take action on the problem.

---

8   These words have not been used in the carefully defined ways described here in my previous publications.

There will often be overlap between these groups—in other words, a stakeholder group which provides a helpful perspective on a problem may be identical to a policy maker or practitioner group which is charged with responding to the problem. Nevertheless, for the purposes of clearly describing the I2S structure, I distinguish between them, depending on whether they are *aiding understanding* about the problem or *acting* on it.

Finally, it may be useful to summarise how this book 'locates' integrative applied research in relation to inter-, multi-, and trans-disciplinary research, post-normal science, systemic intervention, integrated assessment, sustainability science, team science, mode 2, action research and related initiatives. While integrative applied research builds on these other approaches, as outlined above, it also provides some key advances, specifically

- restricting the focus to team research on complex real-world problems
- defining a research style, which has a range of methodological options
- identifying three core domains
- specifying an underpinning discipline—namely I2S.

In addition, integrative applied research puts considerable emphasis on the exchange of methodological insights between research groups working on very different problems.[9]

In various places in the book multidisciplinary research and transdisciplinary research are used as examples of different ways in which integrative applied research can be conducted—in other words, as two methodological options for that research style.[10] But otherwise I do not look in detail at the groundbreaking initiatives that have laid the foundations for integrative applied research. I have not analysed exactly where the ideas presented here originated or explored the similarities and distinctions between integrative applied research and the earlier initiatives. Such analysis and exploration are important future projects.

Fleshing Out the Three Domains: The five-question framework

Review of publications describing studies that tackled complex social and environmental problems reveals that there is no agreed systematic way to report on integrative applied research. Let us start with the first domain and use the

---

9   This is not precluded by interdisciplinarity and other approaches but is not a point of emphasis, which, as I proposed earlier, has limited their development.

10   In these examinations the specific meanings described in Chapter 1 (see Note 20) are used. These various discussions are drawn together and built on in Chapter 33.

investigations undertaken by the World Commission on Dams as an example.[11] The Commission marshalled a wide range of academic and stakeholder knowledge, drawing on perspectives both supporting and opposing dams. But if we want to learn from the methodology it employed, it turns out that the published documents offer only limited clues about a number of key questions concerning the synthesis of disciplinary and stakeholder knowledge. In other words, there is almost no information to help answer questions like the following.

- How did the Commission decide which disciplinary knowledge to build on and which to ignore, as well as which stakeholders to include and to exclude?
- How did it synthesise the findings of its various studies?
- Who was responsible for the synthesis?
- How were any barriers to synthesis addressed?

There are now countless examples of synthesis of disciplinary and stakeholder knowledge, but, as is the case with the World Commission on Dams, developing a comprehensive appreciation of how the investigations were conducted and which concepts and methods were employed remains elusive. The intent here is not to be critical of the Commission, or indeed to complain about other research projects. Rather, it is to show how much poorer the research community undertaking integrative applied research is for not being able to learn detailed lessons from the experience of the Commission and other investigations.

How can we systematically plan and report knowledge synthesis? I propose that the following five questions provide a useful framework.[12]

1. What is the synthesis of disciplinary and stakeholder knowledge aiming to achieve and who is intended to benefit?

2. Which disciplinary and stakeholder knowledge is synthesised?

3. How is the disciplinary and stakeholder knowledge synthesised, by whom and when?

4. What circumstances might influence the synthesis of disciplinary and stakeholder knowledge?

5. What is the result of the synthesis of disciplinary and stakeholder knowledge?

---

11   World Commission on Dams (2000).

12   The lack of an explicit methodology for knowledge synthesis was addressed at a 2004 symposium on the topic of 'integration' organised by the (then) Australian Research and Development Corporation, Land & Water Australia. (The organisation was defunded in 2009.) The results of the symposium can be found in Bammer et al. (2005a, 2005b). At the symposium we developed six questions, but I have subsequently combined two separate questions on 'how' and 'who'. For the original questions, see Bammer and LWA Integration Symposium Participants (2005).

The five-question framework can also be adapted to the other two domains of I2S, allowing them to be covered systematically.[13] Taking all three domains together, the five-question framework becomes the following.

1. What is the integrative applied research aiming to achieve and who is intended to benefit?

2. What is the integrative applied research dealing with—that is, which knowledge is synthesised, unknowns considered and aspects of policy and practice targeted?

3. How is the integrative applied research undertaken (the knowledge synthesised, diverse unknowns understood and managed, and integrated research support provided), by whom and when?

4. What circumstances might influence the integrative applied research?

5. What is the result of the integrative applied research?

The questions can be stated in brief.

1. For what and for whom?

2. Which knowledge, unknowns and aspects of policy and practice?

3. How?

4. Context?

5. Outcome?

While these questions look simple, they encompass considerable methodological depth and this is fleshed out in the chapters that follow. As a set, the questions can be used to plan new integrative applied research or to describe ongoing or completed research. The order of the questions is not fixed. Sometimes it may be useful, for example, to describe the context first or to consider questions two and three together.

---

13 For the second domain the questions are: 1) what is the understanding and management of diverse unknowns aiming to achieve and who is intended to benefit; 2) which unknowns are considered; 3) how are diverse unknowns understood and managed, by whom and when; 4) what circumstances might influence the understanding and management of diverse unknowns; 5) what is the result of understanding and managing diverse unknowns. For the third domain, the questions are: 1) what is the integrated research support aiming to achieve and who is intended to benefit; 2) which aspects of policy and practice are targeted by the provision of integrated research support; 3) how is integrated research support provided, by whom and when; 4) what circumstances might influence the provision of integrated research support for policy and practice change; 5) what is the result of the provision of integrated research support.

I2S as a Storehouse

One key function of a discipline is to provide a storehouse for relevant concepts, methods and case examples, and the book concentrates on this aspect of I2S. The three domains are the three main storerooms (Figure 2.1). Each of the five questions provides a 'wall' of each room, with a more detailed structure of the storeroom for the first domain (synthesising disciplinary and stakeholder knowledge) shown in Figure 2.2.

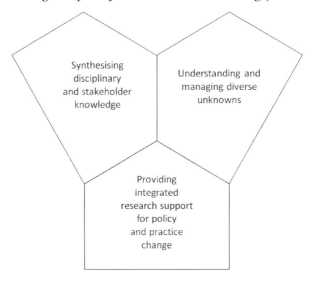

Figure 2.1 The Floor Plan for the I2S Storehouse

Source: Author's illustration.

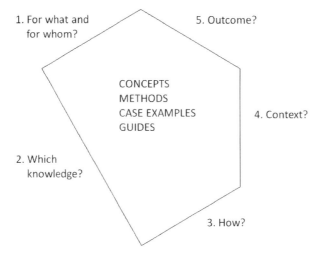

Figure 2.2 The Storeroom for Synthesising Disciplinary and Stakeholder Knowledge

Source: Author's illustration.

Let us examine two issues about what is collected in the storehouse in more detail, beginning with the case examples. I have already briefly indicated their value in helping I2S disciplinary specialists understand the strengths and weaknesses of different concepts and methods. They can also assist in identifying criteria for choosing between options. For instance, one way of undertaking knowledge synthesis is through dialogue methods. Here case examples can start to match different kinds of knowledge synthesis with various dialogue methods. Another benefit of case examples is that they can be used to illustrate less tangible processes that do not lend themselves to being thought of as methods. For example, considering 'by whom' knowledge synthesis is undertaken alerts us to options: it can be carried out by the whole integrative applied research team, by a subgroup or by a single researcher (usually the project leader). Each process has strengths and weaknesses and will be more appropriate in specific circumstances. Documenting a number of instances where each was employed will provide useful information on which I2S disciplinary specialists can base advice to integrative applied research teams and their leaders who are making decisions about how to proceed.

The second issue about what is collected in the storehouse is to add another category of items. As well as concepts, methods and case examples, each storeroom also needs to contain guides to additional specific knowledge from outside the I2S discipline. Some of the I2S foundations are already well established in particular disciplines or other areas of academic work. The aim of I2S is not to reinvent them or appropriate them uncritically, but to tailor these developments to integrative applied research. Two examples will elucidate the point. First, the third domain (providing integrated research support for policy and practice change) includes building on political science theories about government processes to provide useful insights into different ways that integrated research can support policy. Customised guides to these theories are therefore required. Second, systems thinking is integral to all three domains of I2S in that both problems and the policy and practice arenas to be supported are most usefully thought of as systems. Again, well-developed guides to the relevant aspects of systems thinking are key to the development of I2S.[14]

Each storeroom is therefore designed to contain concepts, methods and case examples specific to an I2S domain, as well as guides to relevant knowledge from outside I2S.

---

14   A summary of all relevant guides is provided in Chapter 34 at Table 34.2.

The Structure of the Book

The book has seven sections. The next three cover the domains in turn and include chapters dealing with each of the five questions. The fifth section, which draws the three domains together, focuses on the shared space where the domains interact. It specifically looks at I2S as a whole and deals with synergies and conflicts that can occur when concepts and methods from the different domains are combined.

A discipline is, of course, more than a storehouse—hence the sixth section ('Moving Forward') takes a selective look at some of the other aspects of I2S, especially concerning its functioning in integrative applied research. The starting point in Chapter 31 is a hypothetical scenario about the role of I2S in research in 2025, followed by the description of a virtuous cycle between capacity, demonstrated success and funding. Chapter 32 then explores practical ideas about the operation of I2S as a discipline, drawing on statistics as an analogy. The following chapter, Chapter 33, specifically explores the relationship between integrative applied research and I2S, on the one hand, and multidisciplinary and transdisciplinary research, on the other. It describes how I2S could enhance both types of research, as well as demonstrating how integrative applied research provides a home for hybrids between multidisciplinary and transdisciplinary investigations. I then return to the notion of the storehouse and in Chapter 34 list what the I2S Development Drive needs to cover, as well as discussing how proof-of-concept can be demonstrated and what the forces opposed to building I2S might be. That chapter also draws together the arguments made in earlier parts of the book about an important sub-theme—namely the inevitability of imperfection. It explores the consequences of recognising that there is no way to provide perfect solutions to complex real-world problems.

The final section of the book is devoted to commissioned commentaries, with the aim of launching debate about integrative applied research as an investigative style, the I2S discipline and the I2S Development Drive.

Commentaries and Audiences

Eminent colleagues were asked to write brief essays reviewing the ideas presented in the first six sections of the book. The commentators fall into two main groups

- research leaders and team members tackling real-world problems, including proponents of existing approaches, such as transdisciplinarity or team science, as well as researchers who have developed useful concepts and methods outside these existing approaches

- those concerned that academic research falls short of its potential to contribute to addressing complex real-world problems, including leaders of universities and major research organisations.

The aim of the commentaries is to provide a foundation for further discussion and debate, by providing the initial reactions of individuals from diverse networks. They were invited to focus on issues most pertinent to their interests and experience, as well as urged not to refrain from being critical in responding to the book's ideas. In Chapter 35 I draw out five themes that were raised in several of the commentaries and which could provide the starting point for future conversations and research.

The two categories of commentators also correspond to the main intended audiences for the book. In other words, this book is geared to people who already have an interest in embedding in the academic mainstream what I call integrative applied research. One group is researchers undertaking integrative applied research, who want their work and the work of their colleagues to be more prominent and recognised, and who accept that high standards must be set. The others are leaders of research institutions who want to put their organisations in a position where they can contribute more to tackling complex real-world problems than can be achieved by the disciplines alone. The book aims to give these audiences concrete ideas for a way forward, as well as—through the commentaries—initial reactions from leading members among their peers.

The book sketches a new research style and disciplinary storehouse, as well as proposing a building plan. The aim is to provide enough information to allow fruitful discussion about whether a new research style is warranted; if a new discipline would be beneficial; whether the proposed disciplinary storerooms are indeed workable or need major restructuring; and what sort of effort will be needed to fill the storehouse. In doing so, I seek to provide a constructive and practical answer—and one that can become embedded in the research mainstream—to the question '*How can academic research enhance its contributions to addressing widespread poverty, global climate change, organised crime, escalating healthcare costs or the myriad other major problems facing human societies?*'

Domain 1. Synthesising Disciplinary and Stakeholder Knowledge

3. Introduction

Between 1998 and 2000, the World Commission on Dams undertook an extensive research program to assess how effective large dams had been in providing irrigation, electricity, flood control and water supply, and at what cost, especially displacement and impoverishment of populations, and disturbance of ecosystems and fishery resources. It also aimed to develop internationally acceptable recommendations for all stages of planning, constructing and decommissioning of dams, within a human rights framework. The research included case studies, country studies, a survey, technical reports, submissions, and forums to examine and synthesise a range of technical, social, environmental and economic evidence. It brought together views from those displaced or otherwise affected by dams, as well as from dam funders and construction agencies. The Commission was established by the joint efforts of the World Conservation Union and the World Bank to respond to increasing controversy about, and opposition to, the building of large scale dams. The Commissioners, who represented a range of interests, produced a consensus report.[1]

As mentioned in Chapter 2, although the Commission's work is a prime example of the first domain of integrative applied research, its published documents offer only limited clues about a number of key questions concerning the synthesis of disciplinary and stakeholder knowledge, such as how the scope of the problem was determined and the framing decided, as well as the methods and processes used for knowledge synthesis. This drawback is currently widespread in integrative applied research because there is no agreed way to describe such investigations. In this section I therefore expand on the five-question framework introduced in Chapter 2. For this first domain, the five questions are the following.

1. What is the synthesis of disciplinary and stakeholder knowledge aiming to achieve and who is intended to benefit? (For what and for whom?)

2. Which disciplinary and stakeholder knowledge is synthesised? (Which knowledge?)

---

1 World Commission on Dams (2000). The Commission's research provides a number of lessons for the development of integrative applied research and I2S. As pointed out in Chapter 2, it epitomises the problems associated with the lack of a standardised way to report on integration and implementation. Nevertheless there are useful illustrations that can be drawn from its approach, some of which are presented in this chapter. I do not, however, go into some of the most instructive elements, which relate to undertaking integrative applied research in a highly politicised environment. This is work for the I2S Development Drive. For readers interested in a taste of the issues, see Briscoe (2010); McCully (2001).

3. How is the disciplinary and stakeholder knowledge synthesised, by whom and when? (How?)

4. What circumstances might influence the synthesis of disciplinary and stakeholder knowledge? (Context?)

5. What is the result of the synthesis of disciplinary and stakeholder knowledge? (Outcome?)

The aim is to demonstrate how this framework can provide a systematic approach to planning and reporting integrative applied research, as well as to developing and transmitting the concepts and methods that make up I2S. A summary of the broad categories of concepts and methods covered by each question, along with the chapters in which they are discussed, is presented in Figure 3.1. Each question is represented by one of the walls of the knowledge synthesis storeroom and the classes of concepts and methods are listed under the question.

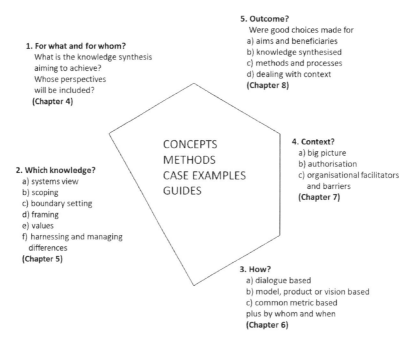

Figure 3.1 The Storeroom for Synthesising Disciplinary and Stakeholder Knowledge, Listing the Key Categories of Concepts and Methods

Source: Author's illustration.

I do not trace the origins of the classes of concepts and methods. They are eclectic, drawn from wide-ranging reading, research experience and reflection. Many can be found in previous work on inter-, multi- and trans-disciplinarity, as well as the more specific areas of post-normal science, systemic intervention, and so on.

It is worth reiterating the point made in Chapter 1 that, although the book describes some relevant concepts, methods and case examples, the focus is on proposing a structure for the I2S discipline. The emphasis is therefore on categories of ideas, theories and techniques. Populating the structure with the full range of existing concepts and methods, along with adequate illustrations, is the brief of the I2S Development Drive. I present the tasks that the I2S Development Drive needs to undertake for this domain in the chapters that follow. These are then brought together in one place (along with the assignments for the other domains) in Chapter 34.

In the final chapter of this section (Chapter 9), the five-question framework is used to elucidate what is involved in specialising in I2S. Three broad categories of I2S specialisation are examined: I2S for team leaders, I2S disciplinary specialists and I2S appreciation for other integrative applied research team members.

4. For What and for Whom?

The purpose of this first question—'*What is the synthesis of disciplinary and stakeholder knowledge aiming to achieve and who is intended to benefit?*'—is to help integrative applied research teams think specifically about their objectives and beneficiaries, so that they target their efforts most effectively. This is important for two reasons. First, teams which undertake integrative applied research have often not thought clearly about what they are trying to achieve and find it very helpful to be pushed to do so. Second, in order for teams to choose the most appropriate options in terms of I2S concepts, methods and case examples, as well as guides to relevant knowledge from outside the discipline, they need to have well-formulated goals.[1]

What the synthesis of disciplinary and stakeholder knowledge is aiming to achieve is more comprehensive insight into the problem by bringing together what is already known, as well as what can be readily ascertained through new research. It sets out to draw on a diverse range of relevant disciplines and stakeholders. The beneficiaries are those whose knowledge is included in the synthesis.[2]

More generally, it is helpful to differentiate between the I2S domains, distinguishing aims and beneficiaries for knowledge synthesis, dealing with diverse unknowns more fully and supporting policy or practice change. This not only enables more effective choices of options within each domain, but also allows independent assessment, for each domain, of how well the goals were met. In this first domain, it enables the success of the knowledge synthesis to be evaluated independently of the rest of the research and its application (see Chapter 8).

In the case of the World Commission on Dams, the aims and beneficiaries form one area that *can* be surmised, to a large extent, from the published reports. The knowledge synthesis set out to '[r]eview the development effectiveness of large dams and assess alternatives for water resources and energy development'.[3] Among the beneficiaries—in other words, those whose knowledge was included—were all the major stakeholders, such as those affected by dams, as well as governments, dam builders and funders. The reports do not, however,

---

1 It is important to note that clarity does not require rigidity. A degree of vagueness and ambiguity is essential for research to proceed, especially in the early stages, and the team can plainly state which areas are still undetermined.
2 The focus here is not on the policy makers and practitioners to whom the synthesised knowledge is provided (along with a more comprehensive understanding of remaining unknowns). They are the beneficiaries in Domain 3, discussed in Chapter 18.
3 World Commission on Dams (2000, p. 28).

specify which disciplines were drawn on, although from the descriptions of the research conducted it can be deduced that they were numerous and wide ranging, with engineering, ecology, anthropology, economics and law providing examples.

The knowledge synthesis underpinned the overarching purpose of the World Commission on Dams, which sought to '[d]evelop internationally acceptable criteria, guidelines and standards where appropriate, for the planning, design, appraisal, construction, operation, monitoring and decommissioning of dams'.[4] This, in turn, aimed to set in train a process to achieve 'development effectiveness', where 'decision-making on water and energy management will align itself with the emerging global commitment to sustainable human development and on the equitable distribution of costs and benefits'.[5] The Commission saw its work as the first step in a longer-term reconsideration of policy and practice regarding dams—both building new dams and the monitoring and decommissioning of existing ones. The chair described this as follows: 'Through this process a shared understanding and truth began to emerge, and with it the thin thread with which to sew the stitches of reconciliation.'[6]

Task for the I2S Development Drive
Compile case examples demonstrating: a) different ways of describing the knowledge synthesis purpose, b) the contribution to the overarching research aims, and c) the beneficiaries (that is, which perspectives were included).

4   World Commission on Dams (2000, p. 28).
5   World Commission on Dams (2000, p. xxxiii).
6   World Commission on Dams (2000, p. iii).

5. Which Knowledge?

Defining the components of the question *'Which disciplinary and stakeholder knowledge is synthesised?'* draws on the ideas previously developed in interdisciplinarity, transdisciplinarity, integrated assessment and related approaches. Based on the thinking that underpins these innovative efforts, I suggest that there are six key, interrelated categories of concepts and methods: taking a systems view, scoping, boundary setting, framing, dealing with values, and harnessing or managing differences.[1]

Taking a Systems View

The challenge is to find an approach that puts the real-world problem centre-stage and that makes it feasible to examine a range of discipline-based and stakeholder perspectives in a coherent and systematic way. To do this, integrative applied research draws on the traditions of systems thinking, which provide ways of looking at the interrelationships between various aspects of the problem, as well as the broader issues the problem relates to and those interconnections. A systems view about heroin use, for example, involves examining the interactions between users, their families, treatment providers, police and the community at large, with different foci on crime, social functioning, health, and so on. It also means examining the broader context of the heroin supply system: the drug cartels, supply lines and international law-enforcement efforts.

It is important to note, however, that it is impossible to focus on the *whole* problem at once. Instead, different systems approaches emphasise different aspects of the whole. Systems approaches can include the following.

- Conceptual maps of key areas, as well as the relationships between them. The description of heroin use just provided is an example of a very rough conceptual map.

- Developing causal (loop) diagrams, which focus on feedback cycles, both positive feedback or reinforcing cycles (which cause vicious and virtuous cycles) and negative feedback or stabilising cycles.[2] For example, heroin users often pay for their drug through crime, which leads to shame that is dulled

---

1   The approaches drawn on do not all deal with each of these categories of concepts and methods, and, when they do, often handle them differently. The notion of harnessing and managing differences is not taken from these earlier developments, but is first described in Bammer (2008). The level of detail provided is uneven across the categories. This should not be seen as a reflection of their significance, but is an artefact of my understanding. It is also important to note that scoping and boundary setting are relevant not only to this question, but also to questions three (how?) and four (context?).
2   Badham (2010).

by the heroin use, leading to more use, more crime, more shame and so on in a vicious cycle. The initial cycle can be embellished with other cycles that bring in a wider array of factors. For example, committing crime can lead to a criminal record, which makes obtaining legal employment harder, leading to more crime—a further vicious cycle. On the other hand, treatment can help users deal with their shame and allow them to hold down a job leading to less drug use, in a stabilising cycle.

- Soft systems methodology, which concentrates on different world views.[3] This method might bring together psychologists who regard drug use to be a result of unresolved trauma, police who see it as disdain for the law, anthropologists who have identified the search for mind-altering experiences as part of every culture, sociologists for whom drug use is an expression of youthful rebellion, civil libertarians who argue it should be a personal freedom, and so on. The aim is to build up the richest possible picture of the situation in which there is perceived to be a problem and then to work through a structured set of processes to decide on a plan of action.

- Agent-based models, which explore how recognisable group patterns can result from simple individual behaviours. Such systems approaches also examine how those patterns are affected by differences in the individual behaviours.[4] For example, a research project I was involved in used an agent-based model to examine the relationship between psychostimulant[5] drug use and resulting harms. Good correlation with real-world prevalence of psychostimulant drug use was found when individual drug using behaviours were classified into five types (no use, occasional weekend use, regular moderate weekend use, regular weekend use with one–three-day 'benders' and daily use), with two primary rules to determine movement between categories—namely individuals increasing use when peers became more involved in drug use and reducing use when friends experienced adverse effects.[6]

There are also other modelling methods that can illuminate different aspects of systems.[7] At this stage the literature about systems approaches is limited in its value for I2S, because illustrative examples relevant to knowledge synthesis are scarce and there is also little analysis that compares different methods.

---

3   Checkland (1984). World views are also referred to as underlying assumptions.
4   Badham (2010).
5   Psychostimulants are drugs like cocaine, amphetamines and ecstasy, which make people feel more alert and energetic. This may be coupled with negative effects like insomnia, paranoia and aggression. For more information, see Australian Drug Information Network (<http://www.adin.com.au/>, accessed 13 December 2011).
6   Moore et al. (2009).
7   Badham (2010).

Tasks for the I2S Development Drive
Collect case examples illustrating how different systems approaches are useful for describing a complex problem and for bringing together discipline-based and stakeholder knowledge.
Work with systems experts to produce a guide to the broad range of systems approaches to a complex problem, emphasising the different ways they bring together discipline-based and stakeholder knowledge.

Scoping

Scoping is a process to look at all the possibilities for gaining a fuller appreciation of a problem, so that the most significant can be identified. It is a critical step in deciding which systems approach to take, as well as which disciplines and stakeholders to involve, by determining the full range of those who have something relevant to contribute. Scoping moves those planning the investigation beyond focusing only on what they know (based on their own interests and expertise) to considering the problem more broadly.

If scoping does not occur, critical issues may be ignored. If we consider the 1940s project of building the atomic bomb, for example, the domination of physical scientists, engineers and the military meant that significant environmental, social and health aspects were not considered, leading to ongoing difficulties in those areas.

In major research tackling significant real-world problems, there will generally be opportunities to build the research team, so the role of scoping is to identify the full range of people who could contribute to the investigation, as well as the breadth of what they could bring to addressing the problem. It aims to help those planning the investigation identify potential collaborators outside their usual circle of partners. This provides the first step in deciding the final composition of the team.

Scoping therefore has two components. One involves setting out all the relevant systems approaches. The other entails identifying—within each systems view—all the pertinent disciplines and stakeholders, what they can potentially contribute to addressing the problem and the various ways in which those contributions could be made.

For disciplines the task is to ascertain the array of topics each relevant discipline could look into and the methods that could be used. For example, in the research program I led on the feasibility of diamorphine prescription to treat heroin dependence, demographers could have made several contributions, such as examining the age and ethnic composition of the heroin-using population or estimating the number of users. There are various ways in which each of these research tasks could have been undertaken. For estimating the number of users, these included network analysis starting with known users, asking experts for estimates using a Delphi technique or interrogating existing data sets. The point here is to think through important issues for the problem, as well as which types of disciplinary experts to include in the research team.[8]

Scoping the potential contributions of stakeholders—those groups who have a practical understanding of the problem—involves different considerations. It is rare for stakeholders to be full members of research teams. They often have little or no research training and are generally employed in other occupations, so are limited in the time they can contribute to any investigation. Those affected by the problem are often large heterogeneous groups whose members have diverse views about the issue. For example, in the research on the feasibility of diamorphine prescription, 31 per cent of police supported a trial, whereas 63 per cent opposed it. For those who provided services to illicit drug users, the comparable figures were 71 per cent and 19 per cent.[9] Those in a position to take action on the problem are often smaller in number, but may also have an array of perspectives. Informal discussions revealed that this was the case, for example, for the government officials who were responsible for illicit drugs policy.

The scoping challenge includes figuring out not only which stakeholders and perspectives to involve, but also a range of possible ways to access their expertise in the research process. This could include, for example: surveys; focus groups; workshops; hiring stakeholders as co-researchers, research assistants or research associates; and working with representatives on advisory committees or more informally. Interactions can range from one-off to intense and sustained.[10] Appropriate recognition of the contributions made is required.[11]

Tasks for the I2S Development Drive
Gather together literature and undocumented practical experience providing concepts for scoping knowledge, methods for undertaking it and illustrative case examples.
Produce a guide to all the potential contributions of different disciplines and stakeholders, focusing on generic issues rather than specifics. Development of the guide requires collaboration with experts who have a broad understanding of each discipline and the various stakeholder groups.

---

8   This process differs from 'business as usual' in at least two ways. It is not only explicit rather than implicit, but also involves thinking about the disciplinary skills needed, rather than just using an expert who is conveniently available and letting them do what they are best at, regardless of how central it is to the problem being examined.

9   The remainder was undecided (Bammer et al. 1996).

10   All of the methods listed were used in the feasibility of diamorphine prescription research and the length and intensity of interactions were also very variable.

11   Depending on the level of involvement, this can be as simple as an acknowledgment in publications or can involve payment. Recognition can also be in-kind, such as teaching the stakeholders particular research skills or providing them with a reference when they are seeking employment. All of these occurred in the feasibility of diamorphine prescription research.

Boundary Setting

The point of scoping is to illuminate a range of options. Practicalities, however, dictate that everything cannot be included in the investigation, so boundaries must be set. This requires systematic thinking about what can best be done with the available time, money and person power. Boundaries define not only what is included and excluded, but also which issues are more central and which are marginal.[12] Both inclusion/exclusion and centrality are relevant to which disciplines and stakeholders are involved in the knowledge synthesis, what they are invited to contribute and how. This translates into allocation of resources, with the lion's share going to the disciplines and stakeholders deemed to be most central.

The point of linking scoping and boundary setting is that it allows the most critical issues to be identified and addressed. It reduces the possibility that the knowledge synthesis effort will miss the mark by focusing on side issues or inadvertently ignoring critical issues. Even when a possibility is ultimately excluded, there is an important difference between ruling something out in the boundary-setting process and not having considered it at all.

Let me illustrate boundary setting by returning to the contributions of the discipline of demography in the feasibility of diamorphine prescription case example mentioned earlier under scoping. We decided that developing an estimate of the number of heroin users was essential to figuring out what the demand for the new treatment might be, so that this was deemed to be the most important contribution the demographers could make. We used existing data sets rather than collecting new data for three reasons: our funding was limited, sampling drug users has many problems and, most significantly, we already had access to a unique data set that was considerably better than any we could have collected.[13]

Elements of scoping and boundary setting occur in all research, usually intuitively. This framework offers two advances, which are important for enhancing the ability of integrative applied research to contribute to tackling complex real-world problems. First, as already described, is to ensure that the problem is central in the considerations. Second is to make the decision process explicit. This allows it to be evaluated and improved in future.

An important aspect of reporting on boundary setting is the systematic documentation of the final decisions about which systems approach was taken, as well as which disciplines and stakeholders were invited to contribute and

---

12   Midgley (2000).
13   Larson (1992); Larson and Bammer (1996).

how those contributions were made. Such accounts are usually missing from descriptions of integrative applied research. But this alone does not allow others to evaluate and learn about the process of boundary setting. Information is also required on how and why decisions were made. There will often be disagreement about the final choices. Unless the boundary-setting process is well described, learning from it to improve future practice is difficult. It is important therefore to document both the concepts and the methods used, as well as to keep a record of the background to and rationale for decisions.

Tasks for the I2S Development Drive
Collate published and unpublished concepts and methods for boundary setting, along with case examples that emphasise how and why decisions were made.

Framing

The frame is the way the problem is presented. The language used to describe the problem is powerful.[14] For example, people who inject illicit drugs can be referred to as 'dirty junkies', 'cool nonconformists' or 'sons and daughters who have lost their way'. Each has specific connotations, which lead to different issues being investigated: perhaps antisocial behaviour for the first framing, creativity for the second and peer pressure for the third. Similarly, research on drug prevention could be defined or framed as 'an examination of individual factors involved in initiating illicit drug use' or alternatively as 'an examination of popular culture and its influence on illicit drug use'. Both are about understanding why young people use illicit drugs as a first step towards more effective prevention, but one approach frames it as a problem of individuals, whereas the other treats it as a societal problem, especially how social norms are communicated through television, music, the Internet and so on.[15]

Critically, the problem will be framed by the way it is described regardless of whether conscious attention is paid to this process. The idea here is to raise awareness of the importance of framing so that the research team can accurately convey what it is setting out to do. This requires more than thinking up a catchy title; it must also be congruent with the knowledge synthesis approach being taken.

---

14   Much of the work on framing has been conducted in the context of selling a political message (see, for example, Lakoff 2004) or advocacy to change policy and/or practice (see, for example, Chapman 2007). These insights need reworking to make them more directly applicable to integrative applied research.

15   Furthermore, in the first framing, psychology would be a key discipline to involve in the investigation, whereas in the second it would be anthropology or culture studies.

Tasks for the I2S Development Drive
Draw together useful concepts and practical methods for framing, along with case examples of when it has worked well and when it has failed.

Dealing with Values

The values brought to the research will both determine and reflect the systems approach used, the way the problem is scoped and the boundaries set, as well as how the problem is framed. In addition, there are likely to be several sets of values in play at the same time: values about the problem, about research and even about the approach that should be taken to values.[16]

In this domain, the task for I2S is to help integrative applied research teams consider the interaction between their values and the knowledge synthesis. For example, are the team's values generating important blind spots about incorporating some kinds of knowledge or leading to disproportionate emphasis on the perspectives of some stakeholders at the expense of others? It is common for research on controversial issues to be affected by values—for example, research on forestry issues may often look only at one side of the debate, concentrating on the views of either loggers or conservationists.

Tasks for the I2S Development Drive
Compile case examples that illustrate different experiences in bringing values into play and their consequences for the knowledge synthesis.
Work with applied philosophers and other experts to produce a guide to concepts and methods for understanding and responding to the various dimensions of values.

Harnessing and Managing Differences

Finally, bringing together different disciplinary and stakeholder perspectives is about more than combining different relevant 'facts'. Among those involved, there will also be differences in, for example, visions for addressing the problem, world views about the problem, epistemological approaches to research, working habits, career goals, and so on.[17] The challenge is to identify and deal separately with two types of differences

---

16 For example, Neuman (2003) compared the way values are dealt with in positivist, 'interpretive' and critical social science. In brief, positivists aim to be value-free and objective; interpretive social scientists favour making values explicit and aim to treat all values equally; whereas critical social scientists have an activist orientation and argue for researcher commitment to a value position.

17 There will also be differences in values. But the importance of values means it warrants its own category.

1. those relevant to developing a rich appreciation of the problem, which need to be harnessed as part of the knowledge synthesis

2. those which may get in the way, which need to be managed so that they do not impact negatively on the knowledge synthesis.[18]

For example, imagine a research program on the future of education to which a demographer, computer scientist and economist are contributing. In figuring out a solid basis for a policy of government provision of computers in schools, they would each have different facts to contribute: the demographer on population distribution and trends, the computer scientist on available hardware and software, and the economist on costs and funding structures. They may well have somewhat different visions about the government policy, so that the demographer might be focused on the geographical distribution of students and how that will change over time, the computer scientist on accommodating differences in intellectual ability and the economist on differential support based on family income. These are all examples of the kinds of information and perspectives that, if harnessed, would effectively contribute to a rich appreciation of the problem.

On the other hand, the demographer and computer scientist may have personality differences that provoke them to dislike each other. In addition, there might be considerable debate about where the results of the knowledge synthesis should be published. Each may want to claim the publication for their discipline and to present the results in a particular way. Multiple publication of the same results is, however, considered bad practice, and even if it could be accommodated, each of the researchers may want to publish first. These differences in personality and personal professional interests are examples of the kinds of differences that need to be managed so that they do not get in the way of the knowledge synthesis.[19]

> **Tasks for the I2S Development Drive**
> Gather together concepts and methods for understanding differences, as well as for harnessing and managing them, along with illustrative case examples.

---

18 Differences can be managed in various ways and a taste of these is provided in Box 26.1 in Chapter 26.
19 The intellectual differences are not always the ones that are harnessed and the personal the ones that are managed. Sometimes the valuable differences are personal. Research on a 24-hour time cycle can make good use of preferences for morning, afternoon and evening work, for example. And sometimes intellectual differences need to be managed, as in the case when researchers have diverse epistemologies.

Dealing with the Six Categories

While it is possible to present the implementation of the six categories of concepts and methods as linear steps—as I have done above—in practice they cannot be dealt with in this way. Instead they need to be considered together and iteratively, as each influences the others.[20] For example, let us return to the imaginary case of government policy on providing computers in schools. Rather than beginning with a systems view, the starting point might be a problem framing focused on the poorest schools and values about supporting the needy. But the economist might want to bring in different values about 'willingness to pay'. This in turn might lead to the identification of the usefulness of causal loops as a systems approach, especially exploring a vicious cycle between low willingness of parents to pay, schools with few resources and poor scholastic performance.

The point is that research is messy and it is difficult to have clear definitions, aims and processes up front. Research that is nailed down too soon leaves little room for creativity and real discovery; instead it is likely to be a mechanical filling in of small gaps. The integrative applied research process can be described by the now common aphorism 'ready, fire, aim'—in other words, find a starting point, initiate some investigations and modify, clarify and tighten up, as the research progresses.

This discussion about iteration, and especially untidiness, may appear to contradict everything that has been presented earlier. The point is not that anything goes. Rather it is that the first tentative steps in the investigation are aimed at choosing a systems approach, furthering the scoping, clarifying the values, and so on. It is likely that at various points throughout the research further adjustments are made. For example, the framing may be recognised as inadequate and require updating, a key disciplinary perspective may be added and a method for engaging a stakeholder group may be dropped. The six categories provide a focus for the iteration and messiness, so that by the end of the research there should be a clear—if complex—story to tell.

Task for the I2S Development Drive

Compile case examples of how iterative processes between the six categories of concepts and methods played out.

---

20   Iteration is not only important in considering the six elements in this question. Iteration between the questions is also necessary. For example, context and scoping are closely intertwined, as I discuss in more detail in Chapter 7. Further, the domains also influence each other. For instance, considerations about the eventual implementation of the research can be crucial in deciding how the knowledge synthesis is approached. It is not possible to describe I2S in a coherent fashion without stripping out many of these complexities, but the practice of I2S needs to allow for iterative and untidier processes.

6. How?

There has been surprisingly little attempt to identify, let alone classify, methods for addressing the question *'How is the disciplinary and stakeholder knowledge synthesised, by whom and when?'*. One way to think about methods is to use three classes

- dialogue-based
- model-, product- or vision-based
- common metric-based.[1]

A brief description of each is presented next. Who undertakes the synthesis is then examined, followed by when in the research process it occurs.

Dialogue-Based Synthesis

Dialogue-based methods use conversation to 'jointly create meaning and shared understanding'.[2] Dialogue-based synthesis does not always need to use formal methods, especially when only a few people are involved. Structured methods are most helpful when groups start to get large, as they ensure that all perspectives are appropriately heard and included.

Fourteen methods suitable for different types of knowledge synthesis have been identified.[3] Some methods are broadly useful, bringing together different people's judgments about an issue. They include consensus conference, Delphi technique and nominal group technique. For example, the Delphi technique was used to develop an implementation plan for sustainability policies at a Canadian university drawing on the judgments of knowledgeable representatives of students, staff, faculty and administrators.[4]

Other dialogue methods are useful for specific tasks, such as combining different visions about an issue (appreciative inquiry) or reconciling various interests (principled negotiation). For example, a UK research team used appreciative inquiry to engage older people's groups, the hospital trust, voluntary agencies and others to figure out how better to meet the needs of the elderly in transition from hospital back to their own homes. There were diverse visions for better

---

1   These three classes of methods are unlikely to exhaust the range of ways in which knowledge synthesis can be undertaken. In addition, these classes overlap; nevertheless, it is useful to consider them separately.
2   Franco (2006, p. 814).
3   McDonald et al. (2009).
4   Wright (2006).

post-hospital experiences—for example, regarding flexible care, individual carer responsibility and process coordination, all of which were drawn together using the method.[5]

The range of dialogue methods can accommodate different requirements and preferences for the engagement of disciplinary and stakeholder expertise.[6] For instance, some methods are most suitable for tasks requiring discipline-based experts only,[7] other techniques work best for bringing together stakeholder views[8] and still others are designed to combine discipline-based and stakeholder knowledge.[9]

Model-, Product- and Vision-Based Synthesis

Model-, product- and vision-based methods are related as they use a specific goal as the focus for synthesis. Model-based methods use the development of a conceptual or mathematical representation of a problem as the 'device' for bringing together disciplinary and stakeholder knowledge. In other words, designing the model is used to stimulate communication and capture the shared understandings. For example, the agent-based model on psychostimulant use I described in Chapter 5 brought together epidemiological and ethnographic research insights.[10] As also indicated in that chapter, there are many modelling approaches, from concept mapping to formal system dynamics or agent-based models.[11] The relative advantages and disadvantages of different models for the purpose of knowledge synthesis remain to be investigated and documented.

Building a product or implementing a vision both rely on the same principle as developing a model in that the focused task brings different understandings together. The development of the atomic bomb is an exemplar of product-based synthesis. This combined knowledge from physical scientists, engineers, the military and private industry.[12] The World Commission on Dams framework for decision making about future dams is an example of vision-based synthesis. A

---

5   Reed et al. (2002).
6   McDonald et al. (2009).
7   An example is the consensus development panel, which was used to bring together discipline-based experts to develop a 'state-of-the-science' statement on prevention, cessation and control of tobacco smoking (National Institutes of Health State-of-the-Science Panel 2006).
8   An illustration is the citizens' jury, which was used to formulate a community decision on the future of a former local wetland, by assisting 16 representatives of the public to come to a judgment based on the best available evidence (Aldred and Jacobs 2000).
9   This is demonstrated by open space technology, which has been used for a range of problems including putting participants from various organisations on an equal footing in generating ideas and plans for the development of the public health workforce in the United Kingdom (Brocklehurst et al. 2005).
10   Moore et al. (2009).
11   Badham (2010).
12   Rhodes (1986).

guiding ideal was proposed for bringing together different perspectives and for deciding on action—namely a globally accepted framework of norms about human rights, economic and social development, and sustainability. These were derived from United Nations declarations and principles. In particular, the Commission used the 'emerging global vision of equitable and sustainable development'[13] to guide the drawing together of the various inputs and to recognise five core values: 'equity, efficiency, participatory decision making, sustainability and accountability'.[14]

Common Metric-Based Synthesis

Common metric-based methods rely on single measures that can be employed to encapsulate the range of relevant disciplinary and stakeholder knowledge about the problem. The best known and most widely used common metric is monetary value. Synthesis can then be based on simple arithmetic or more complex manipulations, such as cost–benefit analysis.

The sort of research problem where common metric-based synthesis might be useful is an examination of the impacts of the encroachment of housing on farmland and bushland on the fringes of cities. This can benefit from the disciplinary expertise of, among others, ecologists, economists, hydrologists, sociologists, soil scientists and demographers. Relevant stakeholders include those affected, such as farmers and recreational users of bushland (whose activities are impinged on by the expansion of housing) and families requiring housing. Stakeholders also include those in a position to make decisions about the issue such as government policy makers, local councilors, regulators and land developers. One way of dealing with the competition for peri-urban land would be to convert the various uses of the land into dollar values and to base decisions on the best financial return. For example, a cost–benefit analysis could focus on the economics of different types of land use. A simple analysis could compare the economic return over a specified period from using the land for farming, maintaining bushland for recreation or building houses. This could be based on the income for local, State and national governments from land taxes and other revenues, such as park entry fees. Involving relevant stakeholders would provide information on other parameters that they consider important, which could include the 'products' of the different types of land use such as food, recreational amenity and contribution to employment through the construction of houses. Alternatively, stakeholders could be involved by being asked about their willingness to pay for the various types of land use.

---

13   World Commission on Dams (2000, p. 198).
14   World Commission on Dams (2000, p. 199).

A different kind of analysis could use an ecosystem services approach[15] to assess each of the three types of land use—farmland, wilderness and housing development—in terms of goods, such as food, timber and biomass produced; regenerative and stabilising processes, such as water catchment and clean air generation; life-fulfilling functions, such as aesthetic value; and preservation of options, such as species diversity. The important difference from standard cost–benefit analysis is the questions posed, such as 'what services are being provided that people have been overlooking', 'how much of these services do people need' and 'to what extent could technology replace nature's services and at what cost'.

Common metric-based synthesis can also use measures other than money. Other common metrics that have been developed and used for environmental problems include the area of land necessary to sustain a given level of resource consumption and waste assimilation (ecological footprint)[16] and metric measures of carbon dioxide equivalent.[17] For health problems, they include disability-adjusted life-years and quality-adjusted life-years.[18] An example of the use of the ecological footprint for knowledge synthesis is a collaboration between university-based researchers and the Cardiff Council in the United Kingdom to assess policies and practice on sustainability.[19]

Tasks for the I2S Development Drive
Identify and catalogue the full range of methods that have been used for knowledge synthesis, as well as their conceptual bases and case examples of their application. Update and improve existing compilations.

Who Undertakes the Synthesis?

It is often assumed that the synthesis should be a group process; however, even though perspectives are drawn from researchers representing a number of different disciplines and from various stakeholder groups, each contributor does not necessarily have to be involved in bringing the knowledge together. The options for undertaking the synthesis are to involve the whole group or a subgroup or for it to be the task of an individual. In the last case the synthesiser is often the research leader.

---

15   Costanza et al. (1997); Daily (1999).
16   Wackernagel and Rees (1996).
17   Michaelowa and Koch (2001).
18   Murray et al. (2000).
19   Cardiff Council (2005); Collins and Flynn (2005, 2007); Collins et al. (2006).

Each of these options has advantages and disadvantages. For example, a disadvantage of involving the whole team is that the time it takes can be very demanding. A disadvantage of the synthesis being undertaken by the team leader is that one person is likely to have only a limited grasp of some aspects of the project.

When is the Synthesis Undertaken?

An additional consideration for undertaking knowledge synthesis is when it will be carried out. Just as there is often an assumption that synthesis will be a whole-group process, some people often presume that it will occur at the end of the research, while others suppose that it must be established right from the beginning. But again there is a range of options, each with advantages and disadvantages.

It is useful to begin by exploring two extremes, epitomised by multidisciplinary and transdisciplinary research. In multidisciplinary research, relatively little attention is given to synthesis at the beginning of the project. Each discipline is left reasonably free to define the problem and to apply its methods as it determines to be appropriate. Synthesis at the end of the project can then be particularly challenging, especially when problem definitions and methods do not fit together readily. Indeed multidisciplinary research often leads to the production of a book, with different chapters by different discipline experts, and with the synthesis left to the reader.[20] For this reason, multidisciplinary research has somewhat fallen out of favour.

Transdisciplinary research aims to deal with the limitations of multidisciplinary investigations by getting agreement on a problem definition, along with the contributions of the different disciplines and stakeholders, at the beginning of the research. This often also includes determining the synthesis method up front, although this is not always spelt out. The synthesis is then generally much more straightforward. The price can be lack of flexibility. It can be hard to introduce new perspectives or to change direction as the research progresses and the importance of new dimensions becomes evident. Comparing these two extremes shows that a key challenge for integrative applied research is to find ways to improve the knowledge synthesis success while maintaining flexibility during the research.[21]

---

20 The introduction and conclusion may provide some synthesis.
21 These two research approaches are compared in greater detail in Chapter 33.

Task for the I2S Development Drive

Collect case examples of implementation of different options for who undertook the knowledge synthesis and when in the research process this occurred.

7. Context?

Developing a systematic way to take context into consideration—in other words, weighing up *'What circumstances might influence the synthesis of disciplinary and stakeholder knowledge?'* is an underdeveloped aspect of I2S.[1] Three areas are considered here: one general and two specific.

1. The overall context of the problem. This is the circumstances that led to the research and that may be influential during its conduct, such as the problem's history, the geographical locations in which it occurs and cultural differences between those affected and those charged with responding to the problem.

2. The sources of authorisation or legitimacy for the knowledge synthesis and how they affect what is investigated.

3. The organisational facilitators of and barriers to undertaking the synthesis of disciplinary and stakeholder knowledge.

Overall Context

It may be useful to start with two examples examining context retrospectively. First, let us return to the building of the atomic bomb. The important contextual factor was World War II (1939–45), which explains why, in scoping the problem, there was minimal attention to social, environmental and health impacts. In the circumstances of a major war including these aspects in the synthesis was not a high priority.

Second, the World Commission on Dams was established against a background of increasing controversy about large-scale dams and a worldwide stalemate in the building of dams where opponents were causing delays and therefore huge cost overruns.[2] There had been a change in the power balance, with those adversely affected by dams gaining influence through collective action and the transnational anti-dam movement.[3] This was allied to a shift in perceptions about appropriate governance, with increasing demands that governments consult their citizens before acting on their behalf.[4] These circumstances help explain

---

1   One characteristic that I2S shares with the social sciences is an appreciation of the importance of context. Unlike the natural sciences, which seek universal laws, the social science disciplines and I2S address issues that are often highly context specific.
2   World Commission on Dams (2000). Note that this is partially disputed by McCully (2001).
3   Khagram (2004).
4   World Commission on Dams (2000).

why the Commission came into existence and why the knowledge synthesis included so many perspectives, as the Commission was trying to be an effective mediator between all the interests.

The general challenge is to find useful starting points for taking context into account in planning knowledge synthesis—in other words, figuring out which circumstances are likely to be most pertinent and how to address them. There is significant overlap with scoping the problem, as many contextual factors—such as the problem's history or geography—correspond to the disciplines that would be considered as part of the scoping process. This is an area that is likely to benefit from the insights of social scientists, in particular.

Tasks for the I2S Development Drive
Collect case examples dealing with overall context relevant to the knowledge synthesis.
Work with a range of social scientists to produce a guide for how context can be taken into account.

Authorisation

The sources of authorisation or legitimacy for any research, including integrative applied research in general and synthesis of disciplinary and stakeholder knowledge in particular, are usually closely tied to the finances. Indeed the provision of funding is, in itself, a major source of legitimacy. For most research, receiving support from a recognised funding source is all that is needed for an investigation to be seen as legitimate and to go ahead;[5] however, in certain cases, such as when projects are large in scale or politically sensitive, authorisation may be more complex. In particular, obtaining backing from influential organisations or individuals may be critical for the research to proceed.

This is illustrated by the establishment of the World Commission on Dams, which was unanimously recommended by the 35 representatives of pro- and anti-dam interests at a 1997 workshop hosted by the World Conservation Union and the World Bank.[6] It seems likely that both the co-sponsorship and the unanimous recommendation by opposing forces were essential for the Commission's legitimacy, giving it both power and moral authority. Power would have come through the standing of the World Conservation Union and the World Bank. Moral authority would have been derived from the balance of

---

5 This is not completely correct, as approval from a properly constituted committee that reviews the ethics of the research is now generally also required.

6 IUCN—World Conservation Union and the World Bank Group (1997); Scudder (2001); World Commission on Dams (2000).

interests represented by influential players on both sides of the dams debate. Moral legitimacy was further built by striving for balance in opposing views among the 12 commissioners and the 68-member stakeholder forum, as well as the broad funding base drawing on 53 public, private and civil society organisations.[7,8]

As well as providing legitimacy, however, both funding and backing can also impose limitations. Funding success may be patchy, so that only some aspects of a research program may eventuate. Constraints on what is undertaken or how can be imposed by organisations that auspice research or members of boards that oversee research. Authorisation therefore shapes the way integrative applied research is approached, including what knowledge is synthesised and how, through both what the funding will support and other restrictions resulting from the legitimisation process.

> **Task for the I2S Development Drive**
>
> Gather case examples describing funding, endorsement and other forms of authorisation, along with any restrictions on knowledge synthesis.

Organisational Facilitators and Barriers

The third contextual issue is organisational facilitators and barriers, which can impact on synthesis of disciplinary and stakeholder knowledge. Here the focus is on the research organisations. It may be useful to think about structure and culture separately. For example, structural issues can include the disciplinary mix in an organisation, the availability of seed funding to encourage cross-disciplinary collaboration and organisational financial mechanisms. If a centre established to examine global climate change does not include any social scientists, for instance, it is probably less likely that good social science research will be part of the knowledge synthesis. In contrast, seed funding to encourage collaborations between researchers who have not worked together before may increase the numbers of disciplines included in the knowledge synthesis.[9] Similarly, barriers to sharing money across different parts of an organisation may

---

7 World Commission on Dams (2000). The Commission worked within a budget of just less than US$10 million (Scudder 2001).

8 For a taste of the politicisation referred to in footnote 1 of this Chapter, instructive perspectives are provided by two insider accounts, which argue that the Commission's desire for balance was exploited by the anti-dam movement representatives, who also outmanouvered the pro-dam and government interests (McCully, 2001; Briscoe, 2010). In addition, Briscoe argued that the broader context (the strong influence of "'red-green' coalitions – a combustible mixture of rich-country anti-capitalists and environmentalists"), allowed the anti-dam movements to usurp the legitimate role of governments.

9 The Australian Research Alliance for Children and Youth (ARACY) effectively used seed funding to promote such new collaborations <http://www.aracy.org.au/index.cfm?pageName=apply_for_seed_funding> (accessed 10 August 2011).

work against joint funding applications and reduce disciplinary scope. Cultural factors can include organisational attitudes towards stakeholders and norms regarding idea exchange. If the organisation's leaders are antagonistic towards particular stakeholders, such as big business or particular non-government organisations, it is less likely that their perspectives will be included in the knowledge synthesis. If it is 'the done thing' that everyone attends morning or afternoon tea breaks or annual retreats, this may facilitate cross-fertilisation of ideas between disciplines.

It is easy enough to speculate on the importance of organisational structure and culture for knowledge synthesis, but there is little published evidence of actual impact. Given that organisations involved in knowledge synthesis are likely to differ substantially in structure and culture (in both obvious and subtle ways), it may also not be sensible to look for generic facilitators and barriers. For example, an organisation composed entirely of natural scientists may have a long history of collaborating with one or more social science organisations, so that its own disciplinary limitations are not an issue. Similarly, financial managers may be adept at finding ways to work around obstacles that stand in the way of sharing grant income. Then again, organisations may have regular gatherings of their researchers, but the focus may be on discussing sport, political events and gossip rather than exchanging research ideas.

A more useful way forward may be to design a series of questions that prompts integrative applied research teams to reflect on their organisation's structure and culture, to identify facilitators and barriers, and to find ways to overcome the barriers and maximise the facilitators. This could include questions like

- which disciplines are represented in the organisation; which ones regularly work together; are there collaborators outside the organisation
- with which stakeholders is there a history of working; are any arenas consistently missing; what determines the stakeholder groups involved
- have there been problems in the past in sharing funding; what impact did these have and were ways found to overcome them?

Recording and sharing such observations may help spark ideas about ways to overcome barriers. Even if the circumstances are quite different, learning about how other integrative applied research teams have overcome problems may generate fresh thinking in a team that is facing particular obstacles.

Task for the I2S Development Drive
Compile case examples describing the diversity and impact of organisational barriers and facilitators.

8. Outcome?

One advantage of the structured approach resulting from the five-question framework is that it also provides a systematic process for evaluation, relevant to question five: '*What is the result of the synthesis of disciplinary and stakeholder knowledge?*' Questions relevant for evaluation are presented in Box 8.1.

Box 8.1 Questions for Evaluating Synthesis of Disciplinary and Stakeholder Knowledge

How well did the synthesis meet its aims and include the beneficiaries (relevant disciplinary experts and stakeholders)?

Was the systems view taken suitable? Would a different systems view have been more useful?

Was the full range of pertinent systems views and applicable disciplines and stakeholders recognised and assessed?

Within the necessary limitations of the research, were the most worthwhile disciplines and stakeholders included? Was the balance between different disciplines and stakeholders fitting? Did any of those excluded turn out to be critical?

Was the problem framed accurately?

Were values considered adequately?

Were the differences in the team relevant to developing a rich appreciation of the problem harnessed effectively? Were potentially destructive differences well managed?

Were sufficient flexibility and iteration built into the processes of deciding on a systems view, scoping, boundary setting, framing, considering values, and harnessing and managing differences?

Were applicable synthesis methods used? Would other methods have made better contributions? Were justifiable decisions made in choosing by whom and when the synthesis was undertaken?

Was the overall context for the knowledge synthesis adequately considered? Were critical contextual factors missed?

Was the authorisation for the knowledge synthesis apposite? Did it influence the knowledge synthesis in significant ways?

Did the host organisational structure or culture provide barriers to the knowledge synthesis? If so, were these effectually recognised and managed? Were facilitators beneficially mobilised?

Knowing what to evaluate is one thing, figuring out how to undertake the evaluation is another. In traditional disciplines, the research is assessed by others from that discipline through peer review.[1] Developing I2S as a discipline also makes peer review feasible for knowledge synthesis specifically, and for integrative applied research more generally. Those who have been involved in the knowledge synthesis aspects of projects are in the best position to act as reviewers and I2S provides elements for reviewers to assess, as outlined in the questions above.

In order for a peer-review process to be effective, the research has to be recorded so that all the critical aspects are highlighted. The five-question framework aims to provide an appropriate structure for such documentation.

Task for the I2S Development Drive
Gather and analyse case examples of evaluation both to improve the list of assessment questions and to develop more detailed guidelines for reviewers.

---

1 Although peer review has its limitations, it is still more efficient and flexible than the alternatives. The main point here is that I2S and integrative applied research should be evaluated in the same way as other disciplinary research.

9. Specialising in I2S

Even after exploring only the first domain of I2S, it is clear that there are many specialist concepts, methods and skills that will assist integrative applied research teams to enhance their effectiveness—and that there are too many for experts in existing disciplines to simply add to their repertoires. I propose that there are three broad categories of I2S specialisation.

1. I2S for team leaders. Leaders must know enough about I2S to be responsible for I2S processes, like deciding on the integrative applied research aims and who will undertake the knowledge synthesis.

2. I2S disciplinary specialists. They must have detailed knowledge of concepts, methods and case examples, as well as guides to relevant knowledge from outside I2S, to assist integrative applied research teams in choosing how they will proceed from the full range of available options. In addition, I2S disciplinary specialists are responsible for strengthening their own discipline, including ensuring appropriate application of existing methodologies, as well as developing new ones.

3. I2S appreciation for other integrative applied research team members. They need to have a general understanding of I2S so that they can effectively work with their team leader, the I2S disciplinary specialist(s) and each other.

I2S for Team Leaders

Team leaders have responsibility for the project as a whole. Their knowledge about I2S enables them to guide a process of working systematically through the five questions and ensuring the wherewithal to do so; in other words, that each team includes one or more I2S disciplinary specialists who have the necessary conceptual and method skills for the tasks such as scoping, framing and synthesis of disciplinary and stakeholder knowledge.[1] Leaders also have responsibility for how decisions about knowledge synthesis are made—for example, whether all team members are involved or whether the team leader or a small group is charged with deciding which disciplinary and stakeholder knowledge to bring together and how. The leaders' I2S expertise must be comprehensive enough to direct the tasks described in Box 9.1.

---

1 Of course, the leader may themselves be an I2S specialist; however, for the purposes of a straightforward discussion, I treat team leaders and I2S specialists separately.

Box 9.1 Specific I2S Responsibilities for Integrative Applied Research Team Leaders

Team leaders must have adequate knowledge about I2S to ensure that

- objectives and beneficiaries are specifically considered, so that teams target their efforts most effectively
- their teams are open to options when considering all aspects of knowledge synthesis including various systems views, ways of scoping and methods for knowledge synthesis
- differences are appropriately harnessed or managed
- their teams understand that formulaic processes are not realistic; instead research is messy, iteration is essential and the investigative process will evolve as the project progresses (this must be counterbalanced by making pragmatic, defensible decisions and not getting bogged down in process)[a]
- sources of authorisation and how they affect what is investigated are understood
- organisational barriers and facilitators, and how they can be, respectively, overcome and exploited are understood
- their teams are committed to drawing on, and contributing to the further development of, the best I2S concepts, methods and case examples, as well as guides to relevant knowledge from outside I2S.

a. This is true not only for the considerations in question two, but also for the five questions as a whole. For example, in this domain, it is very difficult to determine all the relevant angles, and to get them 'right', up front. Instead, it is common for important disciplines or stakeholders to be overlooked, for experts with mismatched skill sets to be chosen, for less important areas to be overemphasised, and so on. A critical role of the team leader is, therefore, to help the team implement a research process that is iterative and evolves as the research progresses.

I2S Disciplinary Specialists

I2S disciplinary specialists have the detailed knowledge that makes it possible for integrative applied research teams to function effectively. Their knowledge about I2S provides them with an overview of the full scope of the discipline, mastery of relevant concepts and methods, and the ability to apply them, which they have learnt through case studies and hands-on experience. They are also adept at using guides to relevant knowledge from outside I2S. It is unlikely that individual specialists will be equally proficient in all of the relevant concepts, methods, guides and applications, but they will have a basic working knowledge of them all and be able to bring in colleagues if their team needs skills that they do not have. I2S disciplinary specialists, therefore, have an understanding of all of the tasks described in Box 9.2 and outstanding ability in some of them. One of their chief roles is to make the team leader and other team members aware of available options and their strengths and weaknesses, assisting the choice of the most apposite for the particular problem, as well as team skills and inclinations.[2]

Box 9.2 Skills for I2S Disciplinary Specialists

I2S disciplinary specialists must have a basic working knowledge of all of the following specific skills and particular competence in some

- systems thinking to conceptualise and deal with problems as systems
- scoping to determine the full range of systems views that could be applied to the problem, as well as the relevant disciplines and stakeholders, including what they could contribute and how
- boundary setting to determine what is included and excluded, as well as which of the included disciplinary and stakeholder knowledge is central and which is more peripheral
- framing to communicate the approach to the problem accurately and effectively
- dealing with values
- methods for knowledge synthesis, including dialogue methods, modelling and other targeted techniques (using products and vision), and common metric-based methods
- understanding overall context to ensure that the most important factors are considered.

Another key responsibility is to continue the development of the I2S discipline by

- being on the lookout for opportunities to improve, or develop new, concepts, methods and guides, and to publish any advances
- writing up innovative aspects of projects as new case examples
- ensuring that the knowledge synthesis is documented in a way that makes it easy to evaluate and draw lessons from—by teams themselves and by peers
- helping teams reflect on outcomes and ways to improve the application of the I2S discipline in future projects
- being involved in conferences and the reviewing process for grants and publications.

Such activities will continue to hone their expertise, as well as to enhance the quality and contributions of the discipline.

---

2   Although skills and inclinations should not be the main driving forces (as I have discussed under scoping and boundary setting in Chapter 5), they are relevant factors.

I2S Appreciation for Other Integrative Applied Research Team Members

The extent to which other team members require an appreciation of the I2S discipline depends on the specific type of integrative applied research being undertaken. If the intention is to have strong team involvement in all the knowledge synthesis activities then the team members need to have a good overview of I2S to allow them to trust and fully participate in the processes established by their team leader and the I2S disciplinary specialist(s). On the other hand, if the team leader and the I2S disciplinary specialist(s) undertake all or most of the knowledge synthesis activities, with the other team members predominantly involved in making their expertise available but not engaging in scoping, synthesis or other processes, the other team members do not need as much familiarity with the I2S discipline.

***

In wrapping up this section, it is useful to recall the analogies with statistics described in Chapters 1 and 2. The different I2S specialisations in an integrative applied research team can be likened to the range of statistics expertise in a team-based quantitative research project. The team leader does not have to be a statistics expert, but must know enough to work effectively with the statistician(s) to design the experiments and develop an analysis protocol. The statistics experts have to be masters of their discipline, so that they can help plan the most appropriate designs and analyses. If warranted, they should be able to suggest where the development of new methodologies would fit into the research program. The other team members need to know enough to conform with (and not undermine) the research plan and to support any innovations.[3]

The chapters covering this domain have provided a systematic approach to planning and reporting synthesis of disciplinary and stakeholder knowledge through detailed consideration of a five-question framework. They have also outlined the concepts, methods, case examples and guides that must be collected and developed to make I2S an effective discipline through a Big-Science-like project: the I2S Development Drive.

In the next group of chapters, the framework is applied to the second domain of integrative applied research and I2S—namely understanding and managing diverse unknowns.

---

3 Examples include adhering to the randomisation process in a randomised controlled trial (and not allocating participants according to preference) and collecting data according to the protocols established.

Domain 2. Understanding and Managing Diverse Unknowns

10. Introduction

In 2003, when Professor Aileen Plant went to Vietnam to head the World Health Organisation (WHO) response to a new mystery killer disease, she dived into a sea of unknowns.[1] This was a disease that had no clear-cut clinical diagnosis and for which there was no test. The organism that caused it was unknown, as was its mode of transmission. It was not evident how long those with the illness were able to infect others or indeed what the outcome would be for those affected.

Just as Plant arrived in Vietnam, the WHO gave the new disease a catchy but non-specific name: SARS—for 'severe acute respiratory syndrome'. Despite the unknowns, public health officials and the community had to act. For example, Plant had to advise on a range of issues for which there were no definitive answers, such as:

> *How often should the front counter in a bank be cleaned?*
>
> *Should a mother who has recovered from SARS breast-feed her child?*
>
> *When could people who have had SARS resume sexual activity?*
>
> *If a woman has SARS, should her husband be allowed to serve food in his restaurant?*
>
> *When is it safe to discharge people with SARS from hospital?*
>
> *When was a person with SARS first infectious to other people?*
>
> *Can people have SARS but no symptoms?[2]*

The requirement to act in the face of widespread unknowns applies not only to problems like SARS, but also to other complex social and environmental challenges such as organised crime, global climate change and population ageing.[3] There are two primary purposes in highlighting the importance of unknowns. One is to explain why actions taken to address complex real-world problems will inevitably be imperfect. As I explain later in this chapter, this is an unavoidable consequence of the characteristics of unknowns, especially that

---

1   Plant (2008).
2   Plant (2008, p. 48).
3   Key factors differentiating between problems are the prominence of the unknowns and the urgency for action. These are both extreme in cases like SARS, whereas for other issues there may not be as many unknowns and/or there can be an extended time to plan responses to deal with them.

they are unlimited while ability to investigate them is constrained. Furthermore responding effectively to such inescapable imperfection is difficult. Some reactions to be avoided are briefly described.

Finding appropriate ways to handle unknowns and imperfection leads to the second purpose. The ultimate goal of highlighting the importance of unknowns is to help policy makers and practitioners make the best possible decisions, which cannot be based on the available evidence alone. Ignoring unknowns can lead to misguided actions and unintended negative consequences, which can be catastrophic.[4] Of course, perfect decisions and actions are not possible, but taking unknowns into account aims to allow more realistic assessment of the adequacy of decisions, as well as better preparation for things that can go wrong. At this stage understanding about unknowns is not sophisticated enough for this goal to be achievable. Instead, the chapters for this domain lay out a broader conceptualisation of unknowns and responses to them to set the direction for future work.

At the end of this chapter, I provide additional background for this domain by describing various kinds of unknowns. Furthermore, the diversity of unknowns does not easily map onto the different perspectives of disciplines and stakeholders. Instead, those perspectives introduce further complexities and these are also briefly described.

In the remaining chapters in this section a more comprehensive approach to unknowns is explored systematically using the five-question framework, which for this domain becomes the following.

1. What is the understanding and management of diverse unknowns aiming to achieve and who is intended to benefit? (For what and for whom?)

2. Which unknowns are considered? (Which unknowns?)

3. How are diverse unknowns understood and managed, by whom and when? (How?)

4. What circumstances might influence the understanding and management of diverse unknowns? (Context?)

5. What is the result of understanding and managing diverse unknowns? (Outcome?)

---

4 Interventions that have unintended adverse consequences are common. For example, police action to reduce the visibility of illicit drug use in one geographical area can lead to displacement of the activity, more risky injecting practices and increased violence and fraud (Aitken et al. 2002). Fortunately, catastrophic events are scarcer, but examples include the marketing of thalidomide as a cure for morning sickness in the late 1950s and the reform of the Russian economy following the breakdown of the Soviet Union in the early 1990s.

As with the previous domain, each question is discussed in turn in order to flesh out the I2S structure and the broad categories of concepts and methods that are encompassed. This is summarised in Figure 10.1. (Let me reiterate that populating the structure with the full range of concepts, methods, case examples and guides to relevant knowledge from outside I2S is not the function of this book, but is the task of the I2S Development Drive. This involves not only collating what is already known and practised, but also considerable original investigation to enhance understanding about unknowns.) Chapter 16 concludes this section by describing how the three different kinds of specialisation in I2S deal with diverse unknowns in order to enhance the work of integrative applied research teams.

Before considering the five-question framework, let us examine the three background issues foreshadowed earlier: the inevitability and challenges of imperfection, appreciating different kinds of unknowns, and understanding where disciplines and stakeholders sit in relation to unknowns. The chapter then finishes by considering knowledge synthesis (Domain 1) and unknowns (Domain 2) together to examine where to draw the line between them.

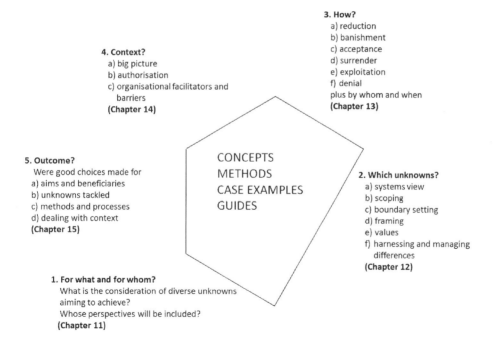

Figure 10.1 The Storeroom for Understanding and Managing Diverse Unknowns, Listing the Key Categories of Concepts and Methods

Source: Author's illustration.

The Inevitability and Challenges of Imperfection

Imperfection is inevitable when addressing the complex real-world problems central to integrative applied research. As described next, this arises because unknowns are unlimited (and some are unresolvable), while research capacity is constrained. The challenge then becomes how to craft an appropriate response to complex problems in light of this unavoidable clash. A first step is to highlight responses to be avoided.

Unlimited Unknowns and Constrained Research Capacity

There are at least four reasons why unknowns cannot be contained

1. change is constant, so new unknowns will continue to arise

2. research will always uncover new unknowns

3. some things are unknowable

4. techniques to research some unknowns have not yet been developed.

An example of constant change is that bacteria and viruses continually evolve to exploit human, animal and plant niches, inexorably leading to new diseases; however, it is not possible to predict what the next new disease will be or where or when it will strike. Similarly, human ingenuity will persist in inventing new technology with some innovations—like the Internet and the mobile phone—being revolutionary. But the next major breakthrough cannot be determined. Change is not only manifested in evolution and technology, but also in culture, and economic and social conditions.

Another source of change is the illumination of new unknowns through research, which warrants consideration in its own right. One demonstration of research uncovering novel unknowns is the common conclusion in research papers pointing to areas where more research is required. But research not only raises previously unasked questions to be addressed. Even the knowledge produced can increase unknowns by generating more, rather than fewer, conflicting views.[5]

The third source of unlimited unknowns is that some things are unknowable. Mathematics and quantum physics provide solid evidence for the irreducibility

---

5   Rayner (2006).

(or unknowability) of at least some unknowns.[6] It is likely that there are also irreducible unknowns in other areas, with current debates in both history and economics providing examples.[7]

Some unknowns may not be irreducible in principle, but are currently so in practice because available methods do not exist to address them adequately. This is the fourth source of unlimited unknowns. For example, there are ancient texts that cannot be translated.[8] Similarly, understanding illicit drug use is limited by many users keeping this behaviour secret and not participating in research. There are no reliable methods for identifying and accessing them.[9] While methodological breakthroughs will occur from time to time, new unsolvable problems will also continue to arise.

It is sobering to couple the unconstrained nature of unknowns with the fact that the capacity to undertake research is a limited resource.[10] Consequently, there can never be enough researchers or funding to study all the important problems existing at any one time. Furthermore, research effort is unevenly distributed on a global scale, with many more researchers in developed countries than in the industrially developing world.[11] Not surprisingly, this means that less research is conducted into the complex real-world problems of the latter countries.[12]

---

6   In mathematics, Gödel and others in the 1930s established that no extensive mathematical system, such as arithmetic, can be both consistent and complete. Here 'consistency' means that the mathematical framework never generates paradoxes or contradictions and 'complete' means that every meaningful statement generated by the mathematical system can be proven true or false. Thus mathematics can never be freed of both paradoxes and undecidable propositions. (This idea was developed by Smithson, based on Nagel and Newman 1959, and described in Bammer et al. 2008.) In other words, developing a mathematical system that is consistent means that it will contain unknowns in terms of propositions that cannot be proven true or false. Similarly, developing a mathematical system that is complete means that it will contain unknowns in the form of paradoxes. For a more detailed discussion, see Smithson (1989). An analogous situation occurs in quantum physics, where the location and momentum (speed and direction of travel) of a subatomic particle cannot both be known with precision at the same time. Knowing the location means that momentum is unknown, and knowing momentum means that one has no idea where the particle actually is (Buckman 2008).
7   In history, some see certain historical knowledge as possible, or at least as limited only by shortcomings in the evidence, while others argue that since history is always written in the present, it will always bear the imprint of particular concerns and perspectives. In their view it will always require rewriting, as new questions from the present prompt new ways of reading and interpreting the historical evidence (Curthoys 2008). Similarly in economics: 'Discussion of problems involving uncertainty is polarized between advocates of formal decision theories, who claim that uncertainty can be tamed by careful consideration of information and elicitation of preferences, and critics who argue that uncertainty is fundamentally irreducible' (Quiggin 2008, p. 201).
8   This is also confounded by uncertainty about whether the texts are genuine; see, for example, Láng (2010) and news articles on the Voynich Manuscript and the Dorabella Code in *New Scientist* (21 May 2011, p. 44).
9   Ritter (2008).
10   For example, Lindblom (1990, p. 162) contended: 'Professional inquiry is a scarce resource even in a wealthy U.S., never abundant enough to permit study of all important social phenomena and problems, even if the entire adult population became social scientists.' This is true for researchers in general.
11   Examination of research capacity across low, lower-middle, upper-middle and high-income economies shows stark differences on a range of measures (Anderson and Bammer 2005).
12   The Global Forum for Health Research, for example, was established specifically to redress that imbalance in health research; see <http://www.globalforumhealth.org/> (accessed 20 December 2011).

Inappropriate Responses to Imperfection

It can be hard to acknowledge that there are no perfect ways forward for major real-world problems, and overconfidence that an answer exists is one response to be avoided. Steve Rayner highlighted that this is an issue for researchers in relation to policy making on environmental risk:[13]

> [P]olicy makers are consistently led to believe that, given time and money, scientific inquiry will reduce relevant uncertainty about environmental risk. Their scientific advisors hold out the promise that more fine-grained information will clarify the nature and extent of the problem and enable policy makers to craft efficient and effective responses.

Rayner then went on to point out why this is mistaken, based not only on the new areas research uncovers, but also on the often conflicting findings of different investigations (already mentioned above). An additional issue is that it may not be possible to even uncover all the unknowns. This may be a consequence of limited resources, but is also a feature of some unknowns (so-called 'unknown unknowns', discussed below).

In raising the unavoidability of imperfection, it is important not only to combat arrogance about certainty, but also to avoid falling into the opposite trap of hopelessness and nihilism. Some actions, even if imperfect, are much better than others. The successful containment of the SARS epidemic[14] showed that it is possible to manage effectively in the face of overwhelming unknowns. Taking no action would have been a great deal worse.

A different challenge associated with imperfection is hindsight bias, where actions are criticised based on information the decision makers did not have at the time. This is illustrated by the 2009 outbreak of the H1N1 (swine flu) virus, where the imposition of quarantine and other restrictions was criticised when the virus turned out to be less deadly than first thought.[15]

A further challenge raised by the need to find ways of accepting and managing imperfection is to avoid providing hiding places for incompetence or corruption. Here the impossibility of obtaining a full picture of a situation may be offered as an excuse for not taking sensible action or for taking action that is self-serving rather than directed at the problem. An example of incompetence is where irrelevant information is used to justify a decision because that is all that is available, such as when cost–benefit analysis is used even though most of the relevant costs and benefits cannot be expressed in dollar values. Corruption can

---

13   Rayner (2006, p. 5).
14   Plant (2008).
15   See, for example, Fineberg (2011).

be illustrated by the casting of doubt to stymie action based on solid evidence, as occurred when the tobacco industry sought to question the link between smoking and lung cancer.[16]

Appreciating Different Kinds of Unknowns

Two ways of describing unknowns are presented to provide insight into their diverse range. The first is a broad characterisation of three kinds of unknowns. The second is a more detailed taxonomy. Understanding the different kinds of unknowns is a critical step in developing more suitable and comprehensive ways of responding to them.[17]

Three Kinds of Unknowns

The matrix presented in Figure 10.2 is a useful—and increasingly acknowledged—way of distinguishing unknowns.

		META-LEVEL	
		Known	*Unknown*
PRIMARY LEVEL	*Known*	Known knowns	Known unknowns (conscious ignorance)
	Unknown	Unknown knowns (tacit knowledge)	Unknown unknowns (meta-ignorance)

Figure 10.2 Distinguishing Different Kinds of Unknowns

Source: Adaptation by Michael Smithson of Kerwin (1993), published in Bammer et al. (2008, p. 293).

Of the three kinds of unknowns, the most familiar is ignorance that we are aware of: the 'known unknowns'. For example, we know that we do not know how much genes contribute to criminal behaviour or how to accurately predict long-range weather. Most research addresses this kind of ignorance, seeking to fill in known knowledge gaps.

Another kind of unknown is knowledge that we do not know we have, the 'unknown knowns' or 'tacit knowledge'. Becoming a disciplinary expert involves being socialised into particular ways of thinking and operating, some of which

---

16 Littlemore (2010).

17 Bammer and Smithson (2008); Bammer and The Goolabri Group (2007); Smithson (2008a). Smithson also points out this topic does not have an agreed nomenclature. In earlier work we used the term 'uncertainty'; for this book I use 'unknowns'.

are explicit and some of which are tacit.[18] Culturally appropriate behaviours are another example of tacit knowledge. These include body language, how people address each other, how conversations are conducted and what is considered to be polite.[19]

The third kind of ignorance is what we do not know we do not know: the 'unknown unknowns'.[20] This can be a difficult concept both to understand and to do something about. We generally become aware of unknown unknowns in two ways. Some unknown unknowns catch everyone by surprise and the only way we can become aware of those is through hindsight. For example, before 2003, SARS was an unknown unknown—we did not know that such a disease was developing and would strike. But other unknown unknowns are specific to individuals or communities, so that people can see them in each other and alert each other to them. I might, for example, believe that there is only one kind of rice. A Pakistani colleague or a good cook could quickly disabuse me of that. Such blind spots can also occur on a much larger scale. For example, when the US Government was planning the 2003 invasion of Iraq, promotion of democracy was part of its rationale. The US officials could not see that they were conflating democracy with 'Americanisation' and it took UK Government officials to point this out to them.[21]

Let us move on now to a categorisation of unknowns that teases out much finer-grained differences.

A Taxonomy of Unknowns

Figure 10.3 presents a taxonomy developed by Smithson, who uses the overarching term 'ignorance' as the starting point. He first distinguishes between passive and active ignorance. Passive ignorance involves areas that we are ignorant of, whereas active ignorance refers to areas we ignore. He uses the term 'error' for the unknowns encompassed by passive ignorance and 'irrelevance' for active ignorance.

18 When I was a biochemistry honours student, for example, I explicitly learnt various biochemical theories and facts, and had good laboratory processes instilled more tacitly. Laboratory-based research requires attention to possible contaminants, so that processes were inculcated to minimise this risk using specific ways of washing and drying glassware, cleanliness and avoidance of clutter on benchtops, required behaviours, such as wearing protective clothing, and unacceptable behaviours such as horseplay. Appropriate procedures became second nature and were usually intuitively applied when new situations arose.

19 O'Sullivan (1994).

20 These unknowns gained some notoriety when former US Secretary of Defence Donald Rumsfeld made remarks about them to US troops in Korea on 18 November 2003. See <http://www.iwar.org.uk/news-archive/2003/11-21-9.htm> (accessed 21 December 2011).

21 Campbell and Scott (2008).

The different elements of the taxonomy are explained in Box 10.1. The main point here is to demonstrate that there are multiple kinds of unknowns, many, if not all, of which will be inherent in any complex problem.

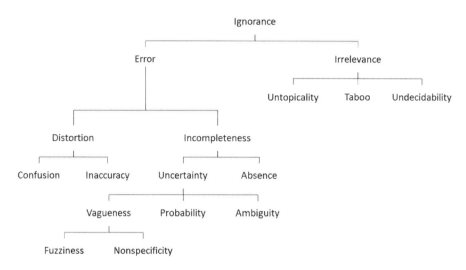

Figure 10.3 Different Kinds of Unknowns

Source: Smithson (1989, p. 9); also in Bammer et al. (2008, p. 294).

Box 10.1 An Explanation of Smithson's Typology

Having differentiated passive (error) from active (irrelevance) ignorance, let us examine the types of unknowns under 'error'. Smithson distinguishes two sources of error: 'distortion' and 'incompleteness'. One type of distortion, 'confusion', involves wrongful substitution—mistaking one attribute for another. Mistaking a block of cheese for a bar of soap is an example of confusion. The other, 'inaccuracy', is distortion in degree or bias. Assuming that all swans are white is an example of inaccuracy.

In terms of 'incompleteness', Smithson first differentiates between what he calls 'incompleteness in degree' or 'uncertainty', and 'incompleteness in kind' or 'absence'. Let us deal with absence first. Absence is simply gaps in knowledge, which can be known or unknown gaps.

If we turn now to 'uncertainty', Smithson's taxonomy uses this term to refer to partial information. He subdivides uncertainty into three categories: 'vagueness', 'probability' and 'ambiguity'. In brief, vagueness relates to a range of possible values on a continuum; probability, simply put, refers to the laws of chance; and ambiguity refers to a finite number of distinct possibilities. In expanding on these, let us begin with vagueness.

Smithson subdivides vagueness into 'fuzziness' and 'non-specificity'. Fuzziness refers to fine-grade distinctions and blurry boundaries. For example, an object may be dark, but there is no clear boundary where darkness begins and ends. Non-specificity is another kind of vagueness. An example relates to geographical location. To say that someone lives *near* a school does not give any indication of whether they are a five-minute walk away or a five-minute drive away.

Moving on to probability, the classic example refers to numerous tosses of a fair coin and the likely outcome that half of the tosses will land heads and half tails. It is worth noting, however, that despite the pervasiveness of probability and its underpinning of the discipline of statistics, the concept is by no means well defined, so that there is considerable work to be done to address the question 'What sorts of things are probabilities?'.[a] In reality, much statistics involves tackling problems that combine vagueness and probability. While probability does not help us with the vague statements provided as illustrations in the previous paragraph, it can assist with other vague statements, such as 'this ticket may win money in the lottery' or 'today some drivers will be injured in an accident'. Probability then helps us calculate the chance of winning or being injured.

The final item in the 'error' side of the taxonomy is 'ambiguity', which is best demonstrated though a linguistic example. To say that food is hot does not clearly tell us if this refers to temperature or spiciness. In terms of disciplines, ambiguity is prominent in the law, where nuances of interpretation can be critical.[b]

Let us now move to the second main arm in the taxonomy (Figure 10.3). 'Irrelevance' refers to issues that are deliberately or unconsciously overlooked. Smithson divides irrelevance into three subcategories—namely 'untopicality', 'taboo' and 'undecidability'.

For the first of these, in the consideration of any particular issue, some things will be generally agreed to be off topic. In defence policy decisions, for example, the price of children's toys would generally not be considered topical.

In terms of taboo, this refers to matters people must not know or even inquire about. This is socially enforced irrelevance. Taboo is important in the discipline of history, for example. The attempt to open up some issues—such as the Holocaust, the nuclear bombing of Japan in World War II or the demise of Australian Aborigines—to further examination can be highly controversial. Curthoys[c] has highlighted the conflict that can ensue when national audiences 'want a story that reassures them about the morality of the national past' but also want the truth, which may be that 'the national past may not be entirely or even mainly praiseworthy'.

The final kind of irrelevance is undecidability, which happens when a matter cannot be designated true or false or when deciding on truth/falsity is not pertinent. The first kind of undecidability overlaps with our earlier considerations of 'irreducability'. We have seen that there are truly undecidable matters in both physics and mathematics.

The second kind of undecidability is where the issues of truth and falsehood are largely irrelevant. The law provides an example in that it 'specifically acknowledges that, in the courtroom context, progress to a decision occurs on the basis of finding facts for the purpose of the court's decision—with only coincidental regard for objective "truth"'.[d] In other words, a 'fact' for legal purposes may not be as tightly defined as a scientific fact.

a. Hájek (2008).
b. Jones (2008).
c. Curthoys (2008, p. 134).
d. Jones (2008, p. 275).

Understanding Where Disciplines and Stakeholders Sit in Relation to Unknowns

Let us begin with disciplines and three important considerations, namely: a) different kinds of unknowns do not clearly map onto existing disciplines, b) no discipline covers more than a fraction of the terrain, and c) disciplines raise additional considerations about unknowns that cannot be covered by taxonomies. I only provide a flavour of these considerations here—the detailed work required is part of the I2S Development Drive.

First, if we look at the unknowns covered in the discipline of history[22] and Smithson's typology, we see that there is no neat overlap. What history deals with includes

- absence, which occurs when records are missing

- inaccuracy, which arises when it is not clear how representative the records are for a particular period—for example, the rich are more likely to leave records than the poor, but even those records may not be typical of all rich people at that time

- taboo, which ensues when some historical events are closed to scrutiny; this was described in Box 10.1 in relation to the conflict between the desire of national audiences for a version of events that fits a favourable national self-image and what really happened, which may not be at all admirable.

Further, even though history contends with each of these aspects of unknowns, it is not the only relevant discipline for any of them, nor does it, by itself, provide a comprehensive understanding of any of these unknowns. Any correspondence is only partial. If we take inaccuracy, for example, psychology also has a lot to contribute, particularly in terms of different kinds of cognitive bias that are inherent in processing information and making decisions.[23]

Second, even though dealing with the unknown is the 'bread and butter'[24] of statistics, this discipline covers only a small part of the terrain. Taking Smithson's typology, the discipline of statistics primarily operates in the area of incompleteness, across probability and some kinds of vagueness.[25] In terms of its considerations of sampling bias, statistics also has some overlap with inaccuracy. But, as the typology shows, there is much more to unknowns than the areas statistics deals with. We can take this description of limited coverage further by examining the value of statistics to history. We can see that statistics is of no use for issues of absence or taboo. Even in the area of inaccuracy where history's problem of representativeness can be thought of as a case of sampling bias, statistics cannot help with many of the problems history deals with, such as understanding bygone customs from an unrepresentative assortment of written records and artefacts.

Finally, various disciplines raise additional considerations that are not encompassed by assorted forms of classification, but that are important when tackling complex real-world problems. Let us take some of the insights that psychology provides as an example. One is that unknowns have a normative dimension. A well-adjusted person is often thought of as a 'knowledge seeker' who can tolerate uncertainty, is open to novel experience and is not defensive about prior beliefs. This contrasts with someone with an authoritarian personality, who has the opposite attributes.[26] These different orientations to even considering unknowns can be critical when forming research teams, in interactions with stakeholders and when presenting research results to policy makers and practitioners. Psychology also provides insights into the debilitating consequences of uncertainty, unpredictability and uncontrollability,[27] which may be very important when involving the general public in trying to understand complex real-world problems.[28]

---

23   See, for example, Nickerson (1998); Tversky and Kahneman (1974).
24   Attewell (2008, p. 81).
25   As illustrated in Box 10.1, statistics is useful for some types of vagueness, but not others.
26   Smithson (2008b).
27   Smithson (2008b).
28   Smithson has also highlighted that unknowns can be beneficial as well as detrimental, at both individual and society-wide levels. For example, a climate favouring innovation and entrepreneurship requires tolerating some unknowns, including risks. While it can be relatively easy to understand the importance of unknowns in stimulating the creative process, including in science and art (Grishin 2008 has shown how artists from Leonardo da Vinci to the surrealists drew on unknowns), less immediately obvious is Smithson's analysis that freedom of choice relies on unknowns and can be thought of as 'positively badged uncertainty'—for example, see his blog 'Can we make "good" decisions under ignorance?' (<http://ignoranceanduncertainty.wordpress. com/tag/knowledge-management/>, accessed 22 December 2011); and Smithson (1989).

A lesson—which I hope is obvious from this discussion so far—is that bringing together different disciplines is as essential for developing a rich understanding of unknowns as it is for developing a comprehensive picture of what is known.

What about stakeholder perspectives on unknowns? First, there may be unrecognised similarities between disciplines and stakeholders in the unknowns they deal with and there may be great benefit from combining forces. For example, there are overlaps between the concerns of the historian and those of the intelligence analyst. In particular, each deals with circumstances where information is limited and its veracity unknown. I have already described this in the case of history where deductions about the past have to be made on the basis of, often very few, records, which may be quite biased. Similarly, intelligence can require investigation of clandestine activities by using undercover operatives, who may be restricted in their capacity to access key documents or to be present at critical meetings.[29]

Second, respectfully listening to the concerns of stakeholders can make researchers aware of a range of unknowns that are not covered by standard discipline-based approaches. The challenge is to use these concerns to enrich thinking about unknowns, rather than ruling them out as irrelevant because tools to understand and respond to them are limited. Such broadening of considerations about unknowns occurred in the research on the feasibility of diamorphine prescription through our interactions with a wide range of stakeholders, although we did not appreciate it in these terms at the time. We set out to uncover the full gamut of concerns about a trial and, as a result, inevitably ended up recognising diverse unknowns. This was not planned, but was an unintended consequence of our overarching interest in being thorough in our investigation and in taking into account the variety of stakeholder perspectives about a trial. In addition, because we tried to deal with each unknown openly and honestly, we soon stumbled across the inevitability of imperfection, in particular that there was no way a trial could be risk-free.[30]

Furthermore, just as disciplines can raise additional considerations about unknowns, so too can stakeholders. Let us take just two examples. One comes from religion, where, as Pickard describes, faith and personal doubt need not be fundamental opposites, but can reinforce each other most fruitfully. Having faith need not therefore mean the abdication of reason.[31] The second comes from jazz, which turns our understanding of tactic knowledge on its head. Usually tacit knowledge is thought of as something that needs to be made explicit to enhance

---

29 Longford (2008). In other circumstances, both can experience the opposite problem—in other words, having too much information to deal with. In history this can occur when examining the records of a recent government and in intelligence when monitoring phone records.

30 Bammer (1999); Bammer et al. (1999).

31 Pickard (2008); Ravetz (2008).

understanding of differences between people. But becoming a successful jazz musician involves reversing this process—that is, making known knowledge tacit. As John Mackey points out, learning to improvise requires internalising a wide range of musical knowledge, so that it can be called on without conscious consideration when the time comes to 'take a solo'.[32] Similar thinking lies behind training people in how to respond in emergencies. Even something as simple as a fire drill involves practising what to do, so that the response can be automatic when a real emergency occurs.

Differentiating the First and Second Domains

Before concluding this chapter, let us examine the distinguishing features of the first and second domains when it comes to unknowns. A useful starting point is the research I directed into the feasibility of diamorphine prescription to treat heroin dependence. On the one hand, we undertook a lot of standard discipline-based research—for example, we reviewed the literature, examined the United Nations conventions, surveyed the police and general community[33] and used demographic methods to estimate the number of heroin users,[34] all of which I would include under knowledge synthesis.

On the other hand, we also took into account important unknowns that cannot be easily addressed through standard disciplinary processes. For example, we investigated whether Canberra might become a 'honey pot' attracting heroin users from other parts of Australia,[35] what the impact might be on drug markets[36] and whether being in a trial might further marginalise participants.[37] There were no straightforward, well-accepted methodologies for addressing any of these questions.[38]

A simple differentiation is that the first domain deals with unknowns in a 'business as usual' way, whereas the second domain aims to help figure out which other unknowns may be critical and how to respond to them. The point of this second domain is, therefore, to ensure that much wider and more intensive attention is paid to unknowns than would traditionally be the case. The aim is to find new ways of thinking about unknowns that can help ensure that all the key unknowns in a problem are considered.

---

32   Mackey (2008).
33   These are all described in Volume 2 of *Feasibility Research into the Controlled Availability of Opioids* (1991): see <http://nceph.anu.edu.au/files/intranet_page/214/stage1vol2a.pdf> or <https://digitalcollections.anu.edu.au/bitstream/1885/41235/2/stage1vol2a.pdf> (accessed 23 July 2012).
34   Larson (1992).
35   Bammer et al. (1994).
36   Bammer and Sengoz (1994).
37   McDonald et al. (1994).
38   Now various modelling techniques could be used to address these questions, but they were not widely used at the time of that research.

11. For What and for Whom?

In this and the following four chapters, the five-question framework is used to provide starting points for more systematically understanding and managing diverse unknowns. Let us now address the first question: *'What is the understanding and management of diverse unknowns aiming to achieve and who is intended to benefit?'* Basically there are three aims

1. recognising that in considering complex real-world problems many different unknowns are relevant and require a range of responses

2. acknowledging that there are no perfect answers to complex problems

3. in the long term, assisting policy makers and practitioners in taking unknowns and imperfection into account in order to both make better decisions and respond rapidly and effectively when their actions lead to unexpected detrimental outcomes.

In other words, the primary intent of this first question is to prompt integrative applied research teams to think expansively about unknowns and how they might be dealt with. The issue is to move beyond the discipline-based focus team members will most probably have been trained in (which looks for individual productive unknowns to convert into knowledge) and instead to consider the unknowns that are most important from the perspective of the complex real-world problem, even if they cannot be responded to in conventional ways. The second purpose is to remind teams about the dangers of hubris and in particular that, for the problem they are investigating, unknowns are most likely unlimited, so that ways of dealing with the problem will be imperfect. These two purposes are combined into the ultimate goal of improving decision-making processes for complex real-world problems. That goal is still a way off and the focus in this book is primarily on the first aim.

In the long term, the beneficiaries are policy makers and practitioners, as well as those affected by their decisions and actions. But in terms of the narrower goal, which is the focus of this domain, the beneficiaries are those whose expertise in or concerns about specific unknowns are taken into account. For example, in the diamorphine prescription feasibility research, where we tried to consider all the identified problems about a trial proceeding, all key stakeholder groups who expressed anxieties were beneficiaries.

The first question also sets the scene for evaluating this domain of integrative applied research, as described in Chapter 15. It allows the approach to understanding and managing diverse unknowns to be differentiated from other research aims and assessed independently of the rest of the research.

> **Task for the I2S Development Drive**
>
> Compile case examples demonstrating: a) different ways of describing the purpose of thinking expansively about unknowns, b) how the inevitability of imperfection was incorporated, c) the contribution to the overarching research aims, and d) the beneficiaries (that is, which perspectives were included).

12. Which Unknowns?

To examine the question *'Which unknowns are considered?'*, the elements introduced in Chapter 5 for knowledge synthesis—taking a systems view, scoping, boundary setting, framing, taking values into account and deciding which differences to harness and which to manage—are also relevant.

Taking a Systems View

Chapter 5 made the point that there is no one way to take a systems view, and that the various systems approaches provide diverse ways of looking at complex real-world problems. To the best of my knowledge, there is no comprehensive explication of how different systems views deal with unknowns, but it is possible to list a range of examples, such as

- in drawing conceptual maps the strength of evidence for different elements and relationships can easily be depicted, allowing known unknowns to be highlighted

- in soft systems methodology the different world views that people bring to the table may be used to uncover both tacit knowledge (unknown knowns) and unknown unknowns

- causal loop diagrams can highlight likely unanticipated adverse outcomes

- in mathematical models of systems, techniques like calculations of probabilities and sensitivity analysis can be used to determine the degree of uncertainty around the model outcome

- conceptual or mathematical models can be devised for different scenarios of the future on particular issues, allowing a range of possible outcomes to be explored.

Tasks for the I2S Development Drive
Collect case examples illustrating how different systems approaches are useful for describing a complex problem, as well as for dealing with diverse unknowns.
Work with systems experts to produce a guide to the broad range of systems approaches to a complex problem, emphasising the different ways they provide to understand and manage diverse unknowns.

Scoping

The principle underpinning scoping is to broaden the range of considerations that the integrative applied research team takes into account, making the needs of the problem central rather than the researchers' expertise. This is particularly important when it comes to unknowns because, as described earlier, most researchers are trained to think about unknowns in very specific and limited ways.

The overall aim of scoping then is to broaden the view of unknowns. This can be undertaken in several ways. As outlined in Chapter 10, taxonomies and other classifications can provide starting points and stakeholder concerns can highlight unknowns that disciplines would ignore. It can also be helpful to look at the approaches of disciplines in a new light, not only revisiting unknowns they would normally banish from consideration, but also looking at unknowns at the intersection of disciplines, as well as unknowns that are highlighted when different disciplinary perspectives are contrasted.[1] A particular challenge for scoping in integrative applied research is that, with unlimited unknowns, the task of scoping is potentially endless.

The development of effective scoping methods that are fruitful and not overwhelming is therefore imperative. A way forward may be for teams to start to formulate key questions, including: are there areas that are deliberately ignored or taboo and are they significant? Can particular vulnerabilities to unknown unknowns be identified? Are important areas being ignored because methods for tackling them do not exist? There is substantial room for innovation here.

Tasks for the I2S Development Drive

Gather together literature and undocumented practical experience providing concepts for scoping unknowns, methods for undertaking it and illustrative case examples.

Produce a guide to all the potential ways of considering diverse unknowns including taxonomies, different approaches of disciplines and stakeholders, and unknowns that would be banished in discipline-based research. This requires collaboration with experts in thinking about unknowns, as well as discipline and stakeholder experts interested in unknowns.

---

1 For example, comparing statistics and history, as was illustrated in Chapter 10

Boundary Setting

Boundary setting determines which of the possibilities identified through the scoping process can realistically be considered in the integrative applied research. For complex real-world problems it is critical to identify and deal with the unknowns that are most significant for the issue under consideration, even though this may not be easy. Some unknowns may not be well understood or may be complicated to take action on. The challenge is to avoid defaulting to 'business as usual', where such unknowns are simply banished from consideration. It is only by responding—however clumsily at first—that ways of accounting for such unknowns will improve.

Boundary setting always involves making trade-offs, doing one thing at the expense of something else. The point of linking scoping and boundary setting is that it moves the integrative applied research team away from dealing with the unknowns with which it has the most experience to those that are central for understanding and managing the problem. One essential ingredient is the ability to learn from experience. This requires documenting the decisions made in boundary setting and the rationale for them, as this will form the basis for evaluation and learning to improve future integrative applied research.

Tasks for the I2S Development Drive
Collate published and unpublished concepts and methods for boundary setting, along with case examples that emphasise how and why decisions were made.
Develop boundary-setting methods to allow the most significant unknowns to be identified.

Framing

The way the problem is presented signals the approach being taken to unknowns. Some of the challenges have been alluded to earlier, particularly to avoid the extremes of overconfidence at one end and nihilism and despair at the other. Another potential difficulty is that a focus on unknowns, particularly those that are not well characterised and for which there are no clear-cut responses, can make the researchers seem ignorant or 'flaky'. A good example here is the reaction that talking about unknown unknowns often provokes, where the concept is seen as laughable and those raising it as stupid.

> **Tasks for the I2S Development Drive**
>
> Draw together useful concepts and practical methods for framing, along with case examples of when it has worked well and when it has failed.
>
> Develop new ways of framing unknowns that signal their importance and potential for achieving better outcomes on complex real-world problems.

Dealing with Values

Taking a broad approach to understanding and managing diverse unknowns is in itself a value position, but in general the link between values and unknowns does not seem to be well developed in the research context. Whose unknowns are considered to be important—in other words, which disciplinary and stakeholder concerns are taken into account—will also reflect the values in play. For example, weighing up the unknowns that worry stakeholders affected by the problem is congruent with democratic values, and if these stakeholders are otherwise generally marginalised it is also in line with liberal values.

Philosophy can provide useful insights. For instance, in the diamorphine prescription feasibility research, we were fortunate to receive guidance from philosopher Robert Goodin. He alerted us to different ethical approaches to the trial risks, particularly contrasting utilitarian and deontological approaches.[2] He helped us understand that we were taking a utilitarian approach, which involves looking at comparative risks and leads to support for a trial if the risks are likely to be less than those that would occur without a trial. Some trial opponents on the other hand were using a deontological approach, which effectively argues that a trial should not go ahead if there is any danger of major risks, regardless of what would happen without a trial. We learnt to appreciate that these perspectives are not reconcilable.

> **Tasks for the I2S Development Drive**
>
> Compile case examples that illustrate different experiences in bringing values into play and their consequences for understanding and managing diverse unknowns.
>
> Work with applied philosophers and other experts to produce a guide to concepts and methods for understanding and responding to the various dimensions of values.

---

2   Ostini et al. (1993).

Harnessing and Managing Differences

Members of integrative applied research teams will differ in their understanding of unknowns and the range of management strategies they consider acceptable. This can result from their disciplinary training and professional experience, as well as personality and cultural background.[3] For example, as I have outlined earlier, statisticians and historians generally have very dissimilar orientations to unknowns. The unknowns that concern stakeholders may be different again. Furthermore, personality distinctions between 'well-adjusted' and 'authoritarian' types, as described in Chapter 10, may also come into play.

The challenge is to identify and deal separately with two types of differences

1. those relevant to developing a more comprehensive way of understanding and managing the unknowns most germane to the problem, which need to be harnessed

2. those that may get in the way, which need to be managed.

For example, it may be desirable to harness the expertise of team members with strengths in understanding different unknowns, such as distortion, probability and taboo. On the other hand, if some team members have very fixed and limited views about unknowns, this may need to be managed so that it does not impede consideration of this domain in the integrative applied research.

Tasks for the I2S Development Drive
Gather together concepts and methods for understanding differences, as well as for harnessing and managing them, along with illustrative case examples.

Dealing with the Six Categories

Requirements for iteration and evolution, as well as moving beyond a formulaic way of proceeding, are just as relevant in this domain as they are in knowledge synthesis. In other words, planning the consideration of unknowns can start anywhere (that is, it may start with framing or a value position rather than the systems view or scoping) and it is likely that each of the six categories will need to be considered a number of times in the preparatory phase. Each category is also likely to require review from time to time as the research progresses. This may include asking questions like: how should an unknown that was discovered to be central after the planning phase be incorporated into the research process; how can the loss of a particular team member's skills in dealing with unknowns

---

3   Smithson (2008b).

be accommodated; and does the framing really convey an accurate view of what the research is aiming to achieve? The six categories provide a focus for the iteration, which is necessarily a messy process. They allow the research to be organised so that important elements can be documented and communicated.

Task for the I2S Development Drive
Compile case examples of how iterative processes between these six categories of concepts and methods played out.

13. How?

In this chapter, addressing the framework question *'How are diverse unknowns understood and managed, by whom and when?'* focuses on ways of responding to unknowns that move beyond the standard approaches in disciplines and that can encompass the diversity of unknowns. Dealing with imperfection is an area that has yet to be developed. Let us start by recapping how researchers are educated about unknowns in the disciplines. Becoming a skilled researcher requires mastering the ability to pick key unknowns (those that substantially move the discipline's knowledge base forward and open up fertile areas for future research), which are targeted for reduction, while the rest are put to one side (banished). How to do this is part of the tacit knowledge that researchers acquire as they develop expertise in their disciplines. This approach has been highly productive in understanding many aspects of the world around us, but, as I argue here, it is not sufficient for comprehending and dealing with complex social and environmental problems. Smithson[1] proposes four additional strategies for managing unknowns. These responses provide starting points for developing a systematic approach in I2S. Unknowns can, therefore, be

- reduced
- banished
- accepted
- surrendered to
- exploited
- denied.

A brief description of each is presented next. As well as using these six strategies to respond to unknowns in integrative applied research, it is also useful for I2S specialists to understand how else they can be employed. For example, fundamentalists deny unknowns and offer dogmatic solutions to all questions. These aspects of responding to unknowns are also discussed briefly. After reviewing these six approaches to managing unknowns, I deal with who in the integrative applied research team considers unknowns, followed by when in the research process this occurs.

---

1   Smithson et al. (2008).

Reduction

The focus here is not on reducing unknowns as would occur in conventional disciplines, but rather how else reduction can be used in I2S. The challenge involves thinking about *diverse* unknowns—in other words, unknowns that would not normally be considered in discipline-based research—and how these can be reduced. This includes the following.

- Looking for productive unknowns at the intersection of two or more disciplines. For example, many thriving areas of 'interdisciplinary' research such as behavioural economics and mathematical psychology explore fertile unknowns at the intersections of two disciplines. Such research can also occur in a more ad-hoc manner, such as when a legal scholar looks at informed consent in medical practice or an international relations expert examines organised crime.

- Importing a reduction method from one discipline to another to allow previously intractable problems to be tackled. An example is the revolution in archaeology by applying the methods of genome sequencing, which has provided new insights into the evolution of humans.

- Finding ways to understand some types of unknown unknowns. Some dialogue processes may be able to more specifically target unknown unknowns, especially those which occur on an individual or community basis, by exposing them and bringing countervailing evidence to bear in a way that allows learning rather than entrenching existing positions.

- Making tactic knowledge explicit. An important limitation to partners from different disciplines and stakeholder groups understanding each other is lack of appreciation of tacit knowledge. Not understanding the way things are done can lead to ill feeling and even conflict, and I2S specialists can make integrative applied research team members aware of this. If we take the example of good laboratory practice, a sociologist who lacks this knowledge will often not appreciate why sandals are not appropriate footwear and eating a sandwich while visiting someone in a laboratory is unacceptable. The response to such inappropriate behaviour is often 'they should have known', but I2S training can explain why this is not the case.

Banishment

Banishment rules some unknowns out of bounds. As already discussed, this is what disciplinary approaches to unknowns do. They effectively define which unknowns a particular piece of research will aim to reduce and everything else is generally put aside. One method to explore in developing I2S is whether and when it can be profitable to revisit the unknowns that have been banished in discipline-based investigations to determine if these are important when the complex real-world problem is considered as a whole. How to do this is also a challenge, because much of the banishment in discipline-based research is unconscious. Nevertheless, it is sometimes articulated—for example, when researchers declare that an investigation will not deal with specific topics.

Of course banishment will also be employed in I2S because it is key to the boundary-setting process. As discussed in Chapter 12, the challenge when considering diverse unknowns at different levels of sophistication is to develop effective criteria for banishment. Certainly an aim for I2S is to make banishment an explicit, considered process.

Acceptance

We now move to the first of the four less common strategies. Acceptance is a key approach to dealing with unknowns that cannot realistically be reduced, but are also too important to be ignored. Acceptance is particularly relevant in integrative applied research and I2S. The challenge for I2S is to decide which unknowns in the real-world problem of interest should be accepted, how much effort to put into developing acceptance methods and which techniques to concentrate on.

The development of ways to accept unknowns is well under way and includes methods devised by disciplines such as statistics (figuring out the likelihood of some important unknowns occurring) and economics (diversification and hedging),[2] as well as approaches widely applied to environmental and other problems, such as the development of scenarios[3] and the precautionary principle.[4] These different acceptance methods are illustrated in the following hypothetical example about the environmental impact of banks of solar panels in deserts. Let us consider just one impact—that on surface and soil water. Some of the ways in which acceptance techniques could be employed are

* the probability of rain could be calculated, along with likely run-off and penetration into the soil

---

2   Diversification is 'not putting all your eggs in one basket', as the old adage goes, whereas hedging aims to limit risk by investing against failure (for example, taking out insurance in case the original investment does not succeed).

3   Badham (2010).

4   At the 1992 Earth Summit in Rio de Janiero, the precautionary principle was stated as follows (Principle 15): 'Where there are threats of serious or irreversible damage, lack of full scientific certainty shall not be used as a reason for postponing cost-effective measures to prevent environmental degradation' (United Nations Conference on Environment and Development 1992; <www.un.org/documents/ga/conf151/aconf15126-1annex1.htm>, accessed 19 September 2012).

- scenarios could be developed for normal and extreme events, the latter including abnormally high or frequent rainfall or unusually long dry spells
- if different spacing of the solar panels in the banks has different impacts, diversification could be achieved using a range of spacing regimes
- an irrigation system could be installed to hedge against soil drying.

Scoping and boundary setting apply here too, in that the challenge is not just to identify a range of acceptance methods, but also to decide which ones to concentrate on, as resources will always be limited. Taking the options above, decisions have to be made, for example, about whether to focus on different rainfall scenarios or to design diverse spacing options.[5]

Another method that warrants mention is adaptive management as this is an acceptance technique that also takes imperfection into account. This has been developed largely in the area of natural resource management and follows implementation of the best available response to a problem by an ongoing process of monitoring, learning from what happens and setting in place modified responses based on that learning. At this stage it is primarily an ideal rather than a demonstrated reality.[6]

Surrender

Surrender to the unknown moves beyond acceptance by making unknowns an active partner. The worlds of art and extreme sport provide the best examples. In art, two illustrations come from the Australian John Wolseley, who actively incorporates the unknown into his creations. One instance is a series where he buried half of each painting under a rock in the outback, letting natural processes complete the work. Another is where he brushed his canvas across bushfire-blackened plants to create the artwork.[7] Similarly, the attraction of extreme sport is the high number of variables that cannot be controlled.

I have not been able to find an example in the research context, but it is interesting to speculate what research that involves surrender to the unknown could look like. Let us imagine an ethnographic study involving participant observation where a researcher goes to a party to study illicit drug use. The researcher could use chance explicitly to guide many key decisions—where in

---

5   But priorities have to be decided on another level, too. For example, should the environmental risks of all the energy options (not just this type of solar energy) be considered instead? And, if so, which risks should be the focus of attention?

6   Stankey et al. (2005).

7   Grishin (2008).

the room to start, who to observe, when to move and change observations, and so on.[8] It is not clear how this could be relevant to I2S but having it available may turn out to be useful.

One aspect of surrender that is helpful for I2S is that it can explain fatalism. While the forms of surrender described above are active, fatalism is passive. In other words, certain actions are not taken (usually to avoid disturbing the status quo) because 'what will be will be'. This can help integrative applied researchers understand what is occurring in some situations and potentially design countervailing strategies.

Exploitation

An important example of exploitation of unknowns in integrative applied research is the use of vagueness. Indeed no research can proceed if outcomes and processes are too rigidly specified, as this stifles initiative, innovation and flexibility. Vagueness can be particularly valuable when team members have diverse expertise, as it can be used to get the research started without incurring all the transaction costs of establishing fully shared knowledge and processes up front.[9]

The use of exploitation is also something I2S has to understand. How different stakeholder groups employ exploitation can provide integrative applied research teams with valuable insights into how a problem has developed or how it is being managed in the policy or practice worlds. For example, terrorists gain much of their power by exploiting unknowns.[10] Even relatively small-scale acts of violence can provoke widespread fear because when, where and whether they will occur again are unknown. A different way of exploiting unknowns is found in political and religious fundamentalism. Here power is gained by taking advantage of people's desire for certainty.

On a more benign level, politicians routinely exploit unknowns in at least two ways. First, unknowns can be used to cause delay. If politicians want to postpone a decision on a particular topic, referring the issue to an inquiry or

---

8   For example, the room could be divided into six quadrants and a dice thrown to determine the starting point. If there are 10 people in that quadrant a random number generator could be used to choose one to observe closely.

9   While there have been calls for integrative applied research teams to settle on a 'shared language' before proceeding, an alternative is to dive in, with important differences being dealt with when they become evident. This works best when team members are invigorated rather than annoyed when differences become evident, as these are powerful moments in collaborations. One role of I2S specialists is to be alert to the likelihood of differences and to help the team work through them when they become apparent. Of course, this approach also has costs, as considerable backtracking may be required.

10   McFadden et al. (2008).

commissioning new research are effective techniques. Second, politicians avoid setting well-specified goals with measurable criteria for success. This is because any deviation, especially if some outcomes are not accomplished, provides ammunition for opposition parties during election campaigns.[11] Furthermore, being too specific may prevent policy experimentation or modifications when they are warranted.[12]

Denial

Denial can be helpful in a crisis. As Aileen Plant (cited in the opening to Chapter 10) demonstrated, in a situation like the SARS epidemic where unknowns are overwhelming, the only way forward is to act and to base those actions on the best available analogies to the current situation. This involves effectively denying the unknowns.[13]

Denial is also widely used and therefore important to understand. For example, fundamentalism not only exploits unknowns, but also denies them, asserting that a dictator or a holy book has all the answers. But fundamentalists are not the only ones who deny unknowns. In the diamorphine trial feasibility research, we became aware of how partisan groups exploited and denied unknowns. It is a common observation that advocates use the facts that suit their case and ignore the rest. This is also true of unknowns. Those supporting a trial would often dismiss or deny the unknowns, whereas those opposing a trial exploited the unknowns to raise concerns about a trial.

Furthermore, Smithson argues that denial probably occurs more frequently than we are aware of. He cites an example where the *British Medical Journal* banned the word 'accident' from its publications.[14] Understanding how denial is used, particularly when it is misused, can therefore be important for I2S.

---

11   Moore (2008, p. 178) pointed out that '[t]here is a clear political advantage in maintaining an unclear situation so that a perception can be created of achievement without actually having to deliver anything specific'. While such exploitation of unknowns can be used in a cynical manner, Moore also highlighted the danger of specific goals, especially if all were not achieved—namely that 'an opposition at the next election… would ignore the 11 (or however many) achievements and focus on the failure(s)' (p. 176).

12   For example, policy makers may need 'the freedom to explore and implement a raft of policies', especially when the evidence base is not strong (Ritter 2008, p. 168).

13   As this and other examples show, the distinction between denial and banishment is not clearcut. I use denial when the process of ignoring some unknowns is not freely acknowledged out of strong beliefs or for political purposes, such as acting in the best interests of the public (as in Plant's case).

14   See Davis and Pless (2001). This was done to emphasise that many accidents are preventable.

Complexities in Managing Unknowns

The complex nature of unknowns was introduced in Chapter 10, especially the different kinds of unknowns, the diverse ways disciplines and stakeholders understand unknowns and various dimensions of unknowns that different disciplines and stakeholders highlight. Further complexities become apparent when the management of unknowns is addressed. Two in particular are described here.

First, depending on the circumstances, each of the six strategies presented above can be adaptive or maladaptive.[15] In other words, it is not possible to make blanket statements like reduction is always good and denial is always bad. This was illustrated in the description of denial, which is often negative, but which can be an adaptive response in an emergency. A different example is where a patient may wish to thoroughly investigate the benefits and risks of competing options before having elective surgery (reduction), but is likely to be better off trusting the doctor's judgment in a life-threatening situation (acceptance). A similar instance for a research project is that it might include a detailed study aimed at reducing particular unknowns if there is no urgency to act, but may devise a rapidly implementable strategy for dealing with the unknowns based on acceptance if there is a window for developing new policy based on the best available evidence. An important determinant, therefore, of whether a management strategy is adaptive or maladaptive is the context in which the strategy is being implemented, as well as the implementer's resources, mental state and time constraints.

Second, considerable work is still required to determine if different kinds of unknowns can be matched to particular management strategies. In cases where more than one strategy is applicable, investigation could elucidate the trade-offs based on the benefits and costs of each option. For example, decisions may need to be made about whether a particular unknown will be banished, reduced or accepted. In planning a new treatment service, for example, demand is usually an important consideration. If the clients are illicit drug users, demand can be challenging to ascertain. Planners then need to choose whether: a) they will banish consideration of the number of drug users who will seek such a service and simply set it up hoping for the best; b) undertake research on user numbers and the history of access to services to gain information on which estimates of demand can be based (reduction); or c) model different demand scenarios using different assumptions about numbers of users and factors that influence treatment access (acceptance). In this case, reducing unknowns or accepting them will take time and the opportunity for taking action may pass. On the other hand, banishing unknowns may be expedient, but may result in action that is poorly targeted and ineffective.

---

15   Smithson et al. (2008).

Tasks for the I2S Development Drive
Identify and catalogue the full range of methods that have been used for understanding and managing diverse unknowns, as well as their conceptual bases and case examples of their application. Update and improve existing compilations.
Develop new methods for understanding and managing unknowns, including reduction (beyond methods used in the disciplines), acceptance, surrender, exploitation and denial.
Draw together understandings of how stakeholders might use strategies like surrender, exploitation and denial in furthering their agendas, so that these can be taken into account in understanding and responding to complex real-world problems.
Pull together concepts, methods and cases that will assist in appreciating and dealing with the complexities involved in understanding and managing diverse unknowns (for example, that the same strategy can be adaptive or maladaptive depending on the circumstances).

Who Undertakes the Consideration of Unknowns?

If integrative applied research is to achieve broader consideration of diverse unknowns, teams need to be open to moving beyond their disciplinary training in figuring out which unknowns the integrative applied research will deal with and how. This will include

1. responding to all the critical unknowns in the real-world problem, even if some methods are not very advanced

2. looking for innovative ways to strengthen or develop the less sophisticated approaches to managing unknowns

3. taking the complexity of unknowns into account

4. making explicit the banishment of unknowns through boundary setting.

It is possible for the whole team to be involved in such broader consideration of unknowns, or for it to be primarily the task of a subgroup or of an individual. Each option has advantages and disadvantages. The latter range from the transaction cost for a group process to a reduced grasp of unknowns for a single person.

When is the Consideration of Unknowns Undertaken?

Identifying unknowns and deciding how to deal with them are core to starting the integrative applied research. But one of the lessons that comes from understanding the complexity of unknowns is that flexibility needs to be built into any long-term project, as, for example, new unknowns may be uncovered, problematic trade-offs may become evident and opportunities to influence policy or practice may arise, each of which may require a new approach to the unknowns.

It is also useful to explore the advantages and disadvantages of multidisciplinary and transdisciplinary research in relation to unknowns, even though unknowns have not been a major consideration for those practising either approach. In multidisciplinary research, the emphasis is on disciplinary contributions, which has potential positives and negatives. Even though the mapping between different kinds of unknowns and disciplinary approaches is only partial, if disciplines with different approaches to unknowns are included, this can automatically broaden the consideration of unknowns. The challenge comes in bringing these different approaches together in a meaningful way in relation to the problem as a whole.

The advantage of transdisciplinary research is that it provides the opportunity for a rich and complex approach to unknowns to be built in at the beginning of the research process. But again, as for knowledge synthesis, the price can be lack of flexibility in responding to new unknowns, which becomes evident as the research progresses.

The distinction between multidisciplinary and transdisciplinary approaches to some extent also encompasses the discussion about vagueness presented earlier. In multidisciplinary research, how the different approaches to unknowns will fit together tends to be quite vague when the project commences, whereas in transdisciplinary research there will often be attempts to reduce vagueness up front—for example, by establishing a common language and shared problem framing.

Task for the I2S Development Drive
Collect case examples of implementation of different options for who undertook the comprehensive consideration of diverse unknowns and when in the research process this occurred.

14. Context?

As with the first domain of knowledge synthesis, consideration of the framework question '*What circumstances might influence the understanding and management of diverse unknowns?*' involves the historical, political or other background that led to the integrative applied research and that may be influential during its life, but in this domain context is viewed through the lens of unknowns rather than knowledge. The three areas for consideration then become

- determining which aspects of the context of the problem are important for the consideration of diverse unknowns, especially which unknowns will be taken into account and how
- understanding the sources of authorisation for a broad consideration of unknowns and their management, as well as how such endorsement affects what is investigated
- understanding the facilitators and barriers to a wide-ranging consideration of unknowns and their management within the organisations undertaking the integrative applied research.

The general paucity of understanding about diverse unknowns and how to manage them (described in Chapter 10) is a key contextual issue that influences each of these considerations.

Overall Context

Although there are few useful concepts and methods for determining which of the circumstances surrounding the problem are likely to be important and how they should be taken into account, some aspects of context are relatively easy to grasp. One is the historical context, which involves examining how unknowns were dealt with in the past, especially which unknowns were considered relevant previously and how other unknowns were managed. If we take a problem like family violence, for instance, this was not considered to be a problem at all a few decades ago, with the whole issue being denied.[1] Sociological circumstances, especially taboos, are also relatively straightforward to think about. For example, examination of unknowns like the way the behaviours of victims contribute to violence is often considered to be taboo.

---

1 Until feminist advocacy made it an urgent research and policy issue.

Tasks for the I2S Development Drive
Collect case examples dealing with overall context relevant to considering diverse unknowns.
Work with a range of social scientists to produce guides for how context can be taken into account.

Authorisation

As is the case for knowledge synthesis, funding and support from influential organisations or individuals are also important sources of authorisation for dealing with diverse unknowns. Traditionally, research funding is directed at reducing a carefully circumscribed set of unknowns. It may be more difficult to obtain funding to consider unknowns that are more expansively defined. Indeed success will be influenced by how well reviewers understand the complexity of unknowns and how good a case can be made. Similar considerations apply to receiving backing from influential organisations or individuals. Obtaining their support for a broader consideration of unknowns will depend on how well they understand its importance and whether a way forward that has merit can be produced.

My experience in directing the feasibility research into diamorphine prescribing was that having relatively untied funding was critical for examining some unknowns, especially risk factors like the potential honey-pot effect and possible increased marginalisation. Although these were widely considered to be important, it was hard to conceive how to frame them in a way that would be attractive to a funder, because there was no clear way to tackle them.[2] Support from the directors of the centres in which the research was being undertaken and from the advisory committee was essential for the approach we took.

Untied funding has another benefit, in that it can allow unknowns that become evident only once the research is under way to be followed up quickly. It may be that new funding mechanisms better adapted to the complexity of unknowns are needed to complement (rather than replace) those that currently exist.

---

2   For the honey-pot effect, we thought through a range of likely 'push' and 'pull' factors, analysed a case of drug user migration and responses to it in Australia some years before, examined two open drug scenes and lessons for how to prevent them, and considered ways of establishing and enforcing residency criteria (Bammer et al. 1994).

Tasks for the I2S Development Drive
Gather case examples describing funding, endorsement and other forms of authorisation, along with any restrictions on understanding and management of diverse unknowns.
Examine whether provision of untied funding enhances the ability to explore unknowns in less traditional ways.

Organisational Facilitators and Barriers

The third area relevant to context applies to the organisations undertaking the integrative applied research and involves whether their organisational structures and cultures aid or impede a broad consideration of unknowns. Two germane dimensions are presented here.

First, organisations—consciously or not—take a position in relation to unknowns, embodied in their epistemological and methodological approaches. For example, some organisations are very specific in how they deal with unknowns, such as the Jerry Lee Centre of Experimental Criminology at Cambridge University,[3] which focuses on randomised controlled trials, and the University of Tennessee's Center for Applied Phenomenological Research, which concentrates on phenomenological and other qualitative methods.[4] Other organisations, such as my own centre, are eclectic in the epistemologies and methodologies embraced and hence in the way unknowns are considered.

Second, there are also likely to be differences between organisations in the research risks they are prepared to take. All research organisations have to engage with a level of chance for their work to stay current and fresh, but some organisations are more likely than others to support investigation of new problems, application of novel methods and unconventional collaborations. Taking a comprehensive approach to unknowns—especially at this stage when concepts and methods for understanding and dealing with them are still relatively underdeveloped—is a precarious activity especially as there is no guarantee that the result will be insightful and publishable. Some organisations will therefore be more open to this than others.

Task for the I2S Development Drive
Compile case examples describing the diversity and impact of organisational barriers and facilitators.

---

3 <http://www.crim.cam.ac.uk/research/experiments/> and <http://knol.google.com/k/jerry-lee-centre-of-experimental-criminology#> (accessed 13 October 2011).
4 <http://phenomenology.utk.edu/default.html> (accessed 13 October 2011).

15. Outcome?

In dealing with question five—*'What is the result of understanding and managing diverse unknowns?'*—the structured approach presented in this book provides a way to assess how successfully unknowns were understood and managed. This can then provide the basis for future improvements. Questions relevant for evaluation are presented in Box 15.1.

Box 15.1 Questions for Evaluating the Understanding and Management of Diverse Unknowns

How well did the consideration of diverse unknowns address the stated aims and beneficiaries (those whose concerns are taken into account)? Was a wide range of unknowns considered in new and important ways to achieve the overarching research goals?

Was the systems view taken suitable? Would a different systems view have been more useful?

Was the full range of relevant unknowns recognised and assessed?

Within the necessary limitations of the research, were the most worthwhile unknowns included? Was the balance between different kinds of unknowns fitting? Did any of those excluded turn out to be critical?

Was the problem framed accurately?

Were values considered adequately?

Were the differences in the team relevant to developing a rich understanding of and ways of dealing with the unknowns harnessed effectively? Were potentially destructive differences well managed?

Were sufficient flexibility and iteration built into the processes of deciding on a systems view, scoping, boundary setting, framing, considering values, and harnessing and managing differences?

Were applicable methods for understanding and managing diverse unknowns used? Would other methods have made better contributions? Were complexities like maladaptive effects and trade-offs recognised? Were justifiable decisions made in choosing by whom and when the diverse unknowns were considered?

Was the overall context for addressing unknowns adequately considered? Were critical contextual factors missed?

> Was the authorisation for the consideration of unknowns apposite? Did it influence the handling of unknowns in significant ways?
>
> Did the host organisational structure or culture provide barriers to the consideration of unknowns? If so, were these effectually recognised and managed? Were facilitators beneficially mobilised?
>
> And, returning to the challenges of imperfection raised in Chapter 10, was the inevitability of imperfection adequately described and recognised? Were defensible decisions made? Were problematic responses avoided—particularly overconfidence, hopelessness and nihilism, hindsight bias and opportunities for incompetence and corruption?

Given the current rough state of understanding about unknowns, many integrative applied research teams will find it difficult to answer the full range of questions presented above. Nevertheless, by raising awareness of what needs to be addressed, these questions may spark creativity in finding new and better ways to understand and manage diverse unknowns.

Task for the I2S Development Drive

Gather and analyse case examples of evaluation both to improve the list of assessment questions and to develop more detailed guidelines for reviewers.

16. Specialising in I2S

The same three broad categories of I2S specialisation discussed for the first domain of knowledge synthesis are also relevant here, namely

1. I2S for team leaders

2. I2S disciplinary specialists

3. I2S appreciation for other integrative applied research team members.

I2S for Team Leaders

As part of their responsibility for the whole project, team leaders must understand the importance, inevitability and complexity of unknowns, as well as the concomitant unavoidability of imperfection. They must be able to guide their teams through the challenges of: a) overconfidence, b) nihilism and despair, c) hindsight bias, and d) sanctioning incompetence and corruption. They must be able to bring into the team I2S disciplinary specialists familiar with the available research findings about unknowns in order to guide the team's work in this domain. Further, they have responsibility for decisions about which discipline, practice-based and other expertise on unknowns is required, which approaches to understanding and managing diverse unknowns will be taken and the extent to which team members will be given a say in making these determinations.

The requirement for team leaders to have I2S expertise that is comprehensive enough to address specific aspects of I2S, as described in Box 9.1, is also relevant here. In brief, this involves

- providing guidance on aims and beneficiaries
- being open to options
- harnessing and managing differences
- appreciating that formulaic processes are not realistic
- understanding authorisation
- ensuring a commitment to excellence in the further development of I2S.

I2S Disciplinary Specialists

In this domain, I2S disciplinary specialists provide the detailed knowledge about unknowns that makes it possible for integrative applied research teams to take diverse unknowns into account. The specialists' expert knowledge is used to move teams beyond standard disciplinary ways of dealing with unknowns to increase the scope of considerations through a problem-centred approach. Whereas knowledge synthesis works within recognised disciplinary parameters, this domain entails stepping outside them. This can involve revisiting unknowns that the disciplines would normally banish from consideration, examining unknowns at the intersections of disciplines, synthesising disciplinary and stakeholder perspectives on unknowns and thinking about unknowns in new ways that do not rely on the disciplines, such as through taxonomies. This process may take fellow team members well outside their comfort zones.

I2S disciplinary specialists also provide expertise in expanding the use of reduction and banishment as the primary methods for dealing with unknowns and can help teams understand exploitation, denial, surrender and, especially, acceptance as strategies they can employ. Specialists can also help their teams understand how relevant stakeholders may use these strategies—for example, how politicians may exploit unknowns to delay making a decision or how a community group may have a fatalistic stance (surrendering to unknowns), which affects its position on a problem.

It is unlikely that individual specialists will be equally proficient in all of the relevant concepts, methods, guides and applications, but they should have a working knowledge of all of the skills described in Box 16.1 and be able to bring in colleagues to make up for their deficiencies.

Box 16.1 Skills for I2S Disciplinary Specialists

I2S disciplinary specialists must have a basic working knowledge of all of the following specific skills and particular competence in some

- appreciation of the diversity of unknowns, including different disciplinary and stakeholder perspectives and various typologies
- understanding how different systems approaches deal with unknowns
- scoping to determine the full range of relevant unknowns, taking into account their complexity
- boundary setting without defaulting to 'business as usual', but instead identifying the unknowns that are most critical for the problem under consideration
- framing to communicate the approach to unknowns accurately and effectively
- dealing with values
- methods for dealing with unknowns—namely reduction, banishment, acceptance, surrender, exploitation and denial; appreciation of when these are adaptive and maladaptive and of the inevitability of trade-offs
- understanding overall context to ensure that the most important factors relevant to unknowns are considered.

I2S disciplinary specialists are responsible for ensuring that the other team members, especially the team leaders, are aware of available options and their strengths and weaknesses. They also have an important role in helping teams choose the most appropriate options for the problems they are tackling.

Another key role for I2S specialists is to be active in expanding their discipline's array of useful theory, methods and case examples, as well as guides to relevant knowledge from outside the discipline. In the first instance this will be given a fillip through the I2S Development Drive, but this is also an ongoing role. A particular task is to ensure that the work of teams relevant to I2S is published. As members of the I2S college of peers, I2S specialists also have important work to do in fairly and thoroughly assessing how other integrative applied research teams and their I2S specialist members have dealt with unknowns.

I2S Appreciation for Other Integrative Applied Research Team Members

The other team members must have some understanding of the broader approach to unknowns, especially as a comprehensive focus on diverse unknowns will be unfamiliar to many of them. They will also need to understand that this area is less developed, so that some of the approaches may be less advanced than in standard discipline-based research and in the other two I2S domains. As discussed in Chapter 9, the team will need to have more knowledge about I2S if the integrative applied research approach involves the whole team in I2S activities such as scoping and boundary setting than if the team members contribute their disciplinary expertise, but leave it to the team leader and I2S disciplinary specialists to make and implement I2S-relevant decisions.

***

The chapters in this domain have provided a systematic approach to planning and reporting consideration of diverse unknowns through the five-question framework. They have also outlined the categories of concepts, methods, case examples and guides that must be collected and developed to make I2S an effective discipline through the Big-Science-like project, the I2S Development Drive.

In the next group of chapters, the framework is applied to the third domain of integrative applied research and I2S—namely providing integrated research support for policy and practice change.

Domain 3. Providing Integrated Research Support for Policy and Practice Change

17. Introduction

In 2005, Dr Peter Shergold, then one of Australia's most powerful public servants, eloquently expressed his frustrations about research input into government policy making:[1]

> *Not infrequently I talk to academics who tell me that they work in the area of public policy. It awakens my interest. Often I am rudely disappointed. They may be researching in areas that are at the forefront of policy debate—health, welfare, early childhood development, education, employment—but they appear uncomfortable when asked directly what policy changes they would implement. This is seen, I discern, as a matter for others— less talented others—to ascertain from a proper consideration of their research findings. Practical policy which affects people's lives seems to be regarded as a trade skill, sullied by the dirt and grime of political compromise.*
>
> *Other academics have very clear policy prescriptions, often argued forcefully and sometimes propounded with a level of polemical certainty. While I am engaged by many of their ideas, and somewhat disquieted by the single-mindedness of their underlying philosophical conviction, I discover that my questions about possible compromise positions are met with a strong gaze into the mid-distance. A second-best outcome, I realise, is not good enough.*
>
> *The art that I find so beguiling—developing policy iteratively, moulded by an environment of political contest and organisational advocacy, responsive to unexpected opportunity, stymied by unforeseen barriers and shaped by financial exigency—is an uncomfortable discipline for the purist.*

Peter Shergold's remarks vividly illustrate the challenge for those seeking to bridge the so-called 'know–do gap'. The point is not that researchers should be seeking to directly implement policy or practice change based on their investigations; indeed that is not their role (nor should it be).[2] But researchers must take a more realistic position when it comes to considering the policy and practice implications of their findings. Neither avoiding the issue nor taking

---

1   Shergold (2005). At the time, Peter Shergold was Secretary of the Department of the Prime Minister and Cabinet of the Australian Federal Government.

2   Of course, researchers may change roles and become policy makers or work for business or a non-government organisation in order to have a more active role in implementing their research findings.

a narrow idealistic position is tenable. I argue that a focus on research *support* is a productive way to think about the issues. For researchers, this involves performing at least four important functions—namely

1. making available what is known, including what has worked and has not worked, so that policy makers and practitioners can develop effective actions

2. providing a digest of remaining unknowns to help policy makers and practitioners take these into account in their decision making, as well as to reduce, or at least be better prepared for, unintended consequences of their initiatives

3. providing critique of current and proposed policy and practice

4. providing new ideas for policy and practice.

It is worth noting that most of what is considered in this domain is relevant to all research, not just integrative applied research. Nevertheless, integrative applied research that is comprehensive, of high quality and impartial would be expected to be more useful and influential than other kinds of research.[3]

It is useful to think about the policy and practice worlds that are tasked with improving complex social and environmental problems as being divided into three major arenas: government, business and civil society (which each have policy and practice arms). The chapters in this domain do not deal with the process of bringing about change, but instead concentrate on the practical issues of identifying key players and procedures that may be amenable to research support, along with ways in which support may be provided. As the following chapters illustrate, there are numerous possibilities. One example is that some teams will decide to engage as closely as they can with those responsible for action, while others will keep their distance, apart from communicating the results of their investigations. Taking another example, some teams will undertake a calculated assessment of the options for producing change in the problem they are addressing[4] and then choose one on which to focus their research. Others will start with research they are interested in and consider the relevance for policy makers and practitioners only once findings are available. Most integrative applied research teams make decisions like these implicitly, often based on narrow understanding and little consideration of the full range of options. The purpose of the third domain of integrative applied research is to help teams make their appraisals explicit and better informed, underpinned by understanding of how government, business and civil society operate and how research can exert influence.

---

3   This issue is not explored further here, but does warrant fleshing out in future.

4   For instance: is a change in government policy or law essential? Would a new commercial product be viable and effective? Is individual behavioural change required? Should a particular community sector be mobilised?

Nevertheless, researchers must also bear in mind that bringing about change is an imperfect art (as Peter Shergold's remarks point out) and this capriciousness includes the outcomes of providing integrated research support. Even though researchers may have a clear view of what they are setting out to achieve, there is no sure-fire recipe for success and the determining factors are generally beyond the researchers' control. For example, whether or not research findings are influential can depend on budget priorities, political 'heat' (caused by advocacy groups or opposition parties) and competing demands for actions other than those the researchers are interested in. This level of uncertainty and chance is not something with which most researchers are comfortable. Furthermore, change is not an ordered process, but instead requires those who choose to provide support in highly engaged ways to be responsive to opportunities as they arise. Again this is at odds with the way most researchers operate. The considerations for integrative applied research teams about how to position themselves are far from straightforward.

As with the two previous domains, the starting point here is that there is no one best way to achieve the goals within this domain. Instead, the aim is to highlight different options for providing integrated research support and their associated benefits and costs. In this domain, the five-question framework becomes the following.

1. What is the integrated research support aiming to achieve and who is intended to benefit? (For what and for whom?)

2. Which aspects of policy and practice are targeted by the provision of integrated research support? (Which aspects of policy and practice?)

3. How is integrated research support provided, by whom and when? (How?)

4. What circumstances might influence the provision of integrated research support for policy and practice change? (Context?)

5. What is the result of the provision of integrated research support? (Outcome?)

Each question is discussed in turn to provide more detail about the I2S structure and to give an indication of the classes of concepts and methods that are encompassed within it, as well as the tasks required of the I2S Development Drive. A summary of the broad categories of concepts and methods covered by each question, along with the chapters in which they are discussed, is presented in Figure 17.1. Dealing in detail with both policy and practice, as well as each of government, business and civil society, is unwieldy, hence the examples in the following five chapters focus mostly on the interaction with government policy making.

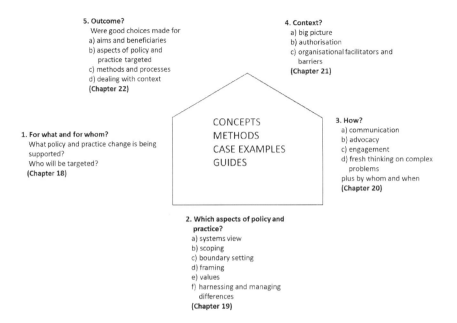

5. Outcome?
 Were good choices made for
a) aims and beneficiaries
b) aspects of policy and
   practice targeted
c) methods and processes
d) dealing with context
(Chapter 22)

4. Context?
a) big picture
b) authorisation
c) organisational facilitators and
   barriers
(Chapter 21)

1. For what and for whom?
 What policy and practice change is being
 supported?
 Who will be targeted?
(Chapter 18)

CONCEPTS
METHODS
CASE EXAMPLES
GUIDES

3. How?
a) communication
b) advocacy
c) engagement
d) fresh thinking on complex
   problems
plus by whom and when
(Chapter 20)

2. Which aspects of policy and
 practice?
a) systems view
b) scoping
c) boundary setting
d) framing
e) values
f) harnessing and managing
   differences
(Chapter 19)

Figure 17.1 The Storeroom for Providing Integrated Research Support for Policy and Practice Change, Listing the Key Categories of Concepts and Methods

Source: Author's illustration.

18. For What and for Whom?

The purpose of the question *'What is the integrated research support aiming to achieve and who is intended to benefit?'* is to help teams move beyond general (often fuzzy) ideas about the impact they want to see towards a clearer assessment of who might benefit from their research findings and how to best transmit these results to that target policy or practice audience.

The intention of this question is to help integrative applied research teams clarify the objectives of their implementation activities, not to force them to take a strong position. Indeed integrative applied research teams will not always have a clear view about what the impact of their research findings should be, nor will they necessarily want to use their research as a basis for engaging in intense political or other action. Instead the question can help teams figure out how their work can be made useful by determining which policy makers or practitioners are likely to find insights from the research valuable, as well as working out how best to make those people aware of the findings.

Beneficiaries are the targets of the research support—in other words, those who can put the integrated research findings into action in producing policy or practice change. Integrative applied research teams need to decide which arenas—one or more of government, business and civil society—are most relevant, as well as which particular organisations, departments and individuals are best able to use their findings.

Task for the I2S Development Drive
Compile case examples demonstrating: a) different ways of describing the purpose of providing integrated research support for policy and practice change (including with and without strong views about the desired impact), b) the contribution to the overarching research aims, and c) the beneficiaries (that is, which perspectives were included).

19. Which Aspects of Policy and Practice?

In considering the question '*Which aspects of policy and practice are targeted by the provision of integrated research support?*', the focus is different from the first two domains of knowledge synthesis and unknowns; it is not on the problem, but on the government, business and civil society arenas where support can be provided to those in a position to bring about change. Nevertheless, the six categories of concepts and methods (taking a systems view, scoping, boundary setting, framing, taking values into account and deciding which differences to harness and which to manage) still apply.

Taking a Systems View

Whereas taking a systems view in the first two domains entails considering the *problem* as a system, in this domain the focus is on the *policy or practice* system that is being supported by the integrated research. There are two relevant dimensions here. One is the organisational structures, how they operate and how they are interconnected. The other is understanding the process by which decisions are made and actions taken. Each of these is described separately, after which I deal with how they are related.

In the government policymaking system, the structures include the government ministry (that is, cabinet), government departments which advise each minister, committees where deliberations on policy matters occur, and so on. On the surface, this seems to be relatively straightforward; however, the structures vary with the type of government (for example, democracy or dictatorship), are country specific and may vary across jurisdictions within countries. Furthermore, they differ from those researchers are generally used to and finding out about them may be challenging, as they are not necessarily transparent. For example, in Australia, a government department website generally provides only limited information in an organisational chart and does not identify the incumbents of most positions. Such information is generally only available informally from contacts within the department.

The process of government policy making is even less transparent than its structure and has many facets. Theories of policy making can help I2S specialists better understand different aspects of the process. No one theory provides a complete view of government policy making, but each theory provides a set of useful understandings for providing integrated research support. Three widely employed and broadly useful theories are summarised in Box 19.1.[1]

---

1   The versions presented here are highly simplified, especially the last two theories.

They provide insight into: i) technical procedures whereby incremental change is made, ii) responses to pressures exerted by specific interest groups, and iii) entrepreneurial activity, where key decision makers look for windows of opportunity to enact change.

Box 19.1 Examples of Different Theoretical Perspectives of Government Policy Making

Three theoretical perspectives of government policy making are presented here to highlight different aspects of the process. They are government policy making as

1. a technical-rational cycle

2. a response to pressures exerted by different interest groups

3. an entrepreneurial activity involving the seizing of windows of opportunity.

Government policy making as a technical-rational cycle

This theory describes a cycle of activity depicted in Figure 19.1. The starting point is an issue or problem coming onto the government agenda ('identifying issues'), at which time the policy process involves examination of existing policy and identification of new options for dealing with the problem—in other words, with policy analysis. This leads to consideration of possible ways of intervening—for example, by changing laws or regulations, by increasing or decreasing certain types of taxation, by introducing an education program or by changing available services. These interventions are often referred to as policy instruments or levers.

Policy makers will also assess the likely impact of proposed policy changes through consultation with affected parties. Consultation generally involves various stakeholders who may be businesses, consumer groups and service providers. There will also be a process of coordination with other relevant government departments. Usually, ministries in charge of expenditure (such as the Department of Treasury) will be involved, but the coordination may also be more widespread. For example, the development of a new public health policy on physical exercise may involve coordination between departments overseeing health, sport and urban planning. Based on all these inputs, a decision will be made and an implementation plan established. Specific evaluation of the effects of the policy change may be undertaken, but more often governments rely on the stakeholders to alert them to problems, which may then be attended to in a new cycle of policy making.

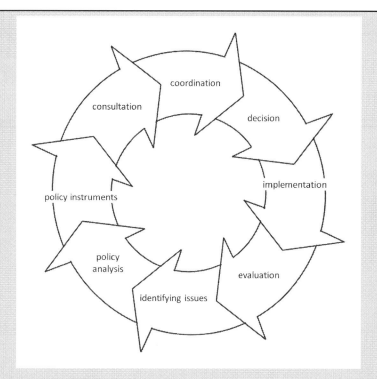

Figure 19.1 Key Elements of a 'Policy Cycle'

Source: Althaus et al. (2007, p. 37).

Government policy making as a response to pressures exerted by interest groups

Anyone who has been involved or interested in government policy making knows that such a technical-rational view represents only one aspect of policy making and de-emphasises the critical political aspects. Another way of looking at government policy making is to see that 'public policy is the outcome of the pressures of society's many and diverse interest groups'.[a] Within the policy cycle shown in Figure 19.1, such groups have most influence during the consultation phase; but exploring pressure groups through the framework of the policy cycle misses the richness of their impacts.

Most interest groups are not passive entities waiting for a government call for input into policy. Instead they are often strong and proactive advocates seeking to shape agendas, highlight failures and counteract the influence of competitors. Interest groups often increase their power to influence policy by forming coalitions with others who seek the same specific outcomes on particular problems.

As a consequence, some policy reflects the overwhelming dominance of one coalition. At other times there are competing coalitions and the resulting policy is a compromise rather than an outright win for any side. In any case, a given policy can be seen as representing the balance between different advocacy coalitions. Looking at policy in this way highlights that policy change occurs in three different ways: when an external perturbation upsets the balance between existing advocacy coalitions; when a new advocacy coalition gains power; or when an existing powerful advocacy coalition changes its beliefs.[b]

Government policy making as an entrepreneurial activity that entails seizing windows of opportunity

Much policy change occurs incrementally by finetuning existing policies;[c] but from time to time a major policy change occurs. For example, in 1996 a lone gunman killed 35 people at a tourist destination in Australia.[d] The newly elected Prime Minister, John Howard, seized the opportunity created by the outrage at this crime to enact major changes to Australian laws on gun ownership.[e]

Sometimes a window of opportunity is opened by an unexpected event, although others are routine occurrences, such as those attached to preparation of government budgets, as well as changes of government following an election. But such a trigger event on its own is not enough.[f] Two additional circumstances are required. First, the event must occur in the right political context, which is influenced by the national mood, the organisation of political forces and the position of influential interest groups. For example, major policy change is more likely to occur when the electorate is deeply and obviously concerned about the issue, soon after a government has been elected rather than just before an election and when the influential interest groups are aligned or when the positions of powerful opposing groups can be managed. In the example presented, many Australians were worried about gun availability, the massacre occurred early in the electoral cycle and, although there were powerful groups (such as farmers) opposed to changes in gun laws, the Government decided it could manage that opposition. This may not be the case in other political environments; indeed similar events in the United States have not led to major policy change, partly because of the significance of the 'right to bear arms' in the US Constitution and the strength of opposition to gun control.

The other requisite circumstances involve the practicalities of achieving change; in other words, change will only occur if it is 'doable'. Considerations include whether space can be made on the government agenda to take on the new issue, whether acting is technically feasible and whether there are any considerations that militate against public acceptance of the problem or the proposed solution. A key factor in the change to gun laws in Australia was that the Government was able to devise an effective scheme to buy newly outlawed guns from those who had previously legitimately held them.

a. Fenna (2004, p. 123).
b. Sabatier (1988); Sabatier and Weible (2007).
c. Lindblom (1959, 1979).
d. Port Arthur in Tasmania.
e. Smeaton (1997) gives a policy maker insider account; Mouzos (1999) briefly reviews other changes when windows open, especially related to firearms; Chapman (1998) is a useful reminder that entrepreneurial activity often occurs in a climate of intense advocacy.
f. Kingdon (2003).

Taking a systems view involves combining structure and process, and again, this can be done in different ways. For example, if the process is viewed as technical-rational then organisation hierarchies and committees are the key structural elements; however, if the process concentrates on pressure groups then structural elements include links between decision makers and pressure groups, including contributors to campaign funds, access to decision makers through direct and informal mechanisms, and so on. This requires additional systems thinking techniques to those presented in Chapters 5 and 12, such as social network theory, which can facilitate analysis of positions of influence.[2]

Effective targeting relies on identifying the relevant people and research support activities within the structures and processes. For example, there is little point interacting with someone who may be interested in the research but has no responsibility for the decision making, in seeking an urgent response from a committee which only meets once a year, in deciding to lobby a minister at an event attended by 1000 other people or in being uncontactable when a policy window opens. Instead, it is more effective for the research findings to be tailored for and presented to those in the key decision-making positions, for relevant committee processes to be taken into account, for lobbying at a time when there is a good chance of being heard and in having built a relationship with policy entrepreneurs that makes it easy for them to get in touch when the time is right.

---

2   The techniques described in the earlier chapters may still be useful, but in different ways. For example, big policy changes often employ several strategies, including legal amendments, incentives and marketing, which are intended to operate synergistically. System dynamics modelling, for example, can check how these different policy levers are likely to interact.

Tasks for the I2S Development Drive

Collect case examples of various ways of considering the major arenas for implementation (government, business and civil society) as systems, showing the organisational structures and processes for decision making and action, as well as the interactions between them.

Produce a guide for systems approaches to each of the major arenas of implementation (government, business and civil society), showing the organisational structures and processes for decision making and action, as well as the interactions between them. Work with relevant experts, such as political scientists for the government arena, business analysts and experts in civil society.

Scoping

The key aim of scoping is to broaden the thinking of the integrative applied research team to help identify various options for supporting policy and practice with their research. It aims to move the team beyond what they know and are comfortable with to a wider range of possibilities. Scoping therefore involves identifying various prospects for support

1. starting with what can be done through each of the government, business and civil society arenas

2. thinking about structure and process together as a system, and identifying various useful systems approaches

3. identifying the range of organisations and individuals within each systems approach.

For example, in scoping possible targets for integrated research support on global climate change, the government, business and civil society arenas are all relevant. Focusing on government and taking a systems view then leads to thinking about structure and process, as described above. For example, if the technical-rational view of policy making is considered, important structural elements are pertinent departments including those responsible for the environment, finance, mining and health. Within those there are various staff, committees and other processes to take into account. On the other hand, focusing on how policy is affected by pressure groups requires scoping out all the relevant advocacy groups and their agendas, understanding what mechanisms are used to keep a coalition between different groups together, and ascertaining how they exert influence.

> **Tasks for the I2S Development Drive**
>
> Gather together literature and undocumented practical experience providing concepts for scoping, methods for undertaking it and illustrative case examples, relevant to
>
> - the roles of government, business and civil society
> - key individuals and groups, along with specific sub-processes.
>
> Provide guides to the roles of government, business and civil society that can help teams understand where action is possible. This requires collaboration with political scientists, public policy experts, business analysts and experts in civil society processes.

Boundary Setting

Boundary setting narrows the options to those that will be implemented given the available time, money and person power. In combination with scoping, the aim of boundary setting is to guide the integrative applied research team to the areas of action that are most likely to be fruitful in providing integrated research support. In other words, the aim of scoping and boundary setting is to move teams away from 'business as usual' to an analysis of how they can be most effective. This may lead to a change in how research support is provided. To take a hypothetical example, a team may come to realise that their usual course of action in writing letters to the relevant minister is likely to be less effective than working with pressure groups which have access and clout, especially if these are open to research input.

Nevertheless, teams should not discount any special advantages that they have. For example, if a team has spent a long time building a relationship with a particular policy or practice group or if it has a particularly effective communications strategy, these should be taken into consideration in the boundary-setting process.

> **Tasks for the I2S Development Drive**
>
> Collate published and unpublished concepts and methods for boundary setting, along with case examples that emphasise how and why decisions were made.
>
> Collate case examples demonstrating how special advantages of teams (such as long-established relationships with particular policy makers) were taken into account.

Framing

Framing is relevant to both the problem being tackled and the integrated research findings that are brought to bear. Further, it may be that the *problem* needs to be framed differently when providing integrated research support to policy and practice change than it does for bringing disciplinary experts and stakeholders on board for knowledge synthesis and considering unknowns. The *findings* need to be presented in a way that is both accurate and meaningful for their target audience.

Framing becomes particularly important when there is competition for policy or practice influence. For example, in our research on the feasibility of diamorphine prescription, we used the same framing for all three domains. We referred to our investigation as 'Feasibility Research into the Controlled Availability of Opioids'. We wanted to signal that we were undertaking a scientific investigation, which was fully and dispassionately considering both sides of the argument, and that the outcome was not predetermined. Once the research was complete, however, and we recommended a pilot study for a trial, we did not think about how we were presenting the trial proposal and were blind-sided by a concerted attack by a powerful media group which reframed the discourse focusing on emotive issues such as 'surrender in the war on drugs', 'government as drug pedlar' and 'deserving and undeserving citizens'.[3]

Tasks for the I2S Development Drive
Draw together useful concepts and practical methods for framing, along with case examples of when it has worked well and when it has failed. Framing is relevant to both the problem and the findings of the integrated research.
Collect case examples of competition between framings trying to influence policy or practice change.

---

3   A three-week intense campaign against a trial of diamorphine prescription ended with the Prime Minister and cabinet withdrawing support. Later, Sydney researcher Simon Chapman invited me to work with him and Glenda Lawrence (then a masters student) on an analysis of newspaper reports (Lawrence et al. 2000). The analysis showed that while the opponents effectively reframed the discourse, supporters stayed with issues such as 'failure of prohibition' and 'time for new approaches', which had little power in countering the denigration by the opponents. The analysis concluded by stating: 'The mid-1997 policy reversal on [diamorphine] prescription was due, in part, to the higher activity of opponents following approval of the trial and because proponents did not reframe discourses used to denigrate the proposal' and '[t]o be successful, advocates of new policy need to recognise and reframe negative discourses to create new dominant themes which address the concerns of the public' (p. 254). It is also worth noting that the media campaign and associated negative framing were unlikely to have been the sole cause of the Federal Government's reversal.

Dealing with Values

Values will influence what the integrative applied research team aims for and how. For example, working with advocacy coalitions may be ruled out if the integrative applied research team is not willing to work with some lobby groups, such as the pharmaceutical industry or Greenpeace. Further, some approaches may be excluded if the team insists on being open and transparent rather than working behind closed doors.

A critical issue is that there must be congruence in values across the team's integration and implementation efforts. For example, if the research team aims to be dispassionate and independent, members cannot make secret deals with specific interest groups to provide them with information for their advocacy. That is not to say that researchers cannot be political players, but their actions and values need to be aligned.

Tasks for the I2S Development Drive
Compile case examples that illustrate different experiences in bringing values into play and their consequences for providing integrated research support for policy and practice change.
Compile case examples examining congruence in values across the three domains, as well as assessing integrity.
Work with applied philosophers and other experts to produce a guide to concepts and methods for understanding and responding to the various dimensions of values.

Harnessing and Managing Differences

The worlds of researchers and those of policy makers and practitioners are often poles apart, as has regularly been pointed out (including the quotation from Peter Shergold that opens Chapter 17). Successfully negotiating those differences is a critical element of providing integrated research support. As described in Chapter 23, a valuable role for I2S disciplinary specialists is to understand these differences and to help the integrative applied research team effectively work with them. Box 19.2 provides a flavour of some of the differences between researchers and government policy makers.

With increased understanding and hindsight, I have come to appreciate that during our research into the feasibility of diamorphine prescription, I had a lot of access to and interaction with relevant policy makers; however, I dismissed what I saw of the policy making process as unimportant, while waiting for the 'real' process to begin.[4] I now realise that I was waiting for a process where the policy makers mirrored the weighing up of benefits and risks that we researchers were engaged in, and that I had no understanding of other considerations relevant to the policy makers.

Box 19.2 Examples of Differences between Researchers and Government Policy Makers

Much has been written about the differences between research and government policy making.[a] Two of the more detailed and useful examples, by Heyman and by Gregrich, are summarised here.

Heyman[b] provided six examples of mismatches between the common approaches of researchers and of policy makers

1. researchers focus on making one change at a time while holding other variables constant, whereas multiple changes and 'horsetrading' between options are standard in the policy domain

2. researchers favour randomised controlled trials, especially double-blinded experiments, but these are politically difficult because sound bites cannot convince the public that something that may fail should be tried nor that something that might succeed should not be made available to everyone; further, trials usually occur in only one setting, but policy has to be effective in a wide range and, if results are mixed, failures get more attention than successes

3. researchers concentrate on means and other measures of central tendency rather than distributions, whereas for political support, how effects are distributed may be equally or more important

4. researchers eliminate 'outliers', whereas in policy spheres outliers can drive the debate (by capturing media attention and symbolising programs)

5. researchers emphasise targeting specific groups for maximum advantage, while policy makers look for widespread benefits

6. while both researchers and policy makers value long-term effectiveness as the gold standard, the practical reality in the policy sphere is that programs must show effectiveness early on, preferably demonstrable in line with budgetary, electoral or other politically significant cycles.

Gregrich[c] (writing from a policymaker perspective) concentrated on issues researchers need to understand, especially that

---

4 For example, in my interactions with a senior public servant in the Australian Capital Territory, I was somewhat irritated by what I saw as gossip about what relevant public servants and politicians in other parts of Australia were likely to think about the proposal to prescribe diamorphine. First, the factual basis for his assessments seemed to be very unscientific and slender, and I could not understand why he did not just ask them. Second, I thought this was unimportant in any case as they would surely be guided by our evidence once it had been gathered.

1. finding relevant studies can be difficult and furthermore the language of research papers is often inaccessible, requiring effort that policy makers simply cannot devote

2. their research may not address the most urgent questions for policy makers

3. findings are often of marginal importance for the overall state of knowledge

4. findings are open to manipulation by advocates of particular positions.

He also urged researchers to

1. avoid self-interested advocacy seeking to influence public policy or allocation of public resources

2. be aware of policy time cycles, including, for example, presenting results at times of greatest receptivity

3. consider policy funding constraints.

a. This information is not, however, gathered together in one place, although some was brought together in Bammer et al. (2010b).

b. Heyman (2000).

c. Gregrich (2003).

As in Chapters 5 and 12, here the critical issue is not only understanding the differences, but also figuring out how to harness those that advance the provision of integrated research support, as well as managing those that impede it. For example, it may be possible to harness some of the mismatches that Heyman identified to get the best of both worlds. If we consider the approaches to outliers and measures of central tendency, for example, researchers and policy makers could work together to provide vignettes for the media describing the typical person or family and how they are affected by a policy, as well as some of the less typical consequences.[5] On the other hand, some differences are less amenable to win–win solutions and have to be managed. The conflicts in priorities and time cycles, as identified by Gregrich, are likely to be in this category.

Tasks for the I2S Development Drive

Gather together concepts and methods for understanding differences, as well as for harnessing and managing them, along with illustrative case examples.

---

5   Indeed this seems to be happening in some Australian Government advertising about its policies as well as in media coverage about proposed policy changes.

Dealing with the Six Categories

The need for iteration and evolution, as well as the inability to use a formulaic way of proceeding, also applies in this domain. In other words, like undertaking the research, providing integrated research support is messy. This is compounded by the unpredictability of success in influencing policy or practice, as well as by the fact that change is ongoing (as described in Chapter 10). No matter how well thought out a support plan is, it may be derailed by circumstances like departmental staff turnover, reshuffling of cabinet positions, governments losing elections, transformations in interest groups as advocates modify positions or coalitions realign, and windows of opportunity opening (or closing).

Nevertheless, the six categories of concepts and methods provide a systematic way for integrative applied research teams to put their aims for the provision of integrated research support into action and to review progress along the way.

Task for the I2S Development Drive
Compile case examples of how iterative processes between these six elements played out.

20. How?

One of the functions of the discipline of I2S is to provide options for answering the question *'How is integrated research support provided, by whom and when?'*, along with information on the strengths and weaknesses of each approach.[1] Staying with the focus on government policy making, the task is to help teams move beyond the two common positions Peter Shergold articulated (lack of interest in policy and narrow prescriptions for policy) to a better appreciation of the range of possibilities for providing integrated research support for Shergold's 'beguiling' art. Let me be clear that I am not advocating any particular position for researchers here. On the contrary, this section aims to illustrate that integrative applied research teams need to be aware of the options and to choose the most suitable for their circumstances. Furthermore, none of the options is perfect, with each having different benefits and costs.

Let us concentrate on three classes of methods for provision of integrated research support, showing how they are linked to the theories in Box 19.1. They are communication, advocacy and engagement. I then outline a particular form of engagement that is aimed at providing fresh thinking on complex real-world problems.

Before moving to these, it is also worth considering a different perspective provided by Brendan Gibson[2] through his development of a matrix between the 'irrefutability' of the evidence and the 'immutability' of policy (Figure 20.1). Changed, or new, policy is most likely when the evidence for change is strong and the political forces maintaining the existing policy are weak. Changed policy is least likely when the evidence is weak and the political forces maintaining the existing policy are strong. When the evidence for change is strong, and the political forces maintaining the existing policy are also strong, the stage is set for confrontation. This analysis is useful for developing tactics when seeking to amplify the research voice, especially when the evidence is strong.

		Irrefutability of the evidence	
		High	Low
Immutability of the policy	High	Confrontation	Change very unlikely
	Low	Change likely	No pressure for change

Figure 20.1 Likelihood of Research Influencing Policy Change

Source: Adapted from Gibson (2003a, p. 25).

---

1   The focus here is on how to provide research support. It is not about how to undertake a calculated assessment of options for producing change as a prelude to deciding whom to target or about how to assess the value of the research for policy and practice decisions. These are also important, but will need to be developed at a later date.

2   Gibson (2003a; 2003b).

Gibson[3] went on to explore the considerations that influence policymakers in such circumstances and posited five indicators of their likely responsiveness to research.

1. Responsibility—'The extent to which the policy-making organisation is unequivocally responsible for the policy problem, either in terms of legislative requirements or precedent established by prior action'; the more responsible they are, the more likely they are to act.

2. Capacity—'The extent to which the policy-making organisation has the capacity and power to effect change in the problem.'

3. Performance—'The extent to which it is possible to measure the policy-making organisation's performance in relation to the policy problem.'

4. '"Theatre of justification"—The extent to which performance information and other data relevant to the problem are available for public scrutiny and debate.' In other words, the more the public can see and is interested in whether or not research results are being taken into account, the more likely policymakers are to be responsive to research.

5. 'Vulnerability to the consequences of error—The extent to which there is a cost (political or economic) for policy failure. Research responsiveness will increase as these costs increase.'

Gibson[4] also pointed out that it is simplistic to think of research being *translated* into policy, as if it were a process of converting words from one language to another. Instead, he argued that the process is more accurately thought of as *transformation*, with the policy process absorbing and reconstituting the research to meet its own goals.

Communication

Communication focuses on describing clearly the integrated research findings, their limitations and their applicability to the policy problem.[5] The value of ensuring that policy makers and practitioners have the correct facts on which to make decisions should not be underestimated. Making accurate information easy to access when needed is an important aspect of communication.[6] This may

3   Gibson (2003a, p. 26).
4   Gibson (2003a; 2003b).
5   It is worth noting that the researchers may not be at all certain about the applicability to the policy problem; in such cases, this uncertainty is part of what would be communicated.
6   In my interactions with policy makers and practitioners during the feasibility research for diamorphine prescription, I was struck by how often they were misinformed. Early in the feasibility research, websites were still uncommon and our information was not available online until 1995. While we mailed out reports

entail such techniques as providing succinct summaries, professional use of the media or giving individual briefings to policy makers. Although much has been written about how to do this,[7] the insights are scattered through the published and grey literatures and are not compiled in an accessible form.

There are also important gaps. One is about how best to convey unknowns and to deal with the tension between policy makers who are thought to want clear answers and researchers who can rarely provide them. Another is that, although much of the literature on communication seems to be premised on the technical-rational approach to policy making, little consideration seems to have been given to differentiating between the stages of the policy cycle to figure out when researcher input is likely to be most effective, who should be targeted or who should do the communicating. Much of what is currently available treats communication narrowly and ignores such considerations.

Communication is often thought of as information 'pushed out' by the researchers, but policy makers also seek information. The challenge for them is that they generally cannot easily identify the best sources or find information tailored to their needs. In a few instances, this has led to the development of brokerage organisations, like Australia's Sax Institute,[8] which match researchers to the questions the policy makers want addressed.

The considerations here are relevant when communication by itself is the method for supporting policy and practice change. Communication also underpins advocacy and engagement, but for these strategies additional factors come into play.

Advocacy

The second class of methods—advocacy—is tied to the aspect of policy making that involves responding to pressure from different interest groups.[9] Although it is unpalatable to many researchers, it can be helpful to consider the integrated research evidence as another 'interest' that those making decisions or planning action need to take into consideration. As Peter Shergold pointed out, it is rare that research evidence is all that is needed in the government policy change

---

and newsletters to people we thought needed them, websites have an advantage in that they can be accessed when required, whereas hardcopy has to be filed and retrieved. It is also hard now to easily gauge how good our coverage (that is, the people we sent information to) was.

7   For example: Brownson et al. (2006); Edwards (2004); Heyman (2000).

8   See <http://www.saxinstitute.org.au/> (accessed 27 October 2011).

9   There is no clear line differentiating communication and advocacy. In general communication is more passive and less politically engaged.

process, and this is also true for policy and practice change in the other arenas. Indeed the research evidence often competes with other forces, including vested financial interests, moral arguments, community pressure and political deals.

Advocacy therefore plays out in two different ways in the provision of integrated research support. One is to boost the power of the research voice in general. The other is to lobby for a particular policy or practice outcome. Amplifying the research voice involves ensuring that research evidence gets due consideration in the decisions about policy or action, and is not swamped by all the competing interests. Lobbying for a particular outcome involves putting pressure on policy makers and/or practitioners to increase the chances of a particular change occurring.[10] The distinction is not particularly clear-cut, because for most researchers an outcome in line with the evidence is the key indicator that the research voice has been properly heard. This is particularly so when evidence for (or against) a particular policy or action is overwhelming.

In taking an advocacy position there are a number of decisions that integrative applied research teams must make. These include interrelated considerations about how they will operate, the framing of the issue and engagement with opponents. Teams may also be drawn into advocacy by others and have to decide how to respond. Let us take each of these in turn.

There are several options for undertaking advocacy, especially who is targeted, how and when. For example, researchers may direct their efforts privately at a few policy makers, seek to gain widespread public support through the media or maintain a low profile and work through established lobby or other advocacy groups. They may have an ongoing program of activity or may wait for a window of opportunity to open.

In addition to the types of good communication described in the previous section, effective advocacy requires an emotional engagement with the politics of the problem. This is the critical task for the framing. Shaping a clear and powerful message usually requires demanding decisions about whether and to what extent unknowns are downplayed and whether any evidence that contradicts the main thrust of the research findings is buried.

Decisions also have to be made about whether and how to engage with opponents of the research findings. Effective advocacy often involves analysis of the strategies that will be used by opponents and figuring out how to counteract them. Finally, an advocacy role is not always initiated by the researchers. Interest groups may approach researchers to join their cause. It is also common

---

10   An example is the efforts by some public health researchers to change government policies in order to reduce the availability of tobacco products; see, for instance, Chapman (2007).

for interest groups to use research results without consulting the researchers involved. In such instances researchers can unwittingly be caught up in an advocacy process and must decide how they will react.[11]

An overarching decision concerns the maintenance of impartiality. This is relevant to the conduct of the research, to general advocacy for research versus other forces that influence policy, and to seeking particular outcomes based on specific findings. The integrative applied research team has to figure out whether it wants to preserve a position of impartiality and how this can be done.[12] Strategies include continuing a respectful relationship with all those who have legitimate interests,[13] including opponents, and being upfront about contradictory evidence and unknowns.

Remaining impartial should not be seen as ruling out: a) support by the integrative applied research team for finding least-worst solutions, or b) strong and effective advocacy for a reasoned solution that takes imperfection into account. Advocating for a balanced and rational approach does not involve shrugging one's shoulders or backing down in the face of strong opposition. On the contrary, it involves becoming tougher and more creative.

Regardless of the style of advocacy employed, the process is inevitably political, which is at the heart of both its strengths and its weaknesses. The major strength is that advocacy may well be more effective in influencing change than straight factual communication. The dominant weakness is that vested interests challenged by the research findings will almost always strike back and researchers may be poorly equipped to deal with personal attacks, denigration of their research and other tactics that may be used against them. Even if they maintain an impartial stance, their neutrality and integrity, along with that of their organisations, are likely to be impugned. If not dealt with effectively this may have long-term repercussions for the career of the researcher and the viability of the organisation.

---

11   For example, they are likely to be invited to comment by the media and must then decide whether they will do so and what they will say.

12   While I personally think impartiality is essential, it is not always possible, as researchers have strong feelings about some topics. (I leave aside here longstanding debates about objectivity.) More important than impartiality is integrity—in other words, that integrative applied research teams are honest about their position(s) on a topic and act in a way that is consistent. It is also worth noting that impartiality and conscious attempts at maintaining a balanced position can be undermined by unconscious cognitive processes like confirmation bias, which entails seeking or interpreting evidence in ways that are consistent with expectations or hypotheses even when there is no motivation to do so in terms of supporting existing beliefs (Nickerson 1998).

13   There are also those whose interests are not legitimate, such as organised crime syndicates dealing illegal drugs. (Even though researchers would not seek to accommodate their interests, it is worth understanding how they might react to a policy change.) In the diamorphine trial feasibility research, I tried hard to maintain a respectful relationship with everyone who had a legitimate view on the issue—a measure of success was that evidence we produced was used (appropriately) by those supporting and opposing a trial.

Despite these difficulties and costs, advocacy should not be dismissed as a strategy. It can be argued that researchers have an obligation to add their voices to considerations about complex real-world problems and how society will deal with them.

Engagement

The focus of engagement is on problem solving by researchers and policy makers working together. This approach also seems to be largely premised on the technical-rational framework, although engagement can also lay the groundwork for a rapid, effective response when a window of opportunity opens. It can be useful to differentiate engagement initiated by policy makers from that initiated by researchers. In either case, however, the policy maker is generally the more powerful partner.

Engagement initiated by policy makers can range from commissioning researchers to investigate specific issues (with the policy makers and researchers working together on the research design and interpretation of the results) to developing 'insider-confidant' relationships, where selected researchers become trusted advisors, with a direct channel of communication. Such engagement can be partisan or non-partisan. An example of a partisan approach is that shadow ministers in opposition parties may seek out researchers to help develop new policy platforms to take to upcoming elections, and, if successful, the new government may continue to seek advice on implementing that policy.[14] An example of non-partisan engagement is when researchers are invited to join committees providing policy advice and when those committees continue to function across successive governments.[15]

Researcher-initiated engagement generally seeks to interest policy makers in the design of integrative applied research projects to ensure that the questions being addressed have policy relevance. The researchers may seek ongoing involvement by inviting policy makers to be on advisory committees which provide input into the conduct of the research and the analysis and interpretation of the findings, as well as the way in which the findings will be disseminated. The hope is often that this will give the completed research an advantage in influencing policy.

---

14 A clear example where this occurred in Australia was when a Labor government was elected in 1972 after 23 years in opposition. A number of researchers were drawn on to help formulate policy during the final years in opposition and to help implement it once the party attained government. Two prominent instances were the development of a universal healthcare policy by John Deeble and Dick Scotton (Scotton 2000) and Pat Troy's involvement in urban and regional policy development (see Uren 1994).

15 For example, this has been the case for those serving on the Australian National Council on Drugs (see membership at <http://www.ancd.org.au/members/members-draft.html>).

The advantages of engagement include a potential increase in the relevance of the integrated research to the policy processes and privileged access of policy makers and researchers to each other. The disadvantages often lie in the practicalities. Unlike researchers, whose topics of investigation are usually constrained, policy makers, especially those who are senior, are usually responding to a wide range of issues. For them, working closely with a different research group on each issue is impractical. They may deputise more junior staff to act on their behalf, making the process less valuable for the researchers. Engagement is often also time-consuming, detracting from the core tasks of each group. There can be particular frustrations for researchers when policy priorities are altered and their investigations become insignificant, or when a key policy maker moves to another job, so that building the professional relationship has to start afresh with someone new. For policy makers, frustrations can arise when researchers are not responsive to windows of opportunity, when research and policy cycles are out of kilter or when the view taken by researchers is too narrow and ignores issues policy makers know are important. Researchers can also be tainted by partisanship, so that while they may be effective when one political party is in power, they may become irrelevant when the political situation changes.

A different consideration is that integrated research can sometimes play a valuable role by taking into account views that the policy makers would have trouble consulting about directly for political reasons. These could include the perspectives of powerful opponents of government policy or groups participating in illegal activity. Similarly the integrated research may provide a forum for considering unknowns in a way that may not otherwise be politically feasible. For example, once a policy decision has been made, the policy focus is on implementation and there is little consideration of unintended consequences. Integrative applied research teams can, however, study such effects through, for example, modelling and early evaluation of the implementation, and can help the policy makers modify the implementation if necessary.

Fresh Thinking on Complex Real-World Problems

In dealing with complex real-world problems there are times when a fresh approach is necessary. This occurs when, for instance, incremental change to established policy and practice can no longer deal effectively with the current manifestations of the problem or when it is not clear what change to implement when a window of opportunity opens. For example, in new forms of crime such as terrorism, cybercrime, people trafficking and identity theft, lawbreakers may be located far away from the scene of the offence. Consequently they constitute a major challenge for established policing processes, which rely on the criminal and the crime scene being in close geographical proximity. Dealing with these offences often also requires a level of training that is not included in conventional policing programs—for example, dealing with cybercrime requires a high level of familiarity and skill with information technology. The costs of dealing with these illegal activities are also high, straining limited government budgets. Further, because the public fears crime, government expenditure may be diverted from education and community services to meet demands for extra police, even though in the long run this may exacerbate crime problems. This requires rethinking how policing is undertaken.[16]

How do we recognise that problems are becoming intractable, requiring innovation in policy and practice? How can fresh thinking be generated? In this area I have been greatly influenced by a method called 'Executive Sessions' conceived by Richard Darman and developed and implemented by Mark Moore and Frank Hartmann at the John F. Kennedy School of Government at Harvard University.[17] A brief review of this method is provided in Box 20.1.

Box 20.1 Executive Sessions as a Method for Providing Fresh Thinking on Complex Real-world Problems

As Moore and Hartmann describe:[a]

The process of an Executive Session is designed to…allow academics and practitioners to work on that particular set of public problems that are important, and for which current solutions do not exist [and]…to work on these problems in a way that not only increases the chance that a 'value creating' solution will be found, but also creates conditions favorable to widespread implementation and continued learning.

A group of some 20 practitioners,[b] five academics and three–four people with expertise in allied areas,[c] holds about six two-day meetings over a period of three years or so to combine their expertise to grapple energetically with the problem.

16   Such issues (and more) were addressed in the Executive Session on Policing and Public Safety run by the Program on Criminal Justice Policy and Management at the John F. Kennedy School of Government at Harvard University from 2008 to 2010. See <http://www.hks.harvard.edu/criminaljustice/executive_sessions/policing.htm> (accessed 15 February 2012). I was fortunate to be an observer at those meetings.
17   Hough (2002); Moore and Hartmann (1999).

Between 1984 and 2009, Harvard University hosted 17 Executive Sessions, many in the criminal justice area.[d] Detailed analysis of these events is ongoing, but there are a number of factors that seem to be required for them to be successful in generating and implementing new ideas. One is the convening power of the host institution, which determines whether innovative, influential thinkers can be attracted as participants. Other elements of success include

- melding together the real-world experience of the practitioners and the theoretical and empirical insights of the academics
- organising the process so that ideas gel over the series of meetings
- involving a mix of participants with different value positions and using those differences as a source of creativity.

The success of Executive Sessions therefore relies on senior practitioners and researchers who have a wealth of experience, both practical and academic, upon which to draw. During the Executive Session, researchers and practitioners will ideally work together to document and further develop new insights, as well as to undertake empirical research that may shed light on the ideas. The aim is to involve practitioners who are powerful enough that they are in a position to implement the new approaches in their organisations and to influence more general uptake throughout their arena.

a. Moore and Hartmann (1999).

b. Here the term practitioners is used to include policy makers.

c. For example, in the Executive Session on Policing and Public Safety, these people included a mayor and a journalist, who had an interest in the policing challenges, but could hold up an outsider's mirror.

d. They were America's Juvenile Justice System (1984), Policing (1985–93, including Drugs and Community Policing, 1990–91), State and Local Prosecutors (1987–90), Making the System Work for Poor Children (1988–90), Working Group of State Drug Control Executives (1992), New Paradigms for Child Protective Services (1994–97), Saguaro Seminar: Civic Engagement in America (1997–2000), Medical Error and Patient Safety (1998–2000), Public Sector Performance Management (1998–2000), Public Defense (1999–2001), Future of Philanthropy (1999–2002), Domestic Preparedness (1999–2003), American Indian Constitutional Reform (2001–03), Future of Public Service (2002), Faith-Based and Community Approaches to Urban Revitalization (2002–03), Human Rights Commissions and Criminal Justice (2006–08), Policing and Public Safety (2008–10).

Tasks for the I2S Development Drive

Identify and catalogue the full range of methods that have been used for providing integrated research support for policy and practice change, as well as their conceptual bases and case examples of their application. Update and improve existing compilations. This includes taking a broad view of communication (such as effectiveness at different stages of the policy cycle), identifying and assessing the value of brokering agencies, and developing rules of thumb for when methods of generating fresh thinking on complex problems are likely to be useful.

Who is Involved in the Provision of Integrated Research Support?

The discussion to date has largely been on the 'how' side of the provision of integrated research support, so let us now move to a brief consideration of 'who'. On the research side, team leaders or other senior researchers will generally be responsible for the provision of integrated research support.[18]

It is also useful to consider 'who' is involved on the policy and practice sides. Part of the rationale for I2S is that many researchers do not think about the specifics of their implementation role, especially who would most benefit from being supported by the integrated research. Important aspects of the choices to be made about policy makers include differentiating between politicians and public servants, government and opposition, as well as players who are currently powerful and those tipped as up-and-comers. While more specificity in targeting integrated research seems to warrant attention, the unpredictability of political processes, where key players may change quickly and unexpectedly, must also be factored in.

The integrative applied research team also needs to be aware that there may be groups with which they do not want to be associated. For example, they may not want to be linked to one specific political party or particular interest groups.

When Does Provision of Integrated Research Support Occur?

It is also useful to consider this question from both the researcher and the policy maker perspectives. From the researcher perspective, communication and advocacy occur when there is a solid body of research evidence that warrants implementation. In other words, they usually occur at the end of the research process.[19] Engagement occurs throughout the research process.

From the policy maker perspective, 'when' is dictated by the political process. Governments generally have a broad program of changes they are seeking to implement in their term of office. Public servants may be charged with developing suitable options from which choices can be made or with implementing an option the government has already decided on. Public servants, ministers

---

18   Many research organisations have become quite sophisticated about using the media to communicate their results and this experience is also relevant for integrative applied research. Such communication is not usually confined to senior people, but can be undertaken by researchers at any level.

19   Although, as in the diamorphine prescription feasibility research, communication can occur throughout if the research itself is of particular public interest or concern.

and their advisers will seek research input at times appropriate to their work schedules. And, unlike a research work program that is relatively amenable to forward planning, the schedules of policy makers are often disrupted by political exigencies. Consequently, research input that is urgent one day may be irrelevant the next. 'When' is therefore much less predictable from the policy maker perspective. This mismatch and the potential waste of researcher time are sources of frustration for both sides.

Task for the I2S Development Drive
Collect case examples of implementation of different options for who undertook the provision of integrated research support for policy and practice change and when in the research process this occurred. Take into account the options for policy and practice recipients and the timing issues that are relevant for them.

21. Context?

The relevant question here is '*What circumstances might influence the provision of integrated research support for policy and practice change?*'. Again, this is examined in light of the pertinent big-picture background (in other words, overall context), authorisation, and organisational barriers and facilitators.

Overall Context

A key issue is to examine the problem in relation to the arenas where action will be taken: government, business and civil society. This involves taking a broader view of how research can support policy and practice change than that dealt with under question two (*Which aspects of policy and practice are targeted by the provision of integrated research support?*). If we stay with government policy making, relevant circumstances may include

- the history of policy on the problem
- analysis of current policy, including levers for influencing the problem and key interest group stances
- political party platforms on the problem, as well as entrenched views among the party leadership
- political party openness to research, especially integrated research.[1]

For example, in our investigation into the feasibility of diamorphine prescription, we hired a political scientist to examine the following contextual issues: political party platforms on illicit drugs, the results of a range of Australian political inquiries into illicit drug use and the history of the current government policy.[2] The main conclusion was that while there was significant concern about illicit drugs, the situation was not 'ripe' for major political change; however, a trial was within the bounds of possibility.

Tasks for the I2S Development Drive
Collect case examples dealing with overall context for considering the government, business and civil society arenas.
Work with a range of social scientists to produce guides for how context can be taken into account.

---

1   Analysis of past political party experiences with integrated research, even on different problems, may be useful. Positive experiences may favourably dispose the party, while negative ones would have the opposite effect.
2   Hartland (1991); Hartland et al. (1992).

Authorisation

How does authorisation affect the provision of integrated research support for policy and practice change? This chapter considers such provision when the research is initiated and driven by the investigator. In Chapter 28, I examine how this may be different when the integrative applied research has come about at the behest of government policy makers, a business group or a civil society consortium.

Let us examine, in turn, funding and endorsement as the key sources of authorisation for provision of integrated research support. It is still relatively uncommon for funding to be provided specifically for the implementation of research findings (integrated or otherwise) when the research is investigator initiated and driven.[3] Nevertheless, it is becoming more usual for standard competitive funding to require impact and communication of the research results to be addressed as part of the funding application.[4]

When it comes to endorsement, there is a general expectation that the results of research initiated and driven by the investigator will be publicly available, but there is wide variation in the extent to which researchers promote their findings outside the academic domain. One important source of endorsement comes from the organisations that employ the researchers. Universities, for example, tend to look favourably on their employees seeking to support policy and practice change, even though formal recognition or reward for such activities tends to be limited. Advisory committees can also be important for endorsement, especially when members are selected because they are influential in policy or practice settings.

Task for the I2S Development Drive

Gather case examples describing funding, endorsement and other forms of authorisation, along with any restrictions on providing integrated research support for policy and practice change.

---

3   When research is initiated by government, business or civil society (see Chapter 28) there is more likely to be a focus on implementation.

4   For example, in the guidelines for applicants for 2012 Discovery Projects, the Australian Research Council requested the following: 'Describe the expected outcomes and likely impact of the proposed research' and '[o]utline the plans for communicating research results, including scholarly and public communication and dissemination' (<http://www.arc.gov.au/pdf/DP12_instructions.pdf>, accessed 13 December 2011).

Organisational Facilitators and Barriers

Facilitators and barriers to providing integrated research support can occur both in the research organisations undertaking the integrative applied research and in the target organisations, hence these will be dealt with in turn. In both cases organisational structure and culture are again important.

Relevant structures in research organisations include having a media office, employment of knowledge brokers and rewards for the provision of integrated research support. Media offices are common and have the explicit aim of helping researchers publicise their work. Targets can include the general community, public servants and advisers to politicians. Some organisations employ knowledge brokers to convey the research findings to selected target groups, which can be politicians, specific professional groups or particular community groups.[5] While outreach is not considered to be a primary activity in the formal academic reward system, as discussed above, being more widely known, seeing research have an impact and having outreach recognised in staff meetings and university newsletters all help promote such activities.

Cultural factors can also be influential. On one level, organisations may be more likely to work with some implementation arenas than others. Organisations undertaking public health and environmental research were, until recently, most likely to work with government and civil society groups, but reluctant to engage with business, for example. On another level, research organisations may favour some kinds of research support over others. For instance, some organisations encourage their staff to engage in public debate and have no problem with the expression of controversial views or criticism of government or other powerful players. Other institutions actively discourage this.

On the other side, policy and practice organisations also vary in how they seek out and respond to integrated research support. From the perspective of structure, some organisations have research arms that have been established to find relevant investigations and consider the application of the findings. Regardless of whether such structures exist, cultural differences will influence the extent to which integrated research is sought, with some constantly striving to improve their area of policy or practice, others only open to research that they commission and others still paying little attention to research at all. The extent to which integrated research has more sway than the perspectives of particular disciplines (such as economics) and stakeholders (such as business) is another cultural variable in organisations. Further, the orientation towards and openness to considering diverse unknowns comprehensively are also relevant. Finally, cultural factors also influence responses to various research approaches.

---

5 Examples of knowledge brokers can be found in Bammer et al. (2010a).

Thus, some may welcome engagement, while others will not. Some will build on research advocacy to help push through change,[6] whereas others may see it as an unwarranted intrusion.

Task for the I2S Development Drive
Compile case examples describing the diversity and impact of organisational barriers and facilitators, examining the policy and practice organisations as well as the research organisations.

---

6   In the 1970s and 1980s feminist public servants encouraged feminists in broader society to keep publicly agitating for change, as this gave them leverage within government policy making in arguing that reforms were needed (Sawer 1990).

22. Outcome?

In considering question five—*'What is the result of the provision of integrated research support?'*—the structured framework discussed in the previous four chapters provides a systematic approach to assessment, through questions shown in Box 22.1.

Box 22.1 Questions for Evaluating Provision of Integrated Research Support for Policy and Practice Change

Was there a clear assessment of who might benefit from the integrated research findings and how to best transmit the findings to that policy or practice audience? How well did the provision of integrated research support meet its aims and target the intended beneficiaries?

Was the systems view taken suitable? Would a different systems view have been more useful?

Was the full range of options considered for: a) what could be done through each of the government, business and civil society arenas, b) the systems view, and c) the range of organisations and individuals within each systems approach?

Within the necessary limitations, were the most worthwhile targets set for: a) the government, business and civil society arenas, b) the systems view, and c) the range of organisations and individuals? Was the balance fitting? Did any of those excluded turn out to be critical? Were any special advantages of the integrative applied research team recognised and helpfully used?

Were the framing of the problem and the results of the integrated research accurate and meaningful?

Were values considered adequately?

Were productive differences between policy makers and practitioners, on one hand, and researchers, on the other, harnessed effectively? Were potentially destructive differences well managed?

Were sufficient flexibility and iteration built into the processes of deciding on a systems view, scoping, boundary setting, framing, considering values, and harnessing and managing differences?

> Were applicable methods used for providing integrated research support? Would other methods have made better contributions? Was a defensible position taken on impartiality? If appropriate, was the need for fresh thinking recognised and were suitable methods used? Were justifiable decisions made in choosing by whom and when the provision of integrated research support was undertaken?
>
> Was the overall context for the provision of integrated research support adequately considered? Were critical contextual factors missed?
>
> Was the authorisation for the provision of integrated research support apposite? Did it influence the provision of integrated research support in critical ways?
>
> Did the research organisation structure or culture provide barriers to the provision of integrated research support? If so, were these effectually recognised and managed? Were facilitators beneficially mobilised?
>
> Did the target policy and practice organisation structure or culture provide barriers to the provision of integrated research support? If so, were these effectively recognised and managed? Were facilitators positively mobilised?

As discussed in Chapter 8, developing I2S as a discipline makes peer review feasible as an evaluation process, as is the case in traditional disciplines. For this domain, those who have been involved in the provision of integrated research support for policy and practice change are in the best position to act as reviewers, employing the questions described above. Nevertheless there are particular challenges to evaluating this domain.

First, no research project on a complex real-world problem is likely to please all the groups which have an interest, so there will always be some who find fault. This raises the more general question: what are realistic aims for research that tackles controversial topics, especially when there are high stakes and the outcomes challenge powerful players with vested interests?

Another related issue is that evaluation may be difficult without input from the policy and practice arenas to complement the documentation provided by the researchers. It may be that actions that the researchers consider to be effective are not perceived in the same way by the relevant policy makers and practitioners. The opposite may also be the case, where actions the researchers thought were ineffective actually made a difference in the eyes of the policy makers and practitioners.

More particularly, the success or failure of individual actions and inactions is often difficult to assess, because the policy and practice systems are so complicated. Indeed most policy and practice change is likely to be the result of the accumulation of a large number of activities and the impact of any one sector (like the research sector or the affected community sector), let alone any one action, will be impossible to ascertain. In addition, secrecy plays an important role in government and other policy making, so that it may not be possible to fully evaluate what occurred.

Finally, the success or failure of the integrated research support may be entirely outside the researchers' control. A political crisis, an economic downturn or the departure of a key policy maker can be pivotal events affecting integrated research impact (either positively or negatively).

Tasks for the I2S Development Drive
Gather and analyse case examples of evaluation both to improve the list of assessment questions and to develop more detailed guidelines for reviewers. Include cases that examine complexities arising from: a) opposition by vested interests, b) the requirement for multiple viewpoints to understand impact, and c) the inability to predict impact.

23. Specialising in I2S

In addition to the three broad categories of I2S specialisation discussed for the first two domains—1) I2S for team leaders, 2) I2S disciplinary specialists, and 3) I2S appreciation for other integrative applied research team members—a fourth is also considered here: I2S appreciation for policy makers and practitioners.

I2S for Team Leaders

In taking responsibility for this domain and the project overall, team leaders provide guidance about how the integrated research can best support policy and practice change. They oversee decision making in two important areas. First, assessments must be made about which arena—government, business and/or civil society—their teams are in the best position to target. Second, judgment is required regarding the overall style of interaction—for example, whether it will be a highly engaged partnership or more independent and distant, with directed communication of integrated research results as the main activity. The leaders bring into their teams I2S disciplinary specialists familiar with how the relevant arena(s) operate, who can help map out more detailed options for providing support.

Team leaders set the tone for their teams in terms of openness to considering a range of options, appreciating that formulaic processes are not realistic and ensuring a commitment to the further development of I2S. They require a level of I2S expertise that is comprehensive enough to address the specific aspects of I2S described in Box 23.1. Finally, given that researchers have little control over the impact of their provision of integrated research support, integrative applied research team leaders need to think through the likely consequences if the provision is not successful in supporting policy or practice change and plan how to minimise the risk of wasting the research effort.[1]

---

1   In the diamorphine prescription feasibility research we emphasised publication of our findings. We also interacted with researchers and policy makers from other countries and it turned out that our results were useful for both the Swiss and the Dutch trials, even though they were not used in Australia.

Box 23.1 Specific I2S Responsibilities for Integrative Applied Research Team Leaders

> Team leaders must have adequate knowledge about I2S to address
>
> - aims and beneficiaries
> - who will be responsible for providing integrated research support
> - how the research world differs from the policy and practice worlds; as well as which differences can be harnessed to enhance the provision of integrated research support and which need to be managed, so that they do not prevent the provision of integrated research support
> - when fresh thinking is required, and identifying processes—like Executive Sessions—that can achieve this
> - authorisation
> - facilitators and barriers to providing integrated research support, both in the relevant research organisations and in the arenas, be they government, business, civil society or some combination of these. Leaders also need to be able to tease out which are most important and determine how facilitators can be exploited and barriers managed.

I2S Disciplinary Specialists

In this domain, I2S disciplinary specialists provide detailed knowledge about how the integrated research can best support policy and practice change. They help their teams map out options for action, understanding the strengths and limitations of each. They not only have a deep appreciation of researcher world views and operations, but also understand the policy and practice worlds and can interpret these for other integrative applied research team members. I2S specialists therefore need to be at least 'bilingual' (able to bridge the research world and one relevant policy or practice world) or 'multilingual'. Experienced I2S specialists can identify when the time for action is 'ripe' and help their integrative applied research teams respond appropriately. For example, specialists can recognise when a policy window is open and work with their integrative applied research teams on a well-crafted, speedy response targeted at the key players. Similarly, I2S specialists should be able to match research input to the appropriate stage of the policy cycle.

In order to achieve this, I2S specialists need to draw on the best available knowledge about how the government, business and civil society systems work and to make these insights available to their teams. It is unlikely that individual specialists will be equally proficient in each of the arenas, but they should have a working knowledge of them all and be able to bring in colleagues to make up for deficiencies in their own skills. Within any one arena, individual specialists may also be more adept at some concepts and methods than others, but they should at least have basic knowledge of all of those described in Box 23.2.

Box 23.2 Skills for I2S Disciplinary Specialists

I2S disciplinary specialists must have a basic working knowledge of all of the following and particular competence in some

- organisational structures and processes—along with theories that can help explain them—that make up policy and practice systems
- scoping the range of possible avenues for providing integrated research support, including arenas, systems, organisations within systems and individuals
- boundary setting around the possibilities for providing support that are likely to be most fruitful
- framing the problem and the findings of the integrated research appropriately for the relevant policy or practice arena, in order to communicate the essence in a meaningful way
- dealing with values and how they influence the provision of integrated research support in terms of targets and processes
- options for supporting policy and practice change—including communication, advocacy and engagement—along with their advantages and disadvantages. This also involves assessing the most suitable policy and practice targets, as well as which options they will be most receptive to
- overall context—in other words, the 'big picture' issues that are likely to influence how the arena for implementation (government, business and/or civil society) views the problem and responds to integrated research.

In this domain, I2S covers a huge amount of material, when the government, business and civil society arenas are all taken into account. This is necessary because many real-world problems like global climate change, child labour and the illegal arms trade require policy responses from governments, business *and* civil society, as well as practice change at many levels, ranging from the individual to the organisational and from local communities to the international sphere. I2S disciplinary specialists must be skilled enough to assist integrative applied research teams in figuring out at which level(s) in which arena(s) they can most effectively provide support.

A major task for I2S disciplinary specialists is also to build and strengthen the discipline. This includes ensuring that, to the extent possible, the aspects of their teams' investigations concerned with provision of integrated research support are documented in a way that makes evaluation by peers easy. In addition, I2S disciplinary specialists are responsible for learning from their evaluations of the work of others about new concepts and methods for providing integrated research support for policy and practice change, as well as how well they worked.

I2S Appreciation for Other Integrative Applied Research Team Members

The other team members need to have some understanding of the provision of integrated research support to policy and practice change, especially when highly engaged processes are used. In these cases they need to appreciate why policy makers and/or practitioners may be involved in boundary setting, framing and other I2S tasks. They also need to understand the processes in place for interacting with policy makers and practitioners and their role in them—for example, to be prepared to help the team seize opportunities when they arise or to refrain from engaging in certain kinds of advocacy. Further, the team members may themselves have valuable contacts, experiences and other expertise that can be drawn on in order to provide effective support.

I2S Appreciation for Policy Makers and Practitioners

Policy makers and practitioners also benefit from understanding what integrative applied research can offer them, which involves appreciating how I2S operates. This allows them to, for example, better assess and respond to overtures from researchers seeking to provide integrated research support, as well as to have more realistic expectations when seeking such support. They would also be in a better position to evaluate what sort of interactions they want to enter into.

***

The chapters in this domain have laid out a systematic approach to providing integrated research support for policy and practice change through the five-question framework. They have also outlined the concepts, methods, case examples and guides that must be collected and built on to make I2S an effective discipline through the I2S Development Drive.

In the next group of chapters, the framework is applied to bringing together the three I2S domains—synthesising disciplinary and stakeholder knowledge, understanding and managing diverse unknowns and providing integrated research support for policy and practice change. This includes taking into account the interactions between the domains, as these are inevitable when investigating complex real-world problems.

I2S As A Whole

24. Introduction

This section brings together and examines the interactions among the three domains: synthesising disciplinary and stakeholder knowledge, understanding and managing diverse unknowns and providing integrated research support for policy and practice change. While it is helpful to differentiate between the domains to make research on complex real-world problems manageable, it is also important to remember that such distinctions are a construct, that the boundaries are not sharply defined and that what happens at the interfaces of the domains must be taken into account. There are different kinds of interactions, which include the following.

- Phenomena that are not very evident in any one domain becoming more prominent when I2S is considered as a whole; for example, some of the policy makers and practitioners considered in Domain 3 are also stakeholders dealt with in Domain 1. As described in Chapter 2, treating these separately is helpful for understanding each domain, but the overlap between these two groups must also be taken into account.

- Spin-offs from one domain that affect the others; for instance, if practitioners are able to help formulate the questions for knowledge synthesis and dealing with diverse unknowns, they may also be more motivated to implement the research findings.

- Efficiencies from considering the domains together, such as the ability to use some dialogue and modelling methods across more than one domain.

A related issue is that of congruence between the approaches in the three domains. Incompatibility can lead to conflict and stymie progress. This can occur if different values, for example, govern how each domain is tackled. Imagine if a democratic research approach is used to involve a wide range of stakeholders in Domains 1 and 2, but the integrated research support for policy or practice change is then driven by maximising profitability. Many of the stakeholders involved in the knowledge synthesis and dealing with diverse unknowns could rightly feel that their time was wasted. On the other hand, identifying and overcoming inconsistencies can strengthen the integrative applied research. In the example just presented, the realisation that there was a problem with congruence could have been used to modify either the approaches to knowledge synthesis and dealing with unknowns or the implementation, thereby improving the research overall.

This section will inevitably recap key issues for each of the three domains. Where possible, I will present these with a different slant and will build on them. Let us then examine the aims of integrative applied research and I2S in a new light. Overall, integrative applied research aims to help tackle complex real-world problems through

- assisting policy makers and practitioners in developing and implementing improved decisions and actions

by

- providing more comprehensive understanding of the problem or generating fresh thinking about it

through

- bringing together relevant disciplinary and stakeholder knowledge

and

- an appreciation of, and management strategy for, the diverse range of remaining unknowns.

The discipline of I2S underpins integrative applied research with

1. a five-question framework, which provides a systematic approach to conducting the research and providing integrated research support
2. an array of options in relevant concepts, methods and case examples
3. guides to relevant knowledge from outside I2S.

In presenting I2S as a whole, the five-question framework becomes the following.

1. What is the integrative applied research aiming to achieve and who is intended to benefit? (For what and for whom?)
2. What is the integrative applied research dealing with—that is, which knowledge is synthesised, unknowns considered and aspects of policy and practice targeted? (Which knowledge, unknowns and aspects of policy and practice?)
3. How is the integrative applied research undertaken (the knowledge synthesised, diverse unknowns understood and managed, and integrated research support provided), by whom and when? (How?)
4. What circumstances might influence the integrative applied research? (Context?)
5. What is the result of the integrative applied research? (Outcome?)

As in the foregoing sections, each of these questions is considered in turn. Figure 24.1 provides a summary of the new ideas presented for each question along with the chapters in which they are relayed.

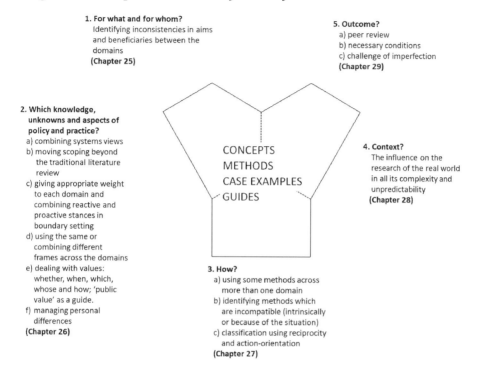

1. For what and for whom?
Identifying inconsistencies in aims and beneficiaries between the domains
(Chapter 25)

5. Outcome?
a) peer review
b) necessary conditions
c) challenge of imperfection
(Chapter 29)

2. Which knowledge, unknowns and aspects of policy and practice?
a) combining systems views
b) moving scoping beyond the traditional literature review
c) giving appropriate weight to each domain and combining reactive and proactive stances in boundary setting
d) using the same or combining different frames across the domains
e) dealing with values: whether, when, which, whose and how; 'public value' as a guide.
f) managing personal differences
(Chapter 26)

CONCEPTS
METHODS
CASE EXAMPLES
GUIDES

4. Context?
The influence on the research of the real world in all its complexity and unpredictability
(Chapter 28)

3. How?
a) using some methods across more than one domain
b) identifying methods which are incompatible (intrinsically or because of the situation)
c) classification using reciprocity and action-orientation
(Chapter 27)

Figure 24.1 The Storeroom for I2S as a Whole

Source: Author's illustration.

Consideration is also given to additional tasks for the I2S Development Drive in compiling the relevant concepts, methods and case examples, as well as guides to relevant knowledge from outside I2S. This section concludes by reviewing the whole role of I2S specialists in integrative applied research teams, especially in providing expertise across the three domains.

25. For What and for Whom?

The purpose of this first question—*'What is the integrative applied research aiming to achieve and who is intended to benefit?'*—is to help teams think specifically about their objectives and beneficiaries, so that they direct their efforts most effectively. Asking the related question of each domain helps ensure that no aspect of integrative applied research is ignored or downplayed and enables separate assessment of the success of the research undertaken in each domain. Hence, this question sets out to provide clarity about

1. the purpose of the knowledge synthesis

2. the importance of thinking expansively about unknowns and how they might be dealt with; this in turn raises the inevitability of imperfection in the response to the problem and encourages the integrative applied research team to consider how best to manage it

3. the specific aspects of policy or practice being supported.

For beneficiaries, this question aims to spell out

1. which disciplinary and stakeholder perspectives are included in the knowledge synthesis

2. which perspectives on unknowns and approaches to them are taken into account

3. which arenas (one or more of government, business and civil society) as well as which particular parts of an arena and individuals are targeted for support by the integrated research effort.

Well-formulated goals help the integrative applied research team choose the most appropriate options in terms of I2S concepts, methods and case examples, as well as guides to relevant knowledge from outside the discipline.

Considering these individual domain purposes together helps identify possible inconsistencies or clashes between them. These could occur, for example, if the knowledge synthesis drew together perspectives useful for business action, but was actually aimed at the government arena, or if the examination of unknowns involved disciplines that were not included in the knowledge synthesis. Another set of considerations involves examining the evenness of research quality across the whole project and the implications of discrepancies for the provision of integrated research support. If, for example, some aspects of the knowledge synthesis were methodologically weak or methods for dealing with some unknowns were poorly developed, greater caution would be necessary in the interpretation of those parts of the research and their implications for action.

Looking at congruence at the team level is also useful. Having individual team members think about the specifics of what they are setting out to achieve assists in identifying the degree of unity among team members in desired aims and beneficiaries. Identifying and discussing differences can be useful for making tacit thinking in the team explicit and for uncovering other areas of divergence, such as dissimilar value positions. If there are conflicts in the team, they will need to be resolved or managed. Further, the identification of inconsistencies at either the domain level or the team level is a useful aid to clarifying the purposes of the integrative applied research. For example, lack of correspondence may mean that there are additional project aims that have not been made explicit.

Let me hasten to add that I do not advocate stipulating rigid aims and beneficiaries that are totally consistent across the three domains and with which everyone in a team has to agree. A degree of vagueness, flexibility and even contradiction is essential for any research to proceed. There is a creative tension between precise specification for choosing the most appropriate concepts and methods versus encompassing the messy realities of the research process. Further, it can be useful to revisit the aims and beneficiaries throughout the investigation, as they may become clearer over time or may change as the research progresses. Rather than considering variability only as a problem to be overcome, it can also be regarded as a way of enriching the research by highlighting new angles and possibilities. Overall, the point of this question is to aid teams in developing and progressing their research.

Task for the I2S Development Drive
Compile case examples illustrating different ways in which integrative applied research teams approached aims for addressing the problem as a whole. Particularly valuable will be information on how they identified and dealt with inconsistencies in aims and beneficiaries across the domains and within the team.

26. Which Knowledge, Unknowns and Aspects of Policy and Practice?

To examine the second question—'*What is the integrative applied research dealing with—that is, which knowledge is synthesised, unknowns considered and aspects of policy and practice targeted?*'—each of the categories of concepts and methods, first introduced in Chapter 5, is reviewed in turn. Hence consideration is given to taking a systems view, scoping, boundary setting, framing, taking values into account, and harnessing and managing differences.

Taking a Systems View

In viewing the three domains together, there are two different systems to consider: the problem and the policy or practice arena. It is important to re-emphasise the key point made in earlier chapters that there is no practical way to focus on either the whole problem or the whole policy or practice arena at once, let alone both of them. Instead, different systems approaches highlight different aspects of the problem or the policy or practice arena.

In viewing I2S as a whole, a key issue is fitting together the various systems views used in each domain. The ability to mix and match different systems approaches to allow the problem to be understood and acted on more effectively requires understanding about the advantages and disadvantages of each systems methodology and how to choose among them. This is an underdeveloped area.

Tasks for the I2S Development Drive
Collect case examples illustrating ways to combine various systems approaches to the problem (which may differ for the knowledge synthesis and unknowns aspects) and the policy and practice arenas.
Work with systems experts to produce a guide for combining different systems approaches to the problem and the policy and practice arenas.

Scoping

Scoping involves considering the problem, and the relevant aspects of policy or practice, as broadly as possible. The aim is to make the problem and the policy or practice change central, and to move considerations beyond the limited expertise of those responsible for designing the research and research support.[1]

---

1   This is particularly important when those who start the study are a small group with limited perspectives.

This involves identifying

1. the range of systems approaches relevant to the problem and the policy or practice arenas

2. the full range of relevant disciplines and stakeholders, what they could contribute to understanding the problem and how those contributions could be made

3. which unknowns are germane, which expertise could be drawn on in considering them and how

4. the key actors and processes in each of the government, business and civil society arenas and the full array of options for providing integrated research support to them.

Scoping is applicable not only to each domain, but also to the overlaps between them. Thus, for example, scoping may need to take into account how previous policy or practice action on the problem was influenced by research, as well as how unknowns may have stymied change in the past.[2]

In essence, the challenge for I2S in scoping complex real-world problems is to help integrative applied research teams build on and move beyond the traditional literature review, which is the way problems are scoped within disciplines. The literature reviews of the relevant disciplines are the starting point, but need to be extended to identify and include relevant stakeholders and their perspectives. The expansion includes an examination of diverse unknowns and particular focus on areas that are contentious. It also encompasses the array of possibilities for providing integrated research support, any interventions that have been tried in the past and how successful they have been. The aim of the scoping is to provide an appreciation of the areas of greatest need for further investigation, management of unknowns and action.[3]

In considering I2S as a whole, an important element of the scoping process is to recognise the overlaps between the *stakeholders* in Domains 1 and 2 and the *policy makers and practitioners* in Domain 3. In other words, some of the stakeholders who have relevant knowledge to contribute to appreciating the problem and considering the unknowns are also often policy makers or practitioners whose task it is to make decisions about and to act on the problem. A chief implication for scoping is recognising that one may influence the other. In particular, the positions of policy maker or practitioner may shape or limit the ability to provide information or consider unknowns. For example, government policy makers

---

2   This overlaps to some extent with big-picture context (see Chapter 28).

3   It can also help the integrative applied research team decide if they want to work within the broad understandings of the problem or if they want to challenge the way the problem is generally viewed by paying more attention to something society or previous researchers have marginalised or excluded.

may be restricted in their contributions by confidentiality requirements, and business and civil society practitioners by the desire to maintain competitive advantage.[4]

The result of the scoping process is to lay out the possibilities for building the integrative applied research team, by identifying the full range of people who could contribute to the team's work, the breadth of what they could bring to addressing the problem, as well as the options for engaging them.

Tasks for the I2S Development Drive
Gather together and develop useful concepts, methods and case examples for managing the vast amount of information that is inevitably involved when the three domains are combined.
Collect case examples to investigate the intersection between 'stakeholders' and 'policy makers and practitioners', especially limits on what is possible for scoping and how these can be overcome.

Boundary Setting

No research project on a complex real-world problem can encompass everything that is revealed to be relevant by the scoping process. Boundary setting will therefore occur, whether it is recognised or not. I2S aims to provide concepts and methods for a conscious and considered process of determining what is included and excluded, as well as what is central and what is marginal. This practical consideration involves figuring out what can best be done with the available resources of time, money and person power. Boundary setting therefore involves deciding

1. which systems approaches will be taken for the problem and the policy and/ or practice arenas

2. which disciplines and stakeholders to include in the knowledge synthesis, what they will contribute to addressing the problem and how those contributions will be made

3. which unknowns will be considered, which expertise will be drawn on in those considerations and how

4. which policy and practice actors and processes in government, business and/ or civil society are to be targeted, as well as through whom, how and when.

---

4   There may be other ways to obtain useful inputs—for example, by working with retirees who can raise the sorts of issues that current policy makers and practitioners would have in mind.

The process is actually much more iterative than this description might imply. Further, boundary setting also involves deciding how much weight to give to different sides when there are contentious issues.

As described in previous chapters, the task for scoping and boundary setting is to move those designing the research away from being driven only by what they know and have experience with, to focusing on the needs of the problem and expanding the integrative applied research team accordingly. The well-worn story of the drunk searching for his keys under a streetlight where he can see, even though he lost them in a dark alley, is pertinent here. The aim is to bring in people with torches to search in the dark alley. Combining scoping and boundary setting to make sure all the possibilities are on the table before decisions are made about what will be undertaken is aimed at maximising the relevance of the integrative applied research to the problem under consideration. A key aspect is to make the boundary-setting process systematic and explicit, so that it can be evaluated and improved in future.

Additional issues are raised when interactions across the three domains are considered. First, it is important to give approximately equal weight to each domain, even though the relevant levels of methodological sophistication may be different. For instance, this involves ensuring that critical unknowns are not sidelined simply because they are not well understood and are difficult to take action on. Second, teams must check that there is congruence in boundary setting between the domains. For example, if policy change was to be supported through an engaged partnership approach, it would be desirable for the collaboration to permeate other aspects of the integrative applied research, particularly setting boundaries around the disciplinary and stakeholder knowledge to be included, as well as which unknowns would be considered and how. On the other hand, care is required to make certain that the aim of congruence does not result in the boundaries being set too narrowly. For example, providing policy makers and practitioners only with what they ask for may miss critical relevant issues. In other words, the integrative applied research team should not be merely reactive, but should also alert policy makers and practitioners to important areas that may be new to them.

Task for the I2S Development Drive
Collate case examples relevant to interactions between the domains in boundary setting, such as: a) ensuring relatively equal coverage of each domain; b) congruence between how knowledge synthesis, unknowns and providing integrated research support were approached; and c) not allowing congruence to be too limiting, especially in restricting coverage of key aspects of the approach to the problem or the potential for change.

Framing

Framing involves deciding how to depict the integrative applied research on the major social or environmental issue. Descriptions automatically provide a frame regardless of whether this is done consciously. The aim here is to raise awareness of the importance of framing so that the team can accurately and succinctly capture the essence of the research and employ the power that language provides.

This is most critical for addressing controversy, which is an aspect of most complex real-world issues. The way the problem and the research results are framed is useful for communicating whether the integrative applied research team is taking a particular stand or seeking to situate itself above the fray. Because framing is so influential, it is important that the position of the integrative applied research vis-a-vis any controversies is conveyed accurately.[5]

There is currently little understanding of how to manage framing across the three domains—for example, when it is useful to have different frames and when they should be the same.

Tasks for the I2S Development Drive
Draw together case examples of the relationships between the frames used in the three domains—for example, when these were the same or different framings—as well as assessments of how well these worked.
Collect case examples of accurate and inaccurate framings for the position of integrative applied research teams on controversial issues.

Taking Values into Account

The systems approaches used, the way the problem and provision of integrated research support are scoped and the boundaries set and the framing employed will all be determined by and reflect the values brought to the research. A major task in the development of I2S is, therefore, providing effective ways of dealing with values. Considerations include the following.

---

5   It is important to be clear that the integrative applied research team does not have to take an unequivocal position. It is fine for the team to say, for example, 'we are worried, we have some relevant information, but we do not know how it fits'. The point is that framing is not just critical for advocacy, but is also about clear, concise communication about the approach to the problem and the research findings.

- Whether and when in the research process values should be made explicit; for example, should there be a proactive process or should it only occur in response to values conflict?

- Which values should be examined—for instance: values about the problem under consideration, research generally, the various disciplines and stakeholders, diverse unknowns or about the different implementation arenas?

- Whose values should be considered—for example: only the key players or everyone involved in the research?

- How should values be considered, specifically what reliable methods are there for doing so?

A key reason for dealing with values explicitly is to ensure that the research has integrity. One element of integrity is congruence in values across the three domains. For example, a research team cannot espouse liberal values about supporting policy action to aid the disadvantaged, while ignoring their perspectives in the knowledge synthesis and dealing with unknowns.

But there is also a broader issue about integrative applied research being true to itself and not becoming an uncritical handmaiden to policy makers and practitioners. While integrated research has an important role in supporting policy and practice change and doing so in a way that takes into account practical realities, such as the 'beguiling' art described by Peter Shergold (see Chapter 17), the research has to be guided by its own principles. It must be able to resist being seduced by the political power of government policy makers, the economic clout of business or the moral sway of civil society in order to continue providing essential critique of these arenas and helping to hold them accountable.[6]

This is an area that still requires considerable development, but Mark Moore's articulation of the notion of 'public value' as the goal for policy making and practice change in the government realm provides a valuable starting point.[7]

Moore describes public value as government activity that 'shields the country from foreign enemies, keeps the streets safe and clean, educates the children, and insulates citizens from many man-made and natural disasters that have impoverished the lives of previous human generations'.[8]

---

6   This relates back to an issue raised in the section on boundary setting about the integrative applied research team not merely being reactive, but also alerting policy makers and practitioners to important areas that may be new to them. What the integrative applied research team deems to be essential in this regard will be driven by their values.

7   Moore (1995). The presentation of Moore's argument here is simplified.

8   Moore (1995, p. 29).

He sees government policy makers and public managers as 'explorers commissioned by society to search for public value'.[9] Consistent with Shergold's remarks quoted in the opening of Chapter 17, Moore expects policy makers to use their initiative and imagination, but also to be responsive to political guidance and feedback. He argues that their 'most important ethical responsibility is to undertake the search for public value conscientiously'.[10] He suggests that this overcomes political corruption, especially 'the triumph of special interests over the general' and irrationalities, such as 'shortsightedness, an unwillingness to make painful trade-offs, and an inability to deal appropriately with risk'.[11]

If integrative applied research teams have the creation of public value firmly in their minds when supporting government policy makers, the temptations to compromise research integrity by supporting corrupt or irrational practices in order to gain additional research funding or some other research advantage can be minimised. Analogous considerations need to be brought to bear for integrated research support for business and civil society policy making and practice change.

Tasks for the I2S Development Drive
Compile case examples that illustrate different experiences of bringing values into play and their consequences for the integrative applied research.
Compile case examples examining congruence in values across the three domains, as well as assessing integrity. The latter includes gauging independence from government, business and civil society pressures, as well as commitment to the provision of 'public value'.
Work with applied philosophers and other experts to produce a guide to concepts and methods for understanding and responding to the various dimensions of values.

Harnessing and Managing Differences

The point of integrative applied research is to effectively harness a range of relevant differences to broaden both knowledge about a problem and consideration of diverse unknowns, as well as to bridge the know–do gap. Indeed members of the integrative applied research team, the stakeholders they interact with and the policy makers or practitioners they seek to support will differ on a wide range of perspectives, skills and characteristics; however, only

---

9   Moore (1995, p. 299).
10   Moore (1995, p. 299).
11   Moore (1995, p. 54).

some of these will be central to the aims of the integrative applied research and some either will be irrelevant or may even get in the way of achieving the main research aims. The challenge is therefore to distinguish between differences that are key to addressing the problem and to be harnessed, and those that are problematic and must be managed.

Let us begin with harnessing differences useful for addressing the problem. Team members and the stakeholders they interact with will have been chosen for such variability. In other words, they may have been picked because they have different, but valuable, access to various facts, visions about addressing the problem, world views (underlying assumptions) about the problem, methods skills, ways of understanding unknowns, skills in managing unknowns,[12] and so on. There will also be differences to be harnessed between the researchers on the one hand and the policy makers or practitioners on the other. At the most basic level, the researchers understand the strengths and weaknesses of the integrated research, while policy makers and practitioners have a detailed appreciation of how to make the policy or practice change more likely to occur.

There will, however, be other differences between the research team members, the stakeholders and the policy makers and practitioners that do not contribute to the overall aims of the research. For example, while team members may have been chosen for their various methods skills, they may also have discrepant epistemologies that get in the way of the research aims.[13] These are the sorts of differences that must be managed so that they do not interfere with the conduct of the research by generating unproductive conflict.[14]

Another class of unproductive differences occurs on a personal scale, such as differences in personality, working style and other attributes. There is a broad sweep of knowledge about conflict resolution, establishing trust, team building and related issues that has been gained in business, community development and other areas,[15] which is also relevant to managing differences in integrative

---

12   For example, some may have a good understanding of probability, while others have an appreciation of distortion.

13   For example, quantitative and qualitative researchers may have different ways of knowing, but those responsible for the integrative applied research may wish it to be conducted within a single epistemology. Of course, in another context, the investigation may seek to harness different epistemologies and this would determine which researchers were chosen. Differences that are problematic in one research context may be the ones to be harnessed in another.

14   Unproductive conflict does not generate new thinking, but instead makes it hard for people to work together. More generally, conflict is not inevitably bad. It can be an important motivator, as well as stimulating new ideas. The challenge is to exploit the benefits of the energy and striving for excellence associated with conflict, especially in the form of competition, while maintaining mutual respect and minimising underhand behaviour and animosity.

15   For example: Gray (1989); Hackman (1990); Mandell (2001); Winer and Ray (1994).

applied research. The main problem is that this knowledge is not compiled in any single place. An outline of what such a resource would look like is presented in Box 26.1.

Box 26.1 Methods for Managing Personal Differences

Only a flavour of potentially useful ways of dealing with problematic differences can be given here. Some simple techniques can be surprisingly effective. Personality assessments (such as the Myers Briggs typology),[a] commonly used in team building, can dissolve conflict, as participants realise that the annoying behaviours of others are not designed to be provocative but simply reflect different psychological make-up and orientation to the world. Enhanced understanding can also ameliorate conflict arising from differences in cultural norms,[b] mental models,[c] emotional intelligence,[d] approaches to problems[e] and team role skills.[f] Principled negotiation, which focuses on differences in interests, is an effective tool for much dispute resolution. It concentrates on creative problem solving and fair accommodation of diverse interests.[g]

Fostering reciprocity within the team can also be helpful in avoiding unproductive conflict. This has two aspects. First is the precept that partners treat each other as they wish to be treated. This provides a general foundation for satisfactory working relationships based on trust and respect, as well as laying the way to overcoming problems through principle-based negotiation, which seeks fair solutions. The second aspect is that rewards resulting from the collaboration are allocated across the partners in proportion to their contributions.

a. Myers with Myers (1993).

b. O'Sullivan (1994).

c. Senge (1990).

d. Goleman (1995).

e. De Bono (1999).

f. Belbin (1993).

g. Fisher et al. (1991); Gray (1989); Ury (1993).

Examination of interactions and congruence involves determining

- to what extent the same differences are relevant across the domains
- whether similar strategies can be used to harness or manage them
- when differences to be harnessed in one domain require management in another (and vice versa).[16]

---

16 For example, epistemological differences may be harnessed in synthesising knowledge and understanding and managing unknowns, but may need to be managed to provide effective integrated research support for policy and practice change.

Looking specifically at managing differences, it is not clear whether this should be done proactively, if it is better to wait until conflict arises or if a mixture of proactive and reactive responses provides the most satisfactory outcomes.

Task for the I2S Development Drive
Gather together case examples to: a) ascertain how the same differences play out across all three domains, b) examine how management strategies fare across the domains, and c) figure out when best to apply methods for managing differences (proactively or reactively).

Dealing with the Six Categories

Let me close this section by re-emphasising that the six categories of concepts and methods considered here—taking a systems view, scoping, boundary setting, framing, taking values into account, and harnessing and managing differences—cannot be dealt with in a linear, stepwise fashion when undertaking integrative applied research. Each affects the others, so that the elements must be considered in parallel, as well as iteratively.[17] Iteration is often also required across the three domains.

Another issue that is implicit in all the considerations above is that there are no perfect approaches to the six categories. Choices must be made and judgment exercised in choosing a systems approach, scoping, setting boundaries, and so on, and each choice will have strengths and limitations. Imperfection is therefore not just an issue in understanding and managing unknowns, but permeates all integrative applied research. I return to this issue in Chapter 29.

Tasks for the I2S Development Drive
Compile case examples of how iteration occurred across the three domains, particularly whether the processes were independent for each domain or if there were interactions between the iterative processes across the three domains.
Compile case examples of choices made and judgment exercised (that is, imperfection) in dealing with the six categories of concepts and methods.

---

17   There are usually some 'stakes in the ground' to provide constraints or starting points for the iteration, such as limited time and money, skills of some key researchers, an identified desirable policy or practice outcome, and so on.

27. How?

In bringing together the three domains to consider the third question—'*How is the integrative applied research undertaken (the knowledge synthesised, diverse unknowns understood and managed, and integrated research support provided), by whom and when?*'—the task is to consider both the interactions between the methods and how congruent they are with each other. To recap, the methods described for each domain are presented in Table 27.1.

Table 27.1 Methods for Knowledge Synthesis, Managing Diverse Unknowns and Providing Integrated Research Support for Policy and Practice Change

Domain	Classes of methods
Synthesis of disciplinary and stakeholder knowledge	Dialogue-based Model-, product- or vision-based Common metric-based
Managing unknowns	Reduction Banishment Acceptance Exploitation Surrender Denial
Providing integrated research support for policy and practice change	Communication Advocacy Engagement

Three issues are dealt with in more depth here

1. the value of some methods for more than one domain

2. achieving congruence between the methods used across the three domains

3. classification using reciprocity and action-orientation.

It is worth making the point explicitly that scoping and boundary setting also apply to the choice of methods used. The point of scoping is to highlight all the possible methods, while boundary setting involves deciding which ones are most likely to be helpful in the particular situation, as well as feasible given the available resources.

Value of Some Methods for More Than One Domain

Although to date I have linked specific methods to single domains, using particular techniques in more than one domain is an area that needs exploration in the further development of I2S. Two obvious candidates are some types of dialogue and modelling. For example, dialogue methods that develop shared judgments implicitly assess unknowns, because judgment is required when facts are missing or not sufficient for addressing the problem. At present the consideration of unknowns is largely implicit and more work is required to make it explicit and systematic.

Some modelling methods are useful not only for synthesis of disciplinary and stakeholder knowledge, but also for providing integrated research support for policy or practice change.[1] A good example is provided for water management in the Middle Rio Grande Basin, where various groups not only provided input into building the model, but also used the completed model to test a range of 'what if' scenarios.[2]

Achieving Congruence between the Methods Used Across the Three Domains

In examining the three domains together, the aim is not just to look for methods that can be used across more than one of them, but also to identify which methods can productively be used together, as well as which methods are likely to be incompatible. Methods may conflict because of some intrinsic feature or because of the way they are used. For instance, advocacy for a particular research outcome is fundamentally incompatible with methods for fairly assessing unknowns.[3] An example of methods that are not inherently conflicting but that are used in a mismatched way is employing a dialogue method to synthesise knowledge from a broad range of disciplinary experts and stakeholders and then advocating a particular solution—which discounts some of the perspectives—to policy makers. These methods are likely to be compatible if participants in the dialogue are told that this is how the results will be used, but incompatible if the ultimate purpose is unstated or kept secret.

---

1 Further, as discussed in Chapter 12, modelling can also help in understanding different kinds of unknowns.
2 Passell et al. (2003).
3 A related issue is that of partisanship. If researchers are aligned with a political party they may find that methods relying on open communication or dispassionate examination of the issues are unsuited to their needs.

Another congruence issue relates to research quality, especially when different methods used have different levels of rigour. This may occur, for instance, when a mixture of formal and informal methods is used. For example, using modelling to provide decision support may lose validity if only informal dialogue methods were used for collecting disciplinary and stakeholder input, as there will be uncertainty about the representativeness of those views, as well as how accurately they were captured.

Classification Using Reciprocity and Action-Orientation

In considering I2S as a whole, it may be useful to develop an overarching classification for the available methods. One way of doing this may be to examine reciprocity and action-orientation. Reciprocity occurs when a method is two-way (and is absent when it is one-way), whereas action-orientation is present when the aim of a method is to stimulate policy or practice change (and absent when it is to increase understanding only). As shown in Figure 27.1, all four types of methods can be useful for particular aspects of integrative applied research.

		Reciprocity	
		No	**Yes**
Action-orientation	**No**	Convey information only *Example*: stakeholders or disciplinary experts provide input to model building	Gain mutual understanding *Example*: disciplinary experts work together to improve understanding of the problem
	Yes	Convey information with the purpose of stimulating others to act *Example*: advocacy	Gain mutual understanding for action *Example*: engagement between researchers and policy makers

Figure 27.1 Classifying Methods According to Reciprocity and Action-Orientation

Source: Author's illustration.

> **Tasks for the I2S Development Drive**
>
> Collect methods (and underpinning concepts) that can be used across two or all three domains, along with illustrative case examples.
>
> Identify which methods can productively be used together, as well as which methods are likely to be incompatible. Explore other issues affecting congruence. Compile case examples that illustrate the range of issues involved.
>
> Further explore the nature and value of an overarching classification based on options for reciprocity and action-orientation.

By Whom and When?

Just as there are no right answers for 'by whom and when' in the individual domains—but instead a range of options that may be more or less appropriate depending on the circumstances—there is also no one right way to ensure compatibility across the domains when considering the research as a whole. There are some general considerations, like ensuring that those undertaking each of the tasks are well informed and that the sequencing makes sense. To take extreme examples, it is unlikely to be appropriate for someone who was not involved in the knowledge synthesis or comprehensive consideration of unknowns to be given the task of engaging with the policy makers or practitioners. And in terms of an appropriate order of events, results have to be gathered before they can be communicated.

> **Task for the I2S Development Drive**
>
> Collect case examples looking at the congruence of 'who' and 'when' across the three domains.

28. Context?

I want to take the discussion of question four—'*What circumstances might influence the integrative applied research?*'—further than in earlier chapters. The starting point is still that context involves the circumstances that led to the research, may be influential during its life and are likely to affect the provision of integrated research support. But let us extend this to consider that context is the influence on the research of the real world in all its complexity and unpredictability. Then it becomes clear that even something as straightforward as understanding the circumstances that led to the research is likely to have different, and possibly contested, interpretations. Further, it shows the impossibility of predicting accurately which historical, political, cultural and other circumstances will end up being important in how the research is conducted[1] and, especially, how the findings can best be used to provide integrated research support for policy makers and practitioners. Taking context into account when investigating major real-world problems is therefore complex and riddled with imperfection. Nevertheless, it cannot be ignored and there will be some ways of dealing with context that are more profitable than others.

In the examination of context overall and of sources of authorisation, I therefore start with a substantial recapitulation and expansion of the material presented in the individual domains in order to highlight this complexity. In these two areas, as well as in organisational facilitators and barriers, interactions and congruence between the domains are also considered. Taking interactions first, I examine the extent to which the circumstances that influence knowledge synthesis, consideration of diverse unknowns and providing integrated research support for policy and practice change are intertwined and whether key background issues for one domain naturally flow on to affect the others. In terms of congruence, attention is paid to situational factors that set up conflict and how such incompatibilities can best be overcome.

Overall Context

The key here is to understand the big-picture issues that influence

- how the problem manifests and is understood
- the unknowns considered to be pertinent
- the possibilities for acting on the problem and hence where integrated research support might best be targeted.

---

1   This is particularly the case for research that will take a number of years.

Interactions immediately become evident. The way the problem manifests and is understood will influence the consideration given to unknowns as well as start to determine what action could be taken. Let us return to the example of building the atomic bomb, where the critical context was World War II. The problem manifestation was developing a more powerful weapon that might be decisive in winning the war. The primary focus for unknowns was on solving technical issues relevant to making the bomb work. Other unknowns such as the long-term consequences on health and the environment were not major considerations and the wartime context led to this narrowing in a way that would probably not have been countenanced during peacetime. Similarly, the background of war meant that massive resources were available and that the military application was paramount. It is instructive to try to imagine how research into nuclear fission might have played out if the investigations had been conducted against the backdrop of society's need for energy supplies in peacetime, rather than the military application in World War II.[2]

It is one thing to appreciate the importance of context; it is another to take it into account systematically in integrative applied research, especially when the circumstances are not as dramatically evident as in the case of war. Let us concentrate on scoping, which I have pointed out in earlier chapters overlaps with context. Highlighting the importance of a big-picture background ensures that scoping is appropriately broad. In addition, the aims of scoping include ascertaining which contextual factors are most likely to be relevant, as well as how they can be illuminated and taken into consideration. Further, the earlier discussion illustrates that the real world in which the research is embedded is unpredictable, so that nimbleness in understanding and responding to changed circumstances is also required.

For now let us leave aside the dimension of context concerning unpredictability and consider how to respond to the background factors that scoping identifies as most likely to be significant. In principle, this is relatively straightforward, at least in the first and third domains. Disciplines like history, geography, political science and cultural studies can all contribute to understanding how a problem manifests and the possibilities for providing research support.[3] If we go back to the example of family violence, history can illuminate how common family violence was in the past and how it was perceived in society. It can also show what actions were taken—both successful and unsuccessful—such as passing laws and changing social customs, which can help in developing measures that might be effective in the current climate. The disciplines might also be pushed

---

2   Presumably the process would have taken much longer and resources would have been scarcer. Development might have been stymied through patenting of key processes or opposition from other energy interests or concerns about health and environmental consequences.

3   What is needed, however, is a guide that will allow the integrative applied research team to think about what the various disciplines can offer, as discussed in Chapter 7.

to clarify the domain of unknowns. In this instance, history may be able to shed light on how family violence was ignored or denied in the past and how taboos on dealing with certain aspects arose.

A practical challenge comes with resource constraints. These will limit discipline-based investigations.[4] The ground covered by any discipline could potentially be wide ranging, as demonstrated by the topics a history of family violence could cover. Furthermore, it is unlikely that only one discipline will be relevant. Instead, many disciplines could provide valuable insights. The historical study outlined above would be considerably strengthened by complementary analyses from other disciplines, such as understandings from psychology about the nature of violence, from anthropology about cultural influences on violent behaviours, from law and criminology on the ability to legislate against violence and the effectiveness of such legislation, and so on. Deciding what to cover and how much depth to go into are the two critical issues here.

Interactions and Congruence

Earlier, I used the example of building the atomic bomb to show how key contextual determinants, such as the background of war, affected all three domains in an intertwined manner. Similarly, the history of family violence shows that one discipline can shed light on all three domains and show the interactions of germane background factors. For instance, the perceptions of family violence are strongly linked to unknowns in the form of taboos, as well as to actions taken against this social problem.

The different disciplinary inputs into the family violence example also illustrate challenges related to congruence. For instance, the feminist scholarship that was instrumental in focusing attention on the high prevalence of family violence and its links to the low status of women has also tended to make taboo any consideration of the contributions victims may make to the occurrence of family violence. But for a comprehensive investigation of the problem, the latter is also a legitimate area of inquiry. This example demonstrates incongruence between different disciplinary perspectives, as well as across the knowledge synthesis and unknowns domains.

Incompatibility between what the research finds and what action is possible is also common. An example here concerns problem drinking. Research shows that increasing the price of alcohol and restricting its availability can reduce consumption, but it is difficult to achieve such policy change because of the countervailing pressure on policy makers from the alcohol industry.[5]

---

4   Hence boundary-setting concepts and methods are also relevant for this question.
5   See, for example, Babor (2009); Hawks (1992).

Such tensions are inevitable in integrative applied research, which then faces the challenge of whether and how it can appropriately and respectfully deal with two seemingly incompatible areas. The situation is exacerbated by the limitations of time, money and personnel, which restrict what the integrative applied research can take into account. The point here is that it is important to be aware of the inevitability of incongruence and the likely imperfection of solutions.

Tasks for the I2S Development Drive
Collect case examples of how: a) the requisite agility to deal with the inevitable unpredictability was fostered, b) interacting influences between the three domains were managed, and c) the inevitability of incongruence and the likely imperfection of solutions were taken into account.
Work with a range of social scientists to produce a guide for combining considerations of context in the three domains.

Authorisation

The sources of authorisation or legitimacy for the research affect what is investigated, as well as whether and how the findings are implemented. Funding is a primary source of authorisation, but for the sorts of complex issues integrative applied research tackles, support from influential organisations or individuals often also plays an important role.

Integrative applied research may seek one primary source of funding and support, as was the case for building the atomic bomb,[6] or may seek to balance finances and endorsement across a range of interests, as illustrated by the World Commission on Dams.[7] Competition may also come into play, as was the case in the Human Genome project, where there were two rival undertakings, with different sources of financial and other backing.[8] It is also conceivable that there may be different sources of funding and influential support for each of the three integrative applied research domains in a project, where knowledge synthesis may be covered by one funding body, another may underwrite a comprehensive examination of unknowns and a third may finance the provision of integrated research support for policy or practice change. There are therefore many ways in which authorisation can play out in integrative applied research.

---

6   This is not completely correct. While the effort was mostly funded by the US Government, some relevant research was also conducted in the United Kingdom; see Rhodes (1986).

7   Funding was drawn from 53 public, private and civil society organisations and there was also a balance of interests among the 12 commissioners and the 68-member stakeholder forum (World Commission on Dams 2000).

8   Collins et al. (2003); Lambright (2002); Sulston and Ferry (2002); Venter (2007).

The key issue regarding authorisation is understanding its consequences. Funding by itself can affect the integrative applied research in significant ways, but impacts generally become more pronounced when the sources of legitimacy move beyond funding to endorsement by influential organisations and individuals. Let us begin by recapping the influence funding can have.

All researchers are aware of how funding shapes what is undertaken. A broad research plan is often modified, with areas for which grant support cannot be secured being dropped. Funding can also have more wide-reaching consequences in that it can open up (or close off) whole areas of research. Over the years funding bodies have become more sophisticated in setting priorities to encourage research in particular areas. When priorities change, researchers often modify their activities. For example, I was one of a number who moved from occupational health research to illicit drugs research when the Australian research funding priorities changed in the early 1990s. A different consideration is that untied funding—on either an institutional or a project level—can be particularly valuable in that it can open up research possibilities and allow risks to be taken.

Funding can be separate from, or inextricably interwoven with, the agendas of influential organisations or individuals. In the former case, the funding may come from relatively neutral bodies, such as government funding agencies, with the agendas of organisations and individuals coming into play quite separately through advisory boards or steering committees. In the latter case, the funder may be a business, government department or civil society organisation which has a vested interest in the outcome. By this I mean that the research results are directly relevant to their activities. The provision of integrated research support is particularly interesting in these cases. On one hand, the chances of implementation of the research findings can be increased, as was the case in the atomic bomb project, not least because those funding the research may be required to demonstrate that the expenditure on the investigation was warranted. On the other hand, research may be discredited if it is too closely tied to a vested interest. This is the case for research funded by the tobacco industry, where there is ongoing lobbying to ban the acceptance of funding from this source.[9]

Of course, most of those who fund research do not want to manipulate the outcomes. The challenge is that it can be hard to differentiate between funders who are genuinely interested in independent research on the problem and those

---

9   For the situation in Australia, see Walsh and Sanson-Fisher (1994), as well as an update from Action on Smoking and Health (ASH) Australia, which reported that in 2009, 21 universities had specific policies limiting acceptance of research funding from the tobacco industry, with 15 reporting a total ban on any such funding (<http://www.ashaust.org.au/lv4/campus.htm>, go to 'Survey summary and results table', accessed 2 December 2011).

who want the research to deliver particular findings. This is compounded by the fact that even the most dispassionate research involves making decisions about what will be studied and how, making it hard to rule out unconscious influences on researchers that favour the funder.[10] There are no easy answers here, but making the problem visible can be helpful. A positive move has been the requirement from reputable medical journals that funding sources and potential conflicts of interest are disclosed for each paper they publish.[11] While these issues are relevant to research generally, they are very pertinent to integrative applied research, because, as indicated earlier, the scale of such undertakings often means that funding and endorsement have to be sought from those with vested interests.

Authorisation may also have consequences for the conduct of the research, not just how the findings are handled. The atomic bomb project again provides an example. The scientists had to work in secret and for those at Los Alamos their freedom of movement was also severely curtailed.[12] Secrecy is common in security-related and industrial research. Because this restricts the ability to bring in a wide range of perspectives to test the ideas, it is a particular problem for integrative applied research as it can prevent the problem being understood and dealt with to the fullest possible extent, resulting in critical issues being missed.

Interactions and Congruence

A key issue for interactions is how authorisation of one domain can spin off into the others. This has already been alluded to earlier in consideration of research funding by vested interests, but let us tease it out further. Interactions are particularly important when there is one funder for all three integrative applied research domains. The focus is generally on the ultimate application and this can have impacts on how the research is conducted. Groueff[13] provided an example in his analysis of the atomic bomb project: 'purely academic scientists were given fantastic amounts of money for their laboratories, unlimited supplies of material and personnel, then were told to succeed at any cost…Negative results were not acceptable; even when they offered great theoretical value, they could not be taken into consideration.' In that project the researchers were also shocked to find that some decisions were taken out of their hands. A particular instance involved building and running the plutonium production piles, necessary to

---

10   Unconscious confirmation bias can have this effect; see Nickerson (1998).

11   See the statement and uniform disclosure form developed by the International Committee of Medical Journal Editors (<http://www.icmje.org/ethical_4conflicts.html>, accessed 23 November 2011).

12   Rhodes (1986).

13   Groueff (1967, p. 181).

scale up the reaction, making the bomb itself feasible. The scientists expected to do this themselves, leading to 'near rebellion'[14] when the task was made the responsibility of the company E. I. du Pont de Nemours (now DuPont).

The issue for congruence is to ensure that any restrictions imposed by different types of authorisation are not in conflict with one another. Imagine that there are two funders, one expecting open publication of the findings, the other expecting confidentiality. Clearly such incompatibility must be recognised and resolved. The two competing undertakings in the Human Genome Project provide an example that also illustrates how complicated interpretation can be. A key issue here was the extent to which the findings would be patented, with each side accusing the other of making patenting (and therefore monopoly commercial access) more likely.[15] As these examples show, contradictory requirements around control of the publication of research findings and ownership of intellectual property are two of the major areas where incongruence plays out.

Lack of congruence can also be evident on advisory boards or steering committees, especially when these bodies represent a range of interests. On the one hand, it is diversity that makes such bodies valuable, because they embody the complexity of the problem being tackled. On the other hand, it can be challenging to make them work well and effectively. One issue is that a consequence of the boundary setting in the project will almost always mean that some interests are excluded and others are marginalised. The challenge is to keep representatives of those interests actively engaged to highlight the research limitations and to keep the overall thinking about the problem broad, although this may not be easy to do. Another issue is that differences in interests become less manageable the closer a project gets to action. Balancing interests in understanding a problem is one thing, balancing them when responding to the problem is much harder. At the latter stage there is generally much more at stake, especially as some actions may not be readily reversible.

Task for the I2S Development Drive
Gather case examples of how integrative applied research teams managed congruence in terms of different restrictions, different interests and other consequences of authorisation.

Organisational Facilitators and Barriers

In considering I2S as a whole, the key issue for organisational facilitators and barriers relates to various aspects of congruence. This occurs both within and

14 Compton (1956, p. 164).
15 See Sulston and Ferry (2002) and Venter (2007).

between the domains. For example, there needs to be congruence between what the organisation is setting out to do, especially the research it seeks to foster, and what is facilitated by the structure and culture. For example, if an organisation aims to bring together natural and social science disciplines to tackle complex problems, it cannot have massive disparities in the numbers of natural and social scientists employed or in the funding given to these two areas. Similarly, if an organisation aims to deal with unknowns in new ways in order to more comprehensively understand their potential impacts, it cannot itself be risk averse.

Other challenging issues related to congruence involve the interactions between the research organisation and the policy or practice organisations it is aiming to support. There may be incompatibilities here in both content and process. For example, the research being undertaken may not be exactly what the policy makers or practitioners are looking for. In terms of process, the research organisation may be committed to operating openly in the public sphere, while the policy or practice organisation may be looking for a confidential interaction. Further, some research organisations will have one dominant approach (for example, providing policy briefs or advocacy), whereas others will seek to have a balance of approaches across communication, advocacy and engagement, including both partisan and non-partisan activities. Research organisations with one primary approach will be successful only if the policy or practice organisations respond to that kind of support.

Task for the I2S Development Drive
Compile case examples examining interactions and congruence in organisational barriers and facilitators within and between research bodies and policy and practice institutions.

29. Outcome?

Considering question five—'*What is the result of the integrative applied research?*'—re-emphasises that one advantage of the structured approach is that it provides a framework for evaluation. Evaluation is essential for improving how the I2S discipline operates. Although this chapter is framed around assessing completed integrative applied research, evaluation is also important at the beginning—for instance, in deciding whether a proposal to undertake such research will be funded. In either case, the methodology has to be adequately described to allow the research to be fairly appraised, as well as to make it clear when something new is planned, such as application of an innovative I2S concept or method, development of an improved guide to relevant knowledge from outside I2S or documentation of a case study that demonstrates a different slant on process. In this chapter four topics are considered

1. peer review

2. necessary conditions for integrative applied research

3. the challenge of imperfection

4. a summary of questions to guide evaluation.

Peer Review

As discussed in Chapters 8 and 22, developing I2S as a discipline makes peer review feasible as a mechanism for evaluating integrative applied research, just as is the case in traditional disciplines. Those who have been involved in knowledge synthesis, understanding and managing diverse unknowns and providing integrated research support are in the best position to act as reviewers, with I2S providing the elements for reviewers to assess, as described in the summary of questions that concludes this chapter.

Although peer review is relatively straightforward for knowledge synthesis and unknowns, applying it to the third domain of I2S is more problematic, as discussed in Chapter 22. This is because impact on policy or practice processes can be difficult to appraise without also getting input from the policy or practice sides. The first two domains are substantially within the researchers' purview, but this is not the case for supporting policy or practice change. Further, the success or failure of the research support may have little to do with the quality of the research or the methods employed to provide research support. Instead, research can be influential because it is available at the right time or backs a particular political outcome, sometimes irrespective of its quality. On the other hand, excellent research that is well communicated can be ignored for a whole range of reasons, including changed political conditions that take the issue off the agenda or if the findings are opposed by powerful interests.

Tasks for the I2S Development Drive
Compile case examples about, and assess the effectiveness of, peer-review processes in integrative applied research.

Necessary Conditions for Integrative Applied Research

A different dimension of evaluation involves consideration of the conditions necessary for integrative applied research to succeed. These are analogous to good laboratory conditions for empirical scientific endeavours. Not only are laboratories required, but they must also meet best practice standards. Although these will vary depending on the research area,[1] it can generally be said that, for example, the environment must be uncontaminated, the equipment must be in good working order, measuring instruments accurate and staff appropriately trained. In addition, the laboratory needs to be furnished with up-to-date equipment that is appropriate for the investigations being undertaken. This requires adequate funding, and indeed the costs associated with running a laboratory are taken as a given.[2] These conditions are separate from the research conducted in the laboratory, although they are a prerequisite for it. They are also different from the organisational structure and culture, which determine, for instance, how much laboratory space different researchers are allocated and whether the laboratory is well run or if corners tend to be cut.

The point of the analogy with good laboratory practice is that the conditions for integrative applied research require the same matter-of-fact consideration and suitable allocation of resources. These conditions also need to be differentiated from the research itself, as well as organisational barriers and facilitators. What, then, are these necessary conditions, in other words, these aspects of integrative applied research that do not produce results by themselves, but that are requirements for success?

Let us begin with the integrative applied research analogy with up-to-date laboratory equipment. This is the compilation of concepts, methods, case examples and guides to relevant knowledge from outside I2S, such as the best

---

1 For example, a laboratory for experiments on stem cells will require different standards from one for psychology experiments using rats.
2 This does not necessarily mean the funding is easy to get, but the point here is that the necessity for such funding is well accepted.

available concepts for problem framing or dialogue methods. A central argument of this book is that this 'equipment' is not currently available and that its rapid and effective establishment requires an I2S Development Drive.

Let us now imagine that the I2S Development Drive is completed, so that the up-to-date 'equipment' is available. What additional conditions for undertaking integrative applied research are required? I propose five conditions here, but at this stage they are tentative and require further investigation. They are

1. adequate resources for project development

2. suitable communication mechanisms among and between the researchers, stakeholders, and policy makers and practitioners

3. the ability to bring in specialist facilitation as required—for example, to 'translate' between different perspectives or to resolve disputes

4. 'database' development to allow the diverse research evidence to be gathered in a suitable format for integration

5. untied contingency funding to allow responsiveness to unforeseen problems, new ideas and opportunities.

The further elaboration of these conditions must test whether they are specific to integrative applied research and can be used to differentiate it from other kinds of research. In addition, a general understanding needs to be built up of the resources required to undertake different kinds of integrative applied research, in the same way that there are rules of thumb about levels of funding and other requirements for running different kinds of laboratories.

Some additional comments about these five putative conditions are warranted, starting with adequate resources for project development. It will be clear from the earlier discussions on scoping and boundary setting that project development for integrative applied research requires significantly more time and funding than other kinds of research.[3] Regarding suitable communication mechanisms, it is useful to differentiate between communication as a prerequisite for the research and communication as part of the research, as it is the first that is of interest here.[4] In other words, the relevant communication is that which is required for the research to 'work'. At a minimum, it is what is needed for the team members to be in touch with what others are doing. More commonly

---

3   Christian Pohl and Gertrude Hirsch Hadorn (Personal communication, March 2007) have argued that this stage is so important in transdisciplinary research that it should be recognised and separately funded and that successful completion should seamlessly lead to continued project funding. This is also briefly alluded to in Pohl and Hirsch Hadorn (2007a, p. 189).

4   Dialogue methods for knowledge synthesis, as well as advocacy or engagement for the provision of research support for policy or practice change, are part of the research itself, not a condition for it—and do not form part of the considerations here.

this is the level of communication that is necessary for establishing trust and building the team. The diversity of integrative applied research teams when it comes to the involvement of different disciplines, stakeholders, policy makers and practitioners means that making this communication effective is likely to require more resources than is the case for other types of research. This multiplicity of perspectives, epistemologies, interests and so on means that bringing in appropriately skilled facilitators at appropriate times can make 'translation' more efficient and effective, as well as aiding conflict resolution.[5]

On a different note, it is remarkable that at this stage relatively little attention has been paid to how diverse knowledge and perspectives are 'captured' as a prelude to integration. If we just consider the synthesis of knowledge from different disciplines and stakeholders, standard ways of bringing knowledge together include annotated bibliographies, literature reviews and databases, but there has been little attention to how this is done in integrative applied research with its multiplicity of different kinds of knowledge, let alone how this can be expanded to include diverse unknowns. Finally, although all research needs some contingency funding, the complicated nature of integrative applied research means that this needs to be considered explicitly, rather than being accommodated through internal mechanisms, as is usually the case.[6]

From an evaluation perspective, assessment of both completed and proposed integrative applied research projects needs to include examination of the adequacy of the conditions, which in turn means that the conditions must be described. More importantly, yardsticks are required to allow adequacy to be determined.

Task for the I2S Development Drive
Compile case examples illustrating whether the integrative applied research required prerequisite conditions, especially resources for project development, communication mechanisms, translation and conflict-resolution processes, 'database' development and funding mechanisms, from which exemplars can be highlighted and general rules proposed.

---

5   Efficient translation involves providing a mediator to aid mutual understanding that would not otherwise occur when people have significant differences such as divergent world views or epistemologies. Developing such facilitation skills is one task for I2S specialists, although not all I2S specialists will necessarily be expert in this.

6   For example, projects are often able to reallocate funding from one area (where there have been savings) to another.

Challenge of Imperfection

The inevitability of imperfection provides a challenge for evaluating the outcomes of integrative applied research. As I have outlined in this and other chapters, imperfection arises because it is impossible to investigate everything that is relevant to a complex problem; there will never be enough time, money or other resources. This is most evident when examining unknowns and contextual factors. The real-world connections of integrative applied research in both studying actual complex problems and seeking to provide integrated research support for policy and practice change add another dimension of imperfection—namely unpredictability. It is not possible to predetermine which aspects of the problem will have the most currency for action, nor to foresee in which ways provision of integrated research support is likely to be most effective.

The inevitability of imperfection raises two particular challenges for evaluation of integrative applied research. One is that it will be easy to identify the unavoidable deficiencies, but this provides neither a fair nor a productive assessment of the work. On the other hand, imperfection should not become an excuse for an 'anything goes' approach. In other words, it can be tempting to suspend any critical review because imperfection is inevitable, but this is also not appropriate.

These are not issues that can be resolved in a dogmatic manner. Reviewers will always be called upon to exercise judgment. One advantage of using peer reviewers, as discussed earlier, is that their judgment is tempered by relevant experience. Of course, peer review itself is far from perfect. But like Winston Churchill's assessment of democracy, '[n]o one pretends that peer-review is perfect or all-wise. Indeed...peer-review is the worst form of assessment except all those other forms that have been tried from time to time.'[7] The questions for evaluation, which are presented next, aim to provide a template that can guide a measured assessment by peers.

Task for the I2S Development Drive
Compile case examples about how imperfection was managed in the assessment process.

---

7   Hansard, Speech to the House of Commons, 11 November 1947, <http://hansard.millbanksystems.com/commons/1947/nov/11/parliament-bill#column_206> (accessed 28 November 2011 via Wikiquotes).

Summary of Questions to Guide Evaluation

Significant questions for evaluating each domain were introduced in earlier chapters and these are re-presented here with some modifications, along with questions covering examination of

- interactions and congruence
- the necessary conditions for integrative applied research
- imperfection.

Box 29.1, therefore, presents questions that peers could use to systematically evaluate integrative applied research.

Box 29.1 Questions for Evaluating I2S as a Whole

How well did the integrative applied research meet its aims and reach the beneficiaries? Did the knowledge synthesis achieve its purpose and include leading discipline and stakeholder perspectives? Were unknowns considered expansively, including wide-ranging insights and approaches? Were appropriate aspects of policy or practice identified? Were identified aspects of policy or practice successfully targeted and well supported?

Were suitable systems views used for both the problem and the policy or practice arenas? Would different systems views have been more useful?

Was there recognition and assessment of the full range of: a) pertinent systems views, b) applicable disciplines and stakeholders, c) relevant unknowns, d) options for providing support to the policy and practice arenas?

Within the necessary limitations of the research, was there inclusion of worthwhile: a) systems views, b) disciplines and stakeholders, c) aspects of unknowns, and d) policy or practice actors and processes? Was the balance fitting? Did any of those excluded turn out to be crucial?

Was the problem framing accurate for knowledge synthesis and consideration of diverse unknowns? Were the problem framing and the framing of the integrated results accurate and meaningful for providing research support for policy and practice change?

Were values considered adequately? Were defensible decisions made about whether and when values were made explicit, which and whose values were considered and how values were examined?

Was there effective harnessing of productive differences: a) in the research team, b) between stakeholders and researchers, and c) between policy makers and practitioners, on one hand, and researchers, on the other? Was there good management of potentially destructive differences: a) in the research team, b) between stakeholders and researchers, and c) between policy makers and practitioners, on one hand, and researchers, on the other?

Were sufficient flexibility and iteration built into the processes of deciding on a systems view, scoping, boundary setting, framing, considering values, and harnessing and managing differences?

Were appropriate methods used for knowledge synthesis, understanding and managing diverse unknowns and providing integrated research support? Would other methods have made better contributions? Were justifiable decisions made in choosing who would undertake, and when, the knowledge synthesis, understanding and managing diverse unknowns and providing integrated research support?

Was adequate consideration given to the overall context for the knowledge synthesis, comprehensively addressing diverse unknowns, and the provision of integrated research support? Were crucial contextual factors missed?

Was the authorisation apposite for the knowledge synthesis, consideration of diverse unknowns and provision of integrated research support? Did the authorisation lead to restrictions or other significant influences?

Did the host organisational structure or culture provide barriers to the knowledge synthesis, consideration of diverse unknowns or provision of integrated research support? Did the target organisation structure or culture provide barriers to the provision of integrated research support? If so, were these effectually recognised and managed? Were facilitators beneficially mobilised?

For each aspect of the framework (aims and beneficiaries, the systems views taken, scoping, boundary setting, framing, values, harnessing and managing differences, flexibility and iteration built into the processes, the methods used, considerations of context, authorisation and how it was managed, and identifying and managing organisational facilitators and barriers): a) were relevant interactions identified and dealt with effectively, b) were issues that were incompatible recognised and resultant problems helpfully managed, and c) was there appropriate balance in emphasis between the three domains of knowledge synthesis, consideration of diverse unknowns and providing integrated research support for policy and practice change?

Were the conditions suitable for undertaking integrative applied research? Did the integrative applied research team make good use of available compilations of concepts, methods, case examples and guides to relevant knowledge from outside I2S? Were there: a) sufficient resources for project development and b) fitting communication mechanisms among and between the researchers, and with stakeholders, and policy makers and practitioners? Was there: a) ability to bring in specialist facilitation as required—for example, to 'translate' between different perspectives or to resolve disputes, b) 'database' development to allow the diverse research evidence to be gathered in a suitable format for integration, and c) untied contingency funding to allow responsiveness to unforeseen problems, new ideas and opportunities?

Was the inevitability of imperfection adequately described and recognised? Were defensible decisions made? Were problematic responses avoided, particularly overconfidence, hopelessness and nihilism, hindsight bias and opportunities for incompetence and corruption?

30. Specialising in I2S

One purpose of this book is to demonstrate that there are many specialist concepts, methods and skills to assist integrative applied research teams enhance their effectiveness. I also argue that these cannot simply be add-ons to other disciplinary expertise, but require a dedicated discipline of their own. As a consequence there will be I2S disciplinary specialists. Nevertheless, other members of integrative applied research teams also require at least a basic understanding of I2S, with team leaders having specific I2S roles to fulfil. Finally, it is also beneficial for policy makers and practitioners who are likely to interact with integrative applied research teams to have some understanding of what I2S offers. Let me therefore draw together and build on the discussions from earlier chapters about the four broad categories of I2S specialisation—namely

1. I2S for team leaders

2. I2S disciplinary specialists

3. I2S appreciation for other integrative applied research team members

4. I2S appreciation for policy makers and practitioners.

I2S for Team Leaders

Team leaders have responsibility for their projects as a whole, which includes providing appropriate orientation to I2S and guiding a range of I2S-related decisions, as described in Box 30.1.

Box 30.1 Specific I2S Responsibilities for Integrative Applied Research Team Leaders

Team leaders must have adequate knowledge about I2S and strive to ensure the following.

- All three domains are considered,[a] the balance between them is appropriate, and interactions and congruence are taken into account.

- The five questions are systematically worked through and there is the wherewithal to do so—in other words, that their teams include appropriate I2S disciplinary specialists.[b]

- There is an openness to considering (and selecting the best among) options, appreciating that there are no perfect solutions for any I2S tasks—like taking a systems view, boundary setting or managing organisational barriers—but that each concept or method has strengths and weaknesses; nevertheless, some options will be more appropriate for the tasks at hand than others.

- Their teams understand that formulaic processes are not realistic, but that iteration is essential and that understandings will evolve as the project progresses. Further there needs to be enough vagueness and flexibility to allow creativity to flourish. On the other hand, the process must not be allowed to bog down, but rather should lead to pragmatic, defensible decisions being made efficiently.

- Team members understand their roles in decision making about and action on knowledge synthesis, understanding and managing diverse unknowns and providing integrated research support for policy and practice change; some teams will operate in a way that gives everyone a say in these tasks, some will give selected team members more say than others, some will rely on most decisions being made by team leaders—many variations are possible; the issue is that expectations should be clear.

- Their teams maintain research integrity.

- All the relevant issues for the aims and beneficiaries of integrative applied research are thought through, including that: a) the methodology is in line with the intended aims and beneficiaries, and b) conflicts between the domains are identified and resolved.

- Differences in the team are appropriately harnessed or managed.

- Sources of authorisation are understood, along with their implications for the integrative applied research, especially identifying and managing costs to research independence and integrity, as well as resolving any conflicting ramifications from different sources of legitimisation across the three domains.

- Facilitators and barriers in terms of organisational structure and culture are appreciated, both in the researchers' home institutions and in the target policy and practice establishments; in addition, this involves determining how facilitators can be exploited and barriers managed, as well as acting on synergies and conflicts between facilitators and barriers in the three domains.

- There is a commitment to contributing to the further development of I2S concepts, methods and case examples, as well as guides to relevant knowledge from outside I2S.

a. The aim is to avoid 'business as usual' and to grapple with new ways of undertaking knowledge synthesis, understanding and managing diverse unknowns and providing integrated research support for policy and practice change.

b. I have deliberately glossed over how integrative applied research projects begin and the role of I2S specialists both in starting and in leading such projects. At one end of the continuum, I2S specialists may be the originators and leaders of the project and may have full control over choosing the other team members, determining the problem parameters, and so on. At the other end, I2S specialists may be brought in as an afterthought to help an already established team work together more effectively. The concepts and methods described in this book apply regardless, although the ability to implement them may vary depending on how and when the I2S specialist becomes involved in the integrative applied research.

I2S Disciplinary Specialists

While team leaders set the orientation to an I2S-based approach, the I2S disciplinary specialists have the detailed knowledge that makes it possible for that approach to be implemented. Their knowledge about I2S provides them with an overview of the full scope of the discipline and mastery of a range of concepts and methods, including the ability to apply them in diverse situations, which they have learnt through case examples and hands-on experience. They are also adept at using guides to relevant knowledge from outside I2S, such as guides to systems thinking and to political science theories about how government policy is made. The wealth of detailed knowledge makes it unlikely that individual I2S disciplinary specialists will be fully proficient across the range of relevant concepts, methods, applications and guides, but it is a fair expectation that they have a basic understanding of the entirety of their discipline and an extensive network of colleagues who can be called on to provide specific expertise, as needed.

I2S disciplinary specialists must have sufficient competence to ensure that each domain can be fully addressed, along with the intersections between the domains. In the first domain of knowledge synthesis, their task is to ensure that all of the relevant knowledge—from disciplines and stakeholders—is recognised and that defensible decisions are made about which knowledge will be taken into account. In the second domain they provide the detailed understanding about diverse unknowns that allows them to be considered comprehensively. This includes the ability to bring together different disciplinary and stakeholder approaches to unknowns, as well as thinking about unknowns using typologies that do not rely on the disciplines. In the third domain, I2S disciplinary specialists provide detailed knowledge about how integrated research can support policy and practice change. They have general appreciation of the government, business and civil society arenas and bring a detailed understanding of at least one of them. The specific skills of I2S specialists are described in Box 30.2.

Box 30.2 Skills for I2S Disciplinary Specialists

I2S disciplinary specialists must have basic working skills in all of the following and particular competence in some.

- Systems thinking to conceptualise and deal with both problems and the arenas for implementation. This includes understanding where different disciplines and stakeholders 'fit', how different systems approaches deal with diverse unknowns and the organisational structures and processes that make up policy and practice systems.

- Scoping to determine: a) the full range of systems views that could be applied to the problem and the arenas for implementation; b) all the relevant disciplines and stakeholders, including what they could contribute and how; c) the diversity of relevant unknowns, taking into account their complexity, as well as different categorisations and typologies; and d) all the possible avenues for providing integrated research support, especially considering arenas, systems, organisations within systems and individuals.

- Boundary setting to determine what is included and excluded, as well as what is central and peripheral. This applies to disciplinary and stakeholder knowledge, unknowns and possibilities for providing integrated research support. The boundary setting must avoid defaulting to 'business as usual', especially in the response to unknowns, but in all domains the task is to identify the issues that are most critical for the problem under consideration, and the arena for implementation that is likely to be most fruitful.

- Framing to communicate accurately and effectively to the relevant audiences about the approach to the problem and unknowns, as well the findings of the integrated research.

- Dealing with values and how they influence the knowledge synthesis, the comprehensive approach to diverse unknowns and the provision of integrated research support in terms of targets and processes.

- Methods for: a) knowledge synthesis (including dialogue methods, modelling and other targeted techniques using products and vision, as well as common-metric-based methods); b) dealing with diverse unknowns (namely reduction, banishment, acceptance, surrender, exploitation and denial), as well as appreciation of when these are adaptive and maladaptive; and c) supporting policy and practice change (including communication, advocacy and engagement), as well as assessing the most suitable policy and practice targets, and the options that are most likely to be influential.

- Understanding overall context to ensure that the most important factors are considered for knowledge synthesis and unknowns, as well as the 'big picture' issues that are likely to influence how the arenas for implementation (government, business and/or civil society) and the organisations within them view the problem and respond to integrated research.

For each of these tasks, I2S specialists will be able to orient their teams to the strengths and limitations of the various concepts, methods and guides. In addition, they will be able to highlight interactions between the domains, especially synergies and conflicts, as well as methods for responding to them.

As well as providing the necessary expertise for integrative applied research teams to function effectively, the second key role for I2S disciplinary specialists is to participate in the ongoing development and improvement of their discipline. This involves

- being on the lookout for opportunities to improve, or develop new, concepts, methods and guides, and to publish any advances
- writing up innovative aspects of projects as new case examples
- ensuring that the knowledge synthesis, comprehensive consideration of diverse unknowns and provision of integrated research support for policy and practice change are documented in a way that makes them easy to evaluate and draw lessons from—by teams themselves and by peers
- helping teams reflect on outcomes and ways to improve the application of the I2S discipline in future projects
- being involved in conferences and the reviewing process for grants and publications, especially learning from these to strengthen I2S collections of concepts, methods and case examples, as well as guides to relevant knowledge from outside I2S.

Another component of the discipline-building task for I2S specialists is to identify the specific challenges for providing support using *integrated* research compared with other types of research and how these can best be addressed. For example, integrative applied research to some extent performs the functions that occur in good policy making, by gathering together all the relevant research knowledge, consulting stakeholders, assessing the importance of diverse unknowns and generating options for policy change. Nevertheless, these functions are performed differently in the research and policy worlds. For example, an I2S specialist places emphasis on weighing up the evidence, whereas for the policy maker assessing political risk is an important part of the evaluation. Other differences are described in Chapter 19 under 'harnessing and managing differences', especially in Box 19.2. Case examples comparing how the same issue is handled in the integrative applied research and policy worlds would therefore be very useful.

The roles and functioning of I2S specialists have parallels with those of other disciplinary experts in integrative applied research teams. In particular, they have a specific set of know-how to contribute. Like other disciplinary experts, they also have a role in helping their discipline expand its array of useful theory, methods and case examples. They can be expected to do this through the integrative applied research—for instance, by trialling a new method or by documenting the research as a case example.

I2S disciplinary specialists will both be responsible for and be the main beneficiaries of the I2S Development Drive in its tasks of compiling concepts, methods and case examples, as well as guides to relevant knowledge from outside I2S.[1] The aim is for the specialists to continue to hone their expertise, as well as to enhance the quality of the discipline and its ability to contribute to addressing complex real-world problems.

I2S Appreciation for Other Integrative Applied Research Team Members

While the team leaders and the I2S disciplinary specialists carry the primary responsibilities for ensuring that integrative applied research teams make the most of what I2S has to offer, other team members need to have at least a basic appreciation of I2S. This enables them to see their place in the research overall, as well as what their expert knowledge can contribute and where there may be useful interactions or problematic incompatibilities. Further, the level of knowledge about I2S needs to be greater for teams that involve all or most members in making decisions about knowledge synthesis, consideration of diverse unknowns and providing integrated research support for policy and practice change than for teams whose members primarily contribute their discipline-based expertise and where the integration and provision of research support are undertaken by the leaders and I2S specialists. But even in the latter cases, it is helpful for all team members to understand the general strengths and limitations of the overall I2S approach as well as the rationale for particular decisions such as which knowledge, unknowns and policy or practice change are being considered, which methods have been chosen and the framing used.

It is also worth noting that team members may have particular I2S skills to contribute. For example, they may have expertise in a dialogue or modelling method, their discipline may have developed an innovative approach to unknowns or they may have pre-existing experience in working closely with an industry group.

---

1   Of course, I2S disciplinary specialists also have a role in reviewing, expanding and revising the framework presented here and in resolving the issues and weaknesses identified in the previous chapters. These include improved articulation of context, as well as the overlaps between scoping and context, more extensive work on values, and identifying effective strategies for managing the reality of imperfection, in terms of how teams position themselves, recognise 'good enough' actions and outcomes (as well as the best possible) and assess weaknesses in light of strengths. I2S specialists also have a role in identifying the basic conditions necessary for integrative applied research to succeed and the resources that are required, to enable the move to a situation where integrative applied research is treated with the same matter-of-factness as laboratory-based research, as described in Chapter 29.

Ideally, the I2S process will enable team members to learn from each other in ways that enhance their disciplinary practice. For example, exposure to another discipline or a stakeholder group may spark a creative idea for new research, looking at unknowns in broader ways may stimulate innovative approaches to key issues in their discipline, and appreciation of what is useful to policy makers and practitioners may lead to additional questions being addressed in their discipline-based research. The intersections of the domains may also be hubs for inventive insights.

I2S Appreciation for Policy Makers and Practitioners

As discussed in Chapter 23, policy makers and practitioners who are the targets of integrative applied research also benefit from understanding what it can provide, which involves appreciating how I2S operates. This allows them to better evaluate what the integrated research has to offer, as well as to consider different options for interacting with the research team. For policy makers and practitioners seeking integrated research support, an understanding of I2S allows them to match what they would like against what it is possible to produce. It may also give them an expanded appreciation of manifestations of imperfection, including those arising from incompatibilities between the domains.

***

This section has brought together the three domains of I2S, especially to explore the interactions between them in terms of synergies, conflicts and balance. The aim is to be able to identify when approaches to the three domains are in harmony and when they are in conflict, and especially how to manage the latter. The balance between the three domains is also important. In particular, consideration of diverse unknowns should not be ignored or minimised, even though it is less developed methodologically.

The purpose of I2S is to provide options—with clear accounts of their strengths and weaknesses—for conducting integrative applied research. Summary lists of major classes of the I2S concepts, methods and case examples, as well as guides to relevant knowledge from outside I2S, which have been proposed in the preceding chapters, are presented in Chapter 34 in the next section demonstrating the Big-Science-like scale of the work plan. In addition, the chapters in the next section examine a range of issues relevant to the operation of I2S and integrative applied research.

Moving Forward

31. A View of the Future

It is 2025. Professor Srilatha Singh at the National University of India is chairing a video conference of the directors of 20 departments of Integration and Implementation Sciences around the world. The main agenda item is the wrap-up of the I2S Development Drive. The compilation had a strong information science foundation, which allowed thousands of researchers in hundreds of universities, research and development organisations, consultancy companies, non-government organisations and other institutions to add to the collection of concepts and methods, contribute case examples of successes and lessons learnt, and comment on guides to relevant knowledge from outside I2S. In addition to being contributors, they could enhance their own research by drawing on the growing storehouse of materials, as well as the identified network of I2S specialists.

One of those using the storehouse is Dr Peter Mandela, head of the international Resilience Overcomes Vulnerability Project. His team is studying adults aged thirty to forty who grew up in the most impoverished circumstances. Mandela, who is based at the University of South Africa, leads a team of experts in the relevant disciplines, including I2S. The five-year project explores how, as children, the study participants overcame ongoing setbacks and how, as adults, they have incorporated their experiences in their own parenting practices. Its aim is to inform policy makers worldwide about strategies for coping with declining living conditions and life expectancy as a consequence of global climate change.

Competition to join the team is high as, internationally, university-based researchers from every discipline look for opportunities to collaborate on projects dealing with complex real-world problems. Providing specialist input to such efforts is now a key performance expectation. The aim is to set up win–win situations, where experts provide their discipline's perspectives, as well as finding a niche in the partnership to further their disciplinary knowledge. For example, Swiss psychiatric researcher Dr Davida Ritter leads a study on how children counter violence. She has developed a new way of measuring responses, which will be trialled as part of her research program.

I2S disciplinary specialists play a key role in helping these partnerships achieve their full potential, and there is growing demand for training at undergraduate, graduate and professional development levels. There are also courses in the basics of I2S to complement education in traditional disciplines. This allows those experts to be more effective participants in integrative applied research teams. For example, Mandela is a sociologist who took a professional development course, 'I2S for Team Leaders', run by his university.

Mandela's team includes two full-time I2S disciplinary specialists. One is Professor Lawrence Moore from Harvard University. He was a major contributor to developing the guide on policy making at an international level for the I2S Development Drive. He is particularly knowledgeable about the provision of integrated research support for policy change and has wide-ranging experience working with government at global and national levels. The other is Dr Michaela Wang from Beijing University, who has comprehensive all-round knowledge of I2S and who was the lead researcher in the I2S Development Drive on methods for understanding and managing diverse unknowns.

Moore and Wang are part of Mandela's core team of eight who set the project's directions and make the key decisions. Most of their interactions are electronic, with technological advances making virtual meetings almost indistinguishable from face-to-face ones. Others are connected to the project in various ways. Dr Gerald Gregory, an I2S specialist from Australia, joined the team for three months to help scope the Resilience Overcomes Vulnerability Project. Ritter is not part of the core team but runs a stand-alone sub-project, although she liaises closely with Mandela to ensure relevance. Dr Nursyahbani Haryanto from Indonesia is a conflict-resolution specialist, with particular expertise in cross-cultural issues, who is brought in when difficulties arise.

The core team uses the I2S disciplinary network to find researchers with specific I2S expertise needed by the project. That is how they found Gregory and Haryanto, as well as Brazilian Caryn de Silva, who expects to join the team in year three to undertake a PhD integrating the research findings into a decision support model for the United Nations and other global policy makers. The University of Brazil, where de Silva completed her undergraduate education, is renowned for its I2S teaching program. De Silva had originally intended to become a chemist, but her interest in I2S was piqued by the classes on I2S designed to help students majoring in other disciplines maximise their contributions to research collaborations on complex problems. An associated university-wide student project investigating low-level toxins leaching from an old garbage dump onto nearby sports fields— to which she contributed her chemistry know-how—exposed her to fellow students specialising in I2S. She was excited by their role in integrating the expertise contributed by the students from different disciplines, as well as the interactions with local policy makers. Watching the I2S majors in operation was the stimulus for switching her field of study.

At this stage in the development of I2S, there is a virtuous cycle between funding, capacity and demonstrated success. Financial support for teams tackling complex real-world problems is multiplying, along with demand from funders that teams include I2S expertise, based on growing evidence of the quality and impact of I2S contributions. This is encouraging an increasing number of students to become I2S specialists, as well as feeding demand from established researchers to enhance their I2S skills.[1]

The bulk of this book has been about a framework for housing the expert knowledge that makes up the discipline of Integration and Implementation Sciences (I2S) and the need for an I2S Development Drive to pull all the available materials together. This section, comprising four chapters, covers additional ideas about the functioning of I2S in integrative applied research teams. I conclude the current chapter by describing in more detail the virtuous cycle between capacity, demonstrated success and funding.

Chapter 32 examines how I2S operates as a discipline and the parallels to be drawn with other disciplines, especially statistics. The focus is on how I2S discipline experts position themselves and what this means for building capacity. Chapter 33 explores how integrative applied research can encompass both multidisciplinary and transdisciplinary approaches, and develop hybrids, as well as how all these are supported by I2S. In the future, such analysis needs to be expanded to explore the relationship of integrative applied research to the other pre-existing approaches on which it and I2S have been built, including post-normal science, systemic intervention, integrated assessment, sustainability science, team science, mode 2 and action research.[2]

To finish the section, Chapter 34 concentrates on the scope and feasibility of the I2S Development Drive. It provides summary lists of the concepts, methods and case examples, as well as guides to relevant knowledge from outside I2S, which need to be compiled in the I2S disciplinary storehouse. As well as recapping

---

1   This imaginary scenario briefly describes how I2S could develop and function. In terms of its operation, the same principles apply regardless of the scale of the project, which could be local, regional or national, as well as international. Similarly the integrative applied research team can draw on the best people at one research institution or include greater or lesser numbers of experts elsewhere in the country or internationally. Whatever the case, the I2S disciplinary network can help identify the available I2S specialists in any locality.
2   And, as an anonymous reviewer has suggested: management sciences, operations research and complex systems science.

the substance of the Drive, establishing proof-of-concept and countervailing forces are discussed. I conclude by drawing together the threads from the whole book on imperfection and discuss its profound implications for both the I2S discipline and the I2S Development Drive.

A Virtuous Cycle between Capacity, Demonstrated Success and Funding

For I2S to become established requires a virtuous cycle between strong capacity, demonstrated success and adequate funding (Figure 31.1). How is this to be accomplished?

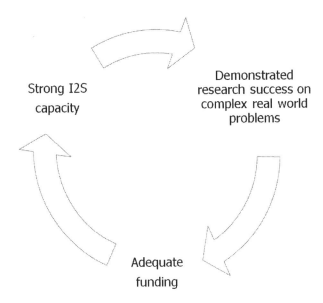

Figure 31.1 A Virtuous Cycle between Capacity, Demonstrated Success and Funding

Source: Adapted from Pohl et al. (2008, p. 422).

One of the hallmarks of an effective discipline is established capacity, which successive generations revitalise and renew. I2S aims to emulate such achievement. Here I examine three relevant aspects

1. the pools of researchers who can provide I2S specialists to develop the discipline

2. how a discipline can facilitate I2S specialists coming together to share insights and build strengths

3. how I2S provides a systematic approach to educating the next generation.

Further development of I2S requires a substantial group of high-quality specialists. The three most likely candidate pools from which they could be drawn are: 1) those who are developing the theoretical foundations of interdisciplinary and related research, 2) those who undertake practical research tackling complex real-world problems, and 3) consultants who concentrate on a defined set of concepts and methods that are relevant to I2S. As described in Chapters 1 and 2, I have used my knowledge of the first two groups, in particular, in developing I2S. The third group has also been of interest. Some consultants specialise in a well-developed set of ideas and methods that are integral to I2S.[3] They are often also important as custodians of these approaches, even though they generally have little time for methodology building or publishing, because they usually run their own businesses and are in high demand from governments and industry.[4] Taking these three groups together suggests that there are potentially many experts who might choose to help found the I2S discipline and to become I2S disciplinary specialists.

While the combined candidate pools comprise a large number of individuals, those people are also widely dispersed and poorly networked. It is not clear what proportion has a comprehensive array of I2S skills versus narrower specialisations such as a primary focus on stakeholder engagement, concept mapping or modelling scenarios for policy discussion.

The aim for I2S is to provide forums—such as journals and conferences— where those who identify as I2S disciplinary specialists can find and learn from each other. Let us explore this idea further using conferences as an example. At present there are numerous conferences devoted to issues relevant to I2S, including conferences on interdisciplinarity, transdisciplinarity, action research and so on, as well as on various key elements like systems thinking, unknowns, decision making and the like.[5] What is striking is their small scale, with attendance likely to be of the order of 200–500 people. In contrast, the annual conferences of established disciplines are likely to have tens of thousands of participants. Although small conferences have their place, I argue that they are

---

3 They include David Snowden's Cognitive Edge <http://www.cognitive-edge.com/whatwedo.php> Stephen Haines' the Haines Centre for Strategic Management <http://www.hainescentre.com> and Bob Dick's consultancy on facilitation and action research <http://bobdick.com.au/bdcons.html> (all accessed 15 December 2011).

4 Because there are generally few or no links with universities, there is little scope for productive interplay between these two sectors. There are, however, notable exceptions where consultancy firms do publish, such as lisode <http://www.lisode.com/index.php/english/Accueil.html> (accessed 31 July 2012) and Sinclair Knight Merz SKM: <http://www.skmconsulting.com> (accessed 31 July 2012).

5 Relevant conferences can be found at <http://i2s.anu.edu.au/resources/conferences>

most valuable as adjuncts to large meetings, where the whole college of peers assembles to review and debate the shape and direction of the discipline, as well as to share insights and expertise. The point of proposing an I2S discipline is to provide a focus for such a critical mass.

Finally, there are thousands of students around the world concerned about complex social and environmental issues who would welcome systematic exposure to integration and implementation concepts and methods, which an I2S discipline could provide. At present there are no agreed curricula—with specified core elements, standards and accreditation—as there are for other disciplines. Instead, current education relevant to complex real-world problems is idiosyncratic. I2S not only provides a way of structuring education, but, for I2S disciplinary specialists, it potentially also makes available well-defined career paths and opportunities for graduates.[6]

Based on considerations such as these, I suggest that the potential exists to build strong capacity. What about demonstrated success?

One of the consequences of not having an agreed systematic way to report on integrative applied research is that the development of new concepts and methods and their successful implementation often go under- or un-documented. There is not only a lack of write-up, but also very limited communication. In particular, when integrative applied research teams develop new methodologies—for example, to help them scope problems, foster dialogue between stakeholders or for effective policy engagement—there is no recognised systematic way for transmitting such insights among teams to build up an array of options for specific I2S tasks. Instead teams dissipate creative effort by reinventing methodological wheels or using suboptimal concepts and techniques. Similar problems relate to implementation: there is little documentation and communication of lessons learnt in case studies.

The flipside of this lack of documentation and communication is that it is also hard for researchers interested in I2S to gain understanding and mastery of the full range of available concepts, methods and lessons. Instead they rely on ad-hoc approaches, intuition and the limited number of insights and skills they happen to have encountered.

Quality control is currently also haphazard, as there is no effective peer-review (or other review) system. This also makes it difficult to assess and record successes, as well as for integrative applied research teams to evaluate how well

---

6   As foreshadowed in the scenario that opens this chapter, I2S-based education would not just be targeted at producing I2S disciplinary specialists, but would also give those majoring in other disciplines enough exposure to I2S to allow them to become more effective members of integrative applied research teams.

they are performing relative to others. As I argue here, demonstrating success and building a strong knowledge base go hand-in-hand and I2S can provide the structure for this to happen.

The last element of the reinforcing loop is adequate funding. Strong capacity and demonstrated success will help I2S specialists be more effective contestants for funding. I maintain that to get support, I2S by and large has to compete on the same terms as other disciplines. It is worth bearing in mind, however, that in this start-up phase, I2S has some disadvantages that may not be experienced by many other new disciplines, especially those that are spin-offs or combinations of existing strong disciplines. I2S is starting from a base that is fragmented and therefore relatively weak. (This is a major reason for the I2S Development Drive.)

The vision is for I2S to provide

- a point of coalescence for a critical mass to form a college of peers, as well as
- the structure for demonstrating success and building a strong knowledge base.

As I2S proves its worth, it will merit and continue to attract funding.

32. How I2S Functions as a Discipline

What practical ideas about the operation of I2S can be drawn from other disciplines? As discussed in previous chapters, I have found statistics to be a particularly useful model for some key aspects of how I2S works. To recap briefly, both achieve effectiveness by interacting with other disciplines in a problem-focused approach. In the case of statistics, this involves improving research projects by enhancing their ability to tackle the quantitative aspects of problems. I2S plays an analogous role, improving the ability of integrative applied research teams to synthesise knowledge about the problem, better understand and manage remaining diverse unknowns and provide integrated research support to policy makers and practitioners. Four primary areas where statistics provides useful lessons for I2S are considered here

1. enhancing the discipline by working on problems

2. transmitting findings

3. fostering widespread awareness and appreciating different levels of expertise

4. building capacity.

Enhancing the Discipline by Working on Problems

Good statisticians not only bring their existing disciplinary knowledge to bear, but they are also on the lookout for how the demands of the research problem might be used to expand their disciplinary skills base. For example, my colleague Keith Dear[1] is the statistician in a research program exploring the potential effects of global climate change on health. He is using the opportunity to develop statistical methods for spatial regression analysis of time-series data, to allow him to simultaneously map deaths geographically, investigate multiple possible potential causes, include lag effects, and to study nonlinear relationships between variables. I2S operates in a comparable way. For instance, an I2S specialist may be able to use their involvement in an integrative applied research team as an opportunity to develop and trial a new boundary-setting method or apply a new concept about unknowns. Like statisticians, I2S specialists will be rewarded for the contributions they make to developing new disciplinary concepts and methods, as well as the insights into important problems they help their teams achieve.

---

1   See <https://researchers.anu.edu.au/researchers/dear-kbg> (accessed 1 August 2011).

Transmitting Findings

The second lesson to be drawn from statistics relates to the transmission of findings, which was raised in Chapter 1. When Keith Dear develops or improves a statistical method, it is not published in the health literature, but in a statistics journal, where it can be picked up and employed as appropriate by statisticians working in completely different areas like education or security. I2S requires a similar discipline-based literature in which to publish, making it possible for integrative applied research to build on the wealth of knowledge available and for I2S specialists to learn from each other's insights and experiences. In addition, there will be an I2S college of peers who can assess these contributions.

Fostering Widespread Awareness and Appreciating Different Levels of Expertise

A third parallel is that most researchers are aware of the discipline of statistics and the relevance of statistics to their work, as well as their own level of statistical expertise and when it needs supplementing.[2] In addition, research grants bodies will not fund quantitative projects unless the team has adequate statistical know-how, and journals will not publish papers unless the analyses are up to standard. The aim of formalising I2S is to produce an analogous situation.[3] The majority of researchers will have a basic education in I2S concepts and methods, so that they know when to call on I2S specialists. Funders and journal editors will become more demanding in relation to the extent and quality of I2S contributions in integrative applied research.

Figure 32.1 encapsulates these points by illustrating the relationship between the core discipline (statistics or I2S) and key areas of application. The central circle, labelled 'Theory and methods', represents the home discipline, either statistics or I2S. Researchers in this circle are primarily concerned with the development of the discipline, rather than its application to problems. In statistics, they work on the general theories of experimental design, statistical modelling, probabilistic inference and stochastic systems.[4] In I2S, they are involved in strengthening and maintaining the storehouse. For example, they may explore how various dialogue methods treat knowledge synthesis and whether they can encompass unknowns or match the insights that different

---

2   The range of relevance and expertise can vary from little to deeply intertwined. At one extreme a historian studying festivals in medieval Europe may find little of relevance, whereas at the other end an epidemiologist investigating the effects of sun exposure will find multiple intersections with statistical concepts and methods.

3   This will replace the current situation where I2S skills are seen as innate attributes of talented researchers.

4   They might also collaborate with mathematicians who work on the underpinning mathematics or philosophers who are developing the theory of probability. For the latter, see Hájek (2008).

modelling techniques can provide with types of research questions relevant to different social and environmental problems. The I2S specialists (or statisticians) in this group are a small percentage of the whole.

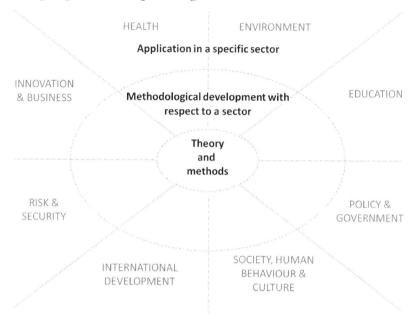

Figure 32.1 The Relationship between the Home Discipline (Statistics or I2S) and Key Areas of Application

Source: Adapted from an unpublished figure by Lorrae van Kerkhoff.

The eight wedges—health, environment, education, and so on—characterise 'sectors' in which complex real-world problems occur. They are mirrored in the organisational structures of many universities and government departments. Of course this is a simplification because many complex real-world problems cross two or more of these sectors. Nevertheless, they are a useful starting point for describing how statistics and I2S work.

The second circle, 'Methodological development with respect to a sector', represents the statisticians or I2S specialists who collaborate with teams working on a particular problem and who use the collaboration to develop new theory and methods, which can contribute to the inner circle. Keith Dear, for example, is located in the segment 'Health'. It is common for statisticians to specialise in a sector—for example, some tend to work on health problems, some on education problems, and so on. This allows them to become familiar with how those with expertise in health (or education or whatever) and relevant disciplines approach problems, and to interact effectively with them. Similarly, many I2S specialists may also choose to focus their efforts in problem-specific areas. The bulk of I2S specialists (and statisticians) are located in this circle.

The outer circle, 'Application in a specific sector', represents the majority of researchers, covering all the other disciplines. The aim is for them to have a basic understanding of I2S, just as they have a general appreciation of statistics. In the case of I2S, this allows them to be more effective when they are part of an integrative applied research team. An elementary comprehension of I2S or statistics provides the foundation for drawing on those with specialist knowledge—and appreciating when this is necessary. Further, some researchers will be skilled enough to deal with various I2S or statistical issues themselves, but they only seek to apply I2S or statistics, not to develop the discipline. Another colleague, Lyndall Strazdins,[5] is typical of such researchers. Lyndall is trained in the quantitative end of psychology and analyses survey data to explore issues such as the relationship between the quality of work and health. She has the requisite skills to conduct some analyses, but calls on more qualified statisticians for others. She is only interested in applying statistics in her research, not in enhancing the development of the statistics discipline. Lyndall also provides an example of how I2S functions in this sector. She and her team have built a relationship with the relevant government department to inform them of pertinent research findings. They apply a specific set of concepts and methods about how research can be useful to policy makers to do this. From time to time, she calls on me (located in the inner circle for I2S) when she wants to expand her skill set and try different ideas.

Building Capacity

The fourth parallel with statistics relates to capacity building, which must be tailored to the needs of researchers in the three circles. Those located in the inner and second circles require strong I2S disciplinary skills. Such I2S specialists need to be educated in a broad framework encompassing all three domains— that is, knowledge synthesis, unknowns and supporting policy and practice change. Their training must equip them to recognise when leading-edge theory and methods are being used, when breakthroughs in thinking have been made and when wheels are being reinvented. Like their statistics colleagues, they will develop deep knowledge and expertise in particular areas—in other words, they will specialise within their discipline. In the case of I2S, there may be specialisation in one of the domains or in one of the five framework questions

---

5   See <https://researchers.anu.edu.au/researchers/strazdins-lm> (accessed 1 August 2011).

across the domains (for example, in all aspects of context). As indicated earlier, those located in the middle circle, both statisticians and I2S specialists, could also focus on a particular sector or type of problem (such as health).

Researchers located in the outermost circle will be educated to have a basic understanding of I2S (just as they have an elementary appreciation of statistics) that they can bring to the problems on which they work. They will generally be experts in another discipline and will contribute that disciplinary expertise to integrative applied research teams, like Davida Ritter in the fictional scenario in Chapter 31. Having a basic understanding of I2S will allow them to better understand what is required of them in contributing to integration and implementation processes and to collaborate effectively with other disciplinary experts, including the I2S specialist(s), in the team.

33. The Relationship of Integrative Applied Research and I2S to Multidisciplinarity and Transdisciplinarity

This chapter looks specifically at two of the initiatives that have informed this book: multidisciplinarity and transdisciplinarity. I argue that rather than rating one better than the other (almost always transdisciplinarity is rated preferable to multidisciplinarity), both have advantages and disadvantages, making each more useful in some circumstances than others. Further, their attributes can be variously combined into hybrid approaches that will change the balance of benefits and shortcomings. The aim of this chapter is to demonstrate one of the core arguments of this book—namely that there are no perfect ways to investigate complex real-world problems, but there are many viable possibilities.

Multidisciplinary and Transdisciplinary Research

Let us begin by drawing together and expanding the thumbnail sketches presented in previous chapters, examining in turn the three domains (synthesising disciplinary and stakeholder knowledge, understanding and managing diverse unknowns and providing integrated research support for policy and practice change).

Multidisciplinary research involves juxtaposing knowledge from different disciplines and stakeholders about a particular issue. Each discipline approaches the problem, interprets the results and reports them in a manner that is conventional for the discipline. The potential for different disciplines to contribute is relatively equal, or at least primarily determined by the extent of what they can usefully offer. While the ways for stakeholders to participate are less well defined, individual stakeholder groups may be represented by the contributions of a prominent individual or subgroup or by one of the disciplines (for example, a sociology-based survey of particular stakeholders could be conducted, with that discipline then speaking for those parties). Overall, multidisciplinary research has the scope to include many disciplinary and stakeholder perspectives. The weakness of this approach is that there is little emphasis on drawing general lessons through synthesis of these different contributions. Such synthesis can be particularly challenging, especially when problem definitions and methods used by the various disciplines and stakeholders do not fit together comfortably.

The approach to unknowns is confined to understandings and methods that are conventional for the participating disciplines and stakeholders. This can provide some breadth in the consideration of unknowns, as disciplines and stakeholders vary in how they tackle them,[1] but there is also usually no attempt to bring their insights together into a comprehensive picture.

Finally, providing *integrated* research support for policy and practice change is constrained both by the absence of knowledge synthesis and by the limited approach to unknowns. Usually the research outcome is that the independent disciplinary and stakeholder reports are presented side by side, often in a one-day seminar or a book. It is up to the individual policy makers and practitioners to extract and pull together the knowledge that is useful for them. While this is generally seen as a limitation because of the expertise and time investment required of policy makers or practitioners, it can have advantages in that they are in the best position to decide what is apposite and can therefore tailor what they hear or read to their own purposes.

Transdisciplinary research starts with the team building a common framework and agreed methods for tackling the problem. The approach to including disciplinary perspectives can vary. In some projects, strong discipline experts are involved and they aim to work together to build a transcending scaffold for the investigation and to agree on the primary methods. But this can lead to battles as disciplines compete for priority. To overcome this, other approaches draw on generalist rather than discipline-based skills. In the worst cases, this can result in a low-grade blancmange of concepts and methods, sometimes falling into methodological holes that specific disciplines overcame a long time ago.[2] The importance of stakeholder perspectives is generally well recognised, but—as in multidisciplinary research—there are no standard ways of including them. They may be consulted in various ways, such as through surveys or focus groups, or representatives may be invited to be team members. While the aim is usually for all those involved to have equal standing, the outcome of negotiating an agreed approach up front is often that some disciplines and stakeholders are restricted in their ability to contribute. Nevertheless, the development of the common framework and agreed methods means that the synthesis of the different disciplinary and stakeholder perspectives that *are* included in the investigation is generally strong. Furthermore, the synthesis is enhanced by the team working together in gathering new evidence and developing a shared interpretation, which aims to transcend the understandings of single disciplines and stakeholder groups.

---

1   Described in Chapter 10.
2   For example, some transdisciplinary researchers ignore standard statistical know-how about choosing study samples to maximise the generalisability of study findings or psychometric skills for designing questionnaires that give clearly interpretable results.

Implicit in negotiating the approach to the problem is which unknowns will be considered and how they will be managed. But consideration of unknowns is often poorly developed because they are not well understood, and their importance is inadequately recognised. Indeed, as I discuss below, having a better appreciation of different ways of understanding and managing diverse unknowns may assist the negotiations of transdisciplinary teams and help them achieve better outcomes.

Transdisciplinary research aims to support policy and practice change, usually through an engaged approach with end-user policy makers and practitioners, seeking to involve them in the development of the framework and interpretation of the results. The strong knowledge synthesis means that there are often useful outcomes on which change can be based; however, the lack of explicit and comprehensive attention to diverse unknowns means that the research support for policy or practice change faces the danger that action (based on evidence alone) may be misguided.

Enhancements that I2S Can Provide

Let us examine how I2S can strengthen these two approaches. The strengths and weaknesses for each domain are summarised in Tables 33.1–33.3.

Table 33.1 Strengths and Weaknesses of Multidisciplinary and Transdisciplinary Research for Knowledge Synthesis

Multidisciplinary	Transdisciplinary
Each discipline can contribute its perspectives in a relatively unconstrained way, enhancing the richness in understanding the problem. In theory this is also possible for stakeholders.	The contributions of the disciplines and stakeholders are constrained by the transcending approach taken to the problem.
Flexible—that is, can easily add disciplinary and stakeholder perspectives that were missed when the research was originally designed.	Adding new perspectives may require renegotiation of the whole approach.
No coherent approach to synthesis and it may be hard to meld diverse approaches.	Synthesis is strong as the process of bringing together the discipline-based and stakeholder knowledge starts at the research design phase with the development of the common framework and agreed methods for tackling the problem.

I2S concepts, methods and guides, as well as lessons from case examples, can strengthen all aspects of knowledge synthesis in both types of research. One obvious contribution is through the collections of knowledge synthesis methods. These provide additional methods for consideration and can therefore significantly enhance both types of research.[3]

It is worth noting that in multidisciplinary research it is likely that some of the findings of the discipline-based research will be so different because of their problem framing that they will not be able to be included in the synthesis. On the one hand, this may be considered as wasted effort. Alternatively, the perspectives that cannot be synthesised can still be presented, making the limitations of the synthesis apparent in a way that is not possible in transdisciplinary research.

Scoping and boundary setting also warrant further discussion. For these, the contribution of I2S is to ensure that considerations in both multi- and trans-disciplinary research are appropriately wide ranging and that specific attention is paid to what is included, excluded and marginalised. This may be particularly helpful in transdisciplinary research in building richer transcending frameworks.

Table 33.2 Strengths and Weaknesses of Multidisciplinary and Transdisciplinary Research for Understanding and Managing Diverse Unknowns

Multidisciplinary	Transdisciplinary
Has scope for including different kinds of unknowns through the diverse disciplinary and stakeholder perspectives.	Although not inevitable, the scope of considerations may be narrowed early in the problem definition phase.
Can better accommodate vagueness and has reduced transaction costs.[a]	Needs specification about processes, outcomes and participants in order to proceed. Less able to accommodate vagueness and has higher transaction costs.

a. The importance of vagueness is discussed in Chapter 13, under exploitation as a method for managing unknowns.

I2S can strengthen both multi- and trans-disciplinary research by supplying concepts and methods for improved understanding and management of diverse unknowns. In multidisciplinary research it is conceivable that additional perspectives on unknowns are laid side by side with the disciplinary and stakeholder perspectives. For example, these could include ways of dealing with the problem by accepting the unknowns (through scenarios, hedging, applying the precautionary principle, and so on), rather than reducing them, as is most likely to occur in the discipline-based approaches. I2S gives transdisciplinary

---

3 Although different perspectives are likely to be better synthesised in transdisciplinary research, access to a range of synthesis methods can also enhance such research by providing more options for pulling insights together. This can allow the synthesis to be better tailored to the circumstances or overcome prescriptive thinking about how synthesis should be undertaken (for example, that dialogue between equals is the only synthesis method).

research the opportunity for a rich and complex approach to unknowns to be built in at the beginning of the research process when the transcending framework is developed. This can influence both how the problem is thought about and how it is dealt with.

Table 33.3 Strengths and Weaknesses of Multidisciplinary and Transdisciplinary Research for Providing Integrated Research Support for Policy and Practice Change

Multidisciplinary	Transdisciplinary
Both are weak in providing *integrated* support because of poor attention to unknowns. Multidisciplinary research also has poor synthesis of available knowledge.	
Tends to rely on fairly low-level communication, with the onus on policy makers and practitioners to identify and use the research in meaningful ways. This can be a strength, as it allows them to select the findings most pertinent for their purposes, as well as to choose the framing for the integration, rather than relying on what is proposed by the researchers. On the down side, many recipients will not have the time or expertise to get the maximum value from the range of insights, so that the advantages of having conducted a multidisciplinary investigation are lost.	Transdisciplinary research seeks a more engaged approach with policy makers and practitioners in the planning, conduct and use of the research. While this can lead to strong engagement, transaction costs are high, which may reduce the willingness of recipients to participate. It can also be hard to accommodate turnover in personnel and changes in policy and practice priorities.

The advantage of I2S is that it can open up a broader range of possibilities for both approaches. It can help both multi- and trans-disciplinary teams target their efforts more effectively, by better understanding the policy and practice arenas and identifying the key players. It can also provide a wider range of options for interacting with policy makers, drawing on communication, advocacy and engagement as the bases. For example, multidisciplinary research might conclude with an advocacy phase. In transdisciplinary research, I2S can assist in considering alternatives when engagement is not possible. It can also help transdisciplinary teams appreciate and plan for the possibility of changed priorities by the time their research is completed—in other words, that their findings are no longer relevant or of interest to current policy and practice concerns.

Hybrid Approaches

The preceding discussion also starts to provide an inkling of how hybrid approaches combining elements of multi- and trans-disciplinary research could be used. These aim to exploit the different strengths, such as the robust disciplinary contributions and flexibility of multidisciplinary research and the strong synthetic focus of transdisciplinary research. It is relatively easy to conceive, for instance, of a program of research that starts with a multidisciplinary phase, which also maximises the benefits of vagueness, using those results to move into a transdisciplinary study, which has a clearer outcome-related focus. For example, the hypothetical Resilience Overcomes Vulnerability study described in Chapter 31 might have started with a multidisciplinary investigation, comprising

- demographic evaluations of the numbers of children growing up in the most adverse conditions and how these estimates have changed in the past 40 years
- geographic examination of how adverse conditions vary by location and how this has changed
- studies combining psychological, sociological and anthropological perspectives on parenting and how it is influenced by the experiences of mothers and fathers when they were children
- economic investigations of living conditions
- theoretical and practical considerations of resilience from history, psychology, psychiatry, anthropology, sociology, economics and philosophy
- epidemiological studies of how living conditions affect life expectancy.

If these investigations were undertaken in the first year of the Resilience Overcomes Adversity study, team leader, Mandela, and the I2S specialists Moore and Wang could use the findings to then pull together a core team to operate in a transdisciplinary manner. Perhaps the other members might be an anthropologist, a public health expert, a psychologist, an international public policy expert and an economist. This team could then develop an overarching conceptualisation for the next three-year research phase, with the final year being devoted to provision of integrated research support for policy and practice change.

Hybrid multi- and trans-disciplinary approaches can also be conceived as a transdisciplinary study embedded in a larger multidisciplinary investigation, rather than a transdisciplinary study following one that is multidisciplinary. The specific hypothetical examples for the Resilience Overcomes Vulnerability study used above can be rearranged to illustrate such an option. In this case, let us imagine that the eight members of the transdisciplinary team started with an overarching conceptualisation for a five-year project based on existing knowledge. The transdisciplinary team may then have commissioned the multidisciplinary add-ons described above. These may address questions that the transdisciplinary team needs for its ongoing research or may provide additional context.

Another advantage of hybrid approaches is that they allow the disciplinary experts and stakeholders to be involved in diverse ways tailored to their own interests and needs. Thus, it is conceivable for integrative applied research projects to be designed so that participants who want a highly engaged process of working together (like Mandela, Moore and Wang) can be accommodated, as can those who wish to offer their disciplinary or stakeholder insights in a less engaged way (such as Ritter) or who want to make a specific contribution and then move on (for example, Gregory).

The purpose of providing these examples is to open thinking about a range of hybrid methodological options and to demonstrate the variability that integrative applied research accommodates and that I2S supports.

34. The Scope and Feasibility of the I2S Development Drive

Here I want to return to the point that there are thousands of research projects that can contribute concepts, methods and case examples applicable to I2S, as well as information for guides to relevant knowledge from outside the discipline. Because the germane material is currently scattered and often undocumented, compilation will require an intense, well-resourced I2S Development Drive to scour a wide range of relevant literatures and to find and write down currently unrecorded information. This chapter describes the scope of this effort and what is required to make the case for feasibility: establishing proof-of-concept and addressing countervailing forces. I conclude by returning to the theme of imperfection, highlighting its central importance for the Drive and I2S itself.

Scope

Tables 34.1 and 34.2 summarise the materials to be compiled and demonstrate the extensive scale of the task.[1] It is not possible to determine at the outset how many relevant concepts and methods there are to be collected. Further, while there will be large numbers of pertinent case examples, again, it cannot be established ahead of time the extent of the variations they will illustrate and therefore how many case examples will need to be gathered.

While such open-endedness is a challenge for planning and seeking funding for the I2S Development Drive, it need not be an insurmountable obstacle. First, the I2S Development Drive does not need to compile absolutely all applicable material. Instead it has to gather enough significant, high-quality options from diverse sources to build a solid foundation—one that can continue to be extended. Second, one of the tasks of establishing proof-of-concept is to formulate feasible and efficient ways of proceeding.[2] Let us now move on to these feasibility issues.

---

1 The beginnings of a compilation of relevant resources can be found at: <http://i2s.anu.edu.au/resources>
2 Once an I2S Development Drive was under way, it would probably gather its own momentum (especially if it was endorsed by groups powerful in determining research policy), making it likely that those who had developed relevant materials would seek to have them included. The focus of Drive activities could then move from finding materials to assessing and categorising them.

Establishing Proof-of-Concept

Demonstrating the feasibility of the I2S Development Drive requires five key questions to be addressed

1. what are effective ways of finding and collecting I2S concepts, methods and case examples?

2. does the I2S structure (the domains and framework) have value for systematically documenting case examples?

3. can an appropriate peer group be identified and are they able to develop consensus-based classifications of I2S materials?

4. what are the best ways to engage discipline-based and other experts in developing guides to relevant knowledge from outside I2S?

5. will resulting compilations be widely used and valued?

What is needed to establish feasibility in each area is outlined below. Some early work pertinent to these considerations is also described.

What Are Effective Ways Of Finding And Collecting I2S Concepts, Methods And Case Examples?

At this early stage, when there is considerable uncertainty about how best to proceed with the task of finding relevant materials, my preferred approach is to leap in and see what happens. In other words, gain some experience and then use that to develop a more systematic approach. Accordingly, I have been getting a feel for the issues by working with colleagues to gather together dialogue methods for knowledge synthesis.

In establishing this compilation, we are essentially using a two-step procedure. Step one concentrated on published literature and led to a book of 14 dialogue methods.[3] We looked for examples of how these techniques had been applied in four areas: the environment, public health, security and technological innovation.[4] It is worth noting that finding case examples was challenging. Most came from public health (seven examples), followed by the environment (five examples), technological innovation (three examples) and security (two examples). For 10 of the methods, we found only one example of application in any of these topic areas.[5]

---

3 McDonald et al. (2009). It should also be pointed out that when the book was written, I was using the term 'integration' quite broadly. As described in Chapter 2, I now use 'synthesis' and 'integration' in specific ways.
4 The case examples included planning the future of a wetland, reducing the human and economic burdens of repetitive strain injuries, examining possible futures for a country's food supply chain and examining the future of the international airline industry.
5 The Delphi technique alone had examples in each of the four areas. For strategic assumption surfacing and testing and principled negotiation we could not find any examples of their use for knowledge synthesis. Only half of the cases were illustrative of integrative applied research; the others were more straightforward and did not involve a broad array of disciplines and stakeholders.

Step two is currently under way and involves testing how we can engage a broad range of relevant researchers to expand the collection of dialogue options and case examples. Identifying pertinent researchers is proving to be straightforward, as we began with those cited in the book. Even though we have found web tools for systematic searching,[6] so far we have been kept busy with referrals from our starting points. On the other hand, eliciting contributions has been more problematic and time-consuming. We developed a web-based forum to record contributions, but so far it has been difficult to get people to use it. On the positive side, when we phone them most are happy to tell us about their work and for us to make a contribution on their behalf.[7]

Although this project is not yet complete, it does suggest that there is value in producing a first-pass compilation as the starting point. This can be tailored to the time and money available and has the benefit of producing a concrete outcome relatively rapidly. The next step is harder. Not surprisingly, busy researchers are not likely to contribute to web-based forums, especially when these have little authorisation. Budgeting for interview-based data collection will probably be more productive. We still need to do more work on sampling issues. For example, although the snowball method is identifying researchers who use dialogue in their investigations, we have not yet assessed the quality and importance of their work and we have yet to compare snowball sampling with more systematic web-based sampling for identifying important lines of research that were missed in the literature review.

Nevertheless, this small study has given me confidence to proceed with investigations into the feasibility of the I2S Development Drive. Furthermore, it is worth exploring proof-of-concept approaches that will themselves yield valuable resources, as we achieved with our book of dialogue methods.

Does The I2S Structure (The Domains And Framework) Have Value For Systematically Documenting Case Examples?

One of the arguments underpinning this book is that there are many examples of research on complex real-world problems where reports do not convey the salient knowledge about which concepts and methods were used and how, making it hard for others to learn from and emulate such studies, let alone for peers to evaluate them adequately. The structure provided by the three domains and five-question framework is designed to be useful for systematic documentation of case examples.

---

6   E-research tools developed by the Virtual Observatory for the Study of Online Networks (VOSON) Project: <http://voson.anu.edu.au/> (accessed 15 December 2011).

7   See <http://i2s.anu.edu.au/projects/>

The structure's applicability now needs to be tested, especially as collecting case examples is a pivotal piece of the I2S Development Drive. A simple version of the framework was used successfully to provide brief case examples in the book on dialogue methods,[8] but the full framework has not yet been applied to a large, detailed case example in a way that illustrates and transmits information about the employment of relevant concepts and methods, as well as guides to knowledge from outside I2S.

Can An Appropriate Peer Group Be Identified And Are They Able To Develop Consensus-Based Classifications Of I2S Materials?

The third key area for proof-of-concept moves beyond the bringing together of concepts and methods to developing consensus-based classifications of those collections. It concerns the work of organising the discipline. The issues here are twofold: 1) is it possible to identify an existing college of peers who are I2S specialists or at least specialists in particular areas of I2S, and 2) can they reach consensus on categorising and setting quality standards for the concepts and methods? This is essentially a follow-on activity to the first area of proof-of-concept research described above—namely *'What are effective ways of finding and collecting I2S concepts, methods and case examples?'*.

The process can be illustrated using the example of the compilation of dialogue methods. A primary ambition of our project is to identify a core group of people experienced in using a range of dialogue methods for knowledge synthesis. This will be followed by seeing if they can reach consensus on: 1) which dialogue methods are pertinent for bringing together disciplinary and stakeholder knowledge, 2) which are of an appropriate level of quality, and 3) how they can best be classified. It is not yet clear whether such a group can be formed. From the work we have done so far, the challenge seems to be identifying researchers with experience in a range of dialogue methods, as most tend to work with one technique or a limited selection.

Testing the ability to develop consensus-based classifications of I2S materials will be straightforward if there is a large enough peer group with broad experience in the relevant concepts and methods. But comparative analysis will be harder and more time-consuming if most practitioners focus on only one or a small number of theories and techniques.[9]

---

8 McDonald et al. (2009).
9 This demonstrates the importance of feasibility examinations for effectively planning the I2S Development Drive. In the long-term development of I2S, such consensus-driven classification needs to occur on at least two levels. One is at the level of specific elements of I2S, such as knowledge synthesis methods based on dialogue, scoping unknowns or assessing authorisation for providing integrated research support for policy and practice change. The other is at the level of the overarching I2S discipline. While this book sets out to provide organising principles for I2S in the form of three domains and a five-question framework, the

What Are The Best Ways To Engage Discipline-Based And Other Experts In Developing Guides To Relevant Knowledge From Outside I2S?

Let us begin with examination of Table 34.2, which shows that there are two broad types of guides: 1) those based on a single discipline or area of knowledge (or a small closely related group), and 2) those aiming to help navigate across a range of disciplines and other knowledge areas.

An example of the first is a guide to theories of government policy making, which is key to scoping policy arenas. This is predominantly based in political science. The feasibility question becomes: can a group of well-regarded political scientists be convened to create the guide?[10] An example of the second type of guide is one useful for scoping unknowns, which provides information on how various disciplines and practice areas deal with unknowns. The key step here is to develop a panel of experts in thinking about unknowns, representing a range of disciplines and stakeholders, as well as areas (like environmental sciences) that grapple with this issue.[11] In both types of guides, an additional task is to establish processes for continual updating.

Will Resultant Compilations Be Widely Used And Valued?

The last dimension of proof-of-concept involves examining whether available compilations of concepts, methods and case examples, as well as guides to knowledge from outside I2S, will be widely used and valued in the conduct of future integrative applied research. For this to happen, the guides must be known about and accessible. Consideration should be given to a range of measures to assess uptake. This can include proxy measures such as sales, downloads and citations of the compilations, as well as more direct assessments such as surveys of pertinent research teams about the materials they use and examination of literature for changes in frequency of use of relevant concepts and methods.

---

structure of the discipline itself needs to be discussed and endorsed (or modified) by I2S specialist peers. In terms of proof-of-concept, the starting point is to see if consensus-based classification can be achieved with something relatively straightforward like dialogue methods for knowledge synthesis, before moving on to the discipline itself.

10   This might start with one country, but eventually needs to be expanded to take different political systems into account. I have done some preliminary work with colleagues interested in bridging research and policy to get a sense of the available theories. See Ritter and Bammer (2010); and Bammer et al. (2007).

11   Some preliminary work has been undertaken through the symposium on uncertainty that I co-organised with Michael Smithson and Steve Dovers in 2005. We demonstrated that we could successfully engaged a diverse cross-section of discipline-based researchers and practitioners to scan the territory, with 17 participants representing different disciplinary and practice perspectives and three representing problems where unknowns are important: communicable disease outbreaks, environmental management and illicit drug use. The process we used is described in Bammer and The Goolabri Group (2007). The symposium produced the book Bammer and Smithson (2008).

Countervailing Forces

To be realistic about the prospects of establishing I2S requires considering why it may be preferable not to progress this discipline. This is relevant not only to the I2S Development Drive, but to any method of advancing I2S. As the previous parts of this chapter have shown, making headway with I2S is a major enterprise, and although the aim is to substantially improve the conduct of integrative applied research, there are no guarantees that this will occur.[12]

Competition for resources, especially time, attention and person power, is a major countervailing force. Time and attention are relevant on at least two levels. First, the requirement to tackle complex real-world problems is urgent given their number and scale. It may be preferable to harness all available resources to address current complex social and environmental problems as best we can, rather than diverting time and energy to further develop I2S.

Second, on a project level, if integrative applied research teams are to fully incorporate I2S into their work, it will place new demands on teams to expand and upgrade the considerations given to knowledge synthesis, understanding and managing diverse unknowns and supporting policy and practice. In other words, these issues will require reallocation of resources. But will it be worth it? The hope is that it will increase the efficiency of the research being undertaken, making it faster and cheaper. This can occur if less time is lost, for example, in searching for useful ideas or applying concepts and methods that are suboptimal. But the worst-case scenario may be that incorporating I2S simply makes the studies more involved, so that they take longer and cost more with no measurable improvement in outcome.

In terms of person power, building I2S capacity requires bright researchers to be attracted into this discipline. Many of them may be drawn from the ranks of those currently involved in developing theory related to interdisciplinarity and related ventures. Others may come from practical projects that can be classed as integrative applied research or from the consultancy world.[13] Still others may be lured away from discipline-based endeavours—as in the case of Caryn de Silva in the hypothetical case in Chapter 31. As pointed out in Chapter 10, research

---

12   Here I have laid out the issues I can think of, but I do not respond to them. As well as being used to assess whether I2S and the I2S Development Drive should proceed, examining the counterarguments is important for identifying possible adverse consequences.

13   An issue here is whether sufficient existing researchers have broad enough expertise, a) across the three domains, and b) with a wide range of options for the various framework questions, to permit immediate establishment of a college of peers. An important role of the I2S Development Drive is to assess the existing baseline level of I2S expertise. This will determine whether the college of peers can be founded forthwith or if a process of building expertise is required. In the latter case, knowing the level of existing I2S expertise will help determine what this process will entail.

capacity will always be limited, so that competition for the most talented people is fierce. Again it may be preferable not to tamper with the status quo, as the implications for the rest of the research enterprise are unknown.

The current state of play also has its strengths and attractions. Some would suggest that the lack of a disciplinary structure allows more freedom for innovation, as new ideas are not stifled by a peer-review system. In other words, a wider range of possibilities can be opened up. There are certainly initiatives, as in implementation science[14] and in team science,[15] which are progressing apace without I2S.

It might also be argued that the market forces that partially drive the present system are more appropriate than a discipline-based structure. At present, the survival of many innovations relevant to integrative applied research seems to depend largely on whether someone is willing to pick them up and to pay for their application. Indeed it is striking that several of the existing concepts and methods that I2S proposes to gather together form the bases for consultancy businesses.[16] Some of these were founded by academics who could not get traction for their ideas within research organisations.

Working outside established academic structures also avoids entanglement with the growing bureaucratic forms of accountability such as quality assurance systems. Increasing prominence is being given, for example, to publication in journals that have high impact factors.[17] Certainly some journals that publish I2S-related work fall into that category, but many others do not. While one of the aims of establishing I2S is to develop the critical mass to enable effective participation in this quality-driven environment, it can also be argued that there are advantages in staying away from it.

Both the current reliance on market forces and the distance from quality assurance mechanisms help avoid the danger that I2S becomes self-referential rather than engaged. What I refer to here is the risk that I2S specialists will research and write for each other on ever more arcane aspects of the I2S discipline rather than being part of integrative applied research teams addressing complex real-

---

14   See, for example, the (US) National Implementation Research Network: <http://www.fpg.unc.edu/~nirn/default.cfm> (accessed 15 December 2011).

15   See, for example, the Science of Team Science: <http://scienceofteamscience.northwestern.edu/> (accessed 15 December 2011).

16   As described in Chapter 31. It is worth noting though that these generally target the policy and practice, rather than the research, communities.

17   Examples of quality assurance systems are the Excellence in Research for Australia (ERA) initiative <http://www.arc.gov.au/era/> (accessed 15 December 2011) and the United Kingdom's Research Excellence Framework <http://www.hefce.ac.uk/research/ref/> (accessed 15 December 2011).

world problems. It is too early to say which kind of development the quality assurance mechanisms will foster, but there is certainly concern that they will be counterproductive for research implementation.

In considering the establishment of I2S, such countervailing forces need to be kept in mind. On the other hand, the fact that I2S has potential problems and faces opposition does not necessarily mean that it should be abandoned. Expecting a perfect solution or unanimous support for I2S is unrealistic, as all major initiatives have limitations and detractors.[18] Overall, whether to proceed is a major decision yet to be made.

Implications of Imperfection for I2S and the I2S Development Drive

The importance of imperfection was introduced in Chapter 10 as a consequence of the inevitability of unknowns, and was further teased out in several subsequent chapters relating to different dimensions of I2S, especially

1. understanding that all systems views are partial and that the whole system cannot be effectively taken into account

2. the need to set boundaries to define what can be done with the available resources of time, money and personnel, and that having enough resources to do everything will be a rare occurrence

3. the significance of values in determining what research is undertaken, along with inevitable downplaying of some values

4. appreciation that context (the influence on the research of the real world in all its complexity and unpredictability) cannot be fully taken into account in planning and conducting integrative applied research

5. awareness of the general unpredictability of policy making and practice change, along with inability to be certain of research impacts, the possibility of incompatibility between what the research finds and what action is possible, and that many forces compete with research for influence.[19]

---

18   Even the now widely lauded Human Genome Project initially struggled to gain acceptance; see Lambright (2002).
19   There is value in providing a guide to different kinds of knowledge about imperfection and this is included in Table 34.2.

It is also worth reiterating the challenges raised by imperfection for integrative applied research and I2S that were discussed in Chapter 10—namely avoiding: 1) overconfidence and hubris, 2) nihilism and despair, 3) hindsight bias in evaluation, and 4) the sanctioning of incompetence and corruption.

These circumstances signal that an important task for the I2S Development Drive is to gather together ways of thinking about and managing imperfection. One example is adaptive management, discussed in Chapter 13. Another is the capacity to effectively recognise and manage hindsight bias, which is particularly important for the evaluation of I2S. Building on existing approaches and developing new ones are critical in the further evolution of I2S.

Let us also examine the implications of imperfection for how I2S is evaluated. As described in Chapter 29, assessment of I2S has to steer a path between two precipices. On one side, there will always be identifiable limitations to an integrative applied research project, making it easy to castigate the project for these inevitable deficiencies. But this is not a fair or productive appraisal process. The challenge instead is to judge whether the decisions taken by an integrative applied research team are defensible in light of the inescapable restrictions. Peers who have been in the same situation are likely to be best placed to undertake such review. A further complication is that genuine mistakes are also inevitable. Sometimes the wrong choice will be made—for example, about which dialogue method to use, where boundaries are set or which policy makers or practitioners to target. Again, peers are likely to be best placed to take mistakes into account and to differentiate them from a history of sloppiness or incompetence.

The other precipice to be avoided is allowing imperfection to be an excuse for 'anything goes'. Given that every I2S concept and method has strengths and weaknesses, it can be tempting not to worry about finding the most suitable. This can play out in various ways, such as considering only a very limited repertoire of options, continuing to use substandard concepts and methods when significantly improved versions are available, and employing the latest fad regardless of its suitability. A commitment to excellence and effective peer review are necessary to counteract these trends. This requires a realistic appraisal of what I2S can offer and what an excellent integrative applied research project looks like in light of inevitable limitations.

Imperfection is inescapable in dealing with complex real-world problems, but in order to manage it, much current research sidelines key issues, especially unknowns and context. A core assumption of this book is that this marginalisation is no longer tenable and that imperfection has to be faced head-on. Grappling with imperfection and communicating its importance are central challenges for I2S.

Table 34.1 I2S Concepts, Methods and Case Examples, as well as Guides to Relevant Knowledge from Outside I2S, to be Collected in the I2S Development Drive

Framework question	I2S Development Drive tasks	I2S Development Drive involves compiling:			
		Concepts	Methods	Case examples	Guides
1. For what and for whom	**Domains 1–3** Compile case examples demonstrating: a) different ways of describing the purpose (knowledge synthesis, thinking expansively about unknowns, providing integrated research support for policy and practice change); b) the contribution to the overarching research aims; and c) the beneficiaries (that is, which perspectives were included).			√	
	Domain 2 addition Compile case examples demonstrating how the inevitability of imperfection was incorporated.				
	Domain 3 addition In case examples describing purpose, include cases where there were strong views about the desired impact of the research and cases where there were not.				
	I2S as a Whole Compile case examples illustrating different ways in which integrative applied research teams approached aims for addressing the problem as a whole. Particularly valuable will be information on how they identified and dealt with inconsistencies in aims and beneficiaries across the domains and within the team.				

Framework question	I2S Development Drive tasks	I2S Development Drive involves compiling:			
		Concepts	Methods	Case examples	Guides
2. Which knowledge, unknowns and aspects of policy and practice: Systems view	**Domains 1–2** Collect case examples illustrating how different systems approaches are useful for describing a complex problem, as well as for bringing together discipline-based and stakeholder knowledge and dealing with diverse unknowns.			√	√
	Produce a guide to the broad range of systems approaches to a complex problem, emphasising the different ways they bring together discipline-based and stakeholder knowledge and provide for understanding and management of diverse unknowns.				
	Domain 3 Collect case examples of various ways of considering the major arenas for implementation (government, business and civil society) as systems, showing the organisational structures and processes for decision making and action, as well as the interactions between them.				
	Produce a guide for systems approaches to each of the major arenas of implementation (government, business and civil society), showing the organisational structures and processes for decision making and action, as well as the interactions between them.				
	I2S as a Whole Collect case examples illustrating ways to combine various systems approaches to the problem (which may differ for the knowledge synthesis and unknowns aspects) and the policy and practice arenas.				
	Produce a guide for combining different systems approaches to the problem and the policy and practice arenas.				

Framework question	I2S Development Drive tasks	I2S Development Drive involves compiling:			
		Concepts	Methods	Case examples	Guides
Scoping	**Domains 1–3** Gather together literature and undocumented practical experience providing • concepts for scoping each of: a) knowledge, b) unknowns, and c) the roles of government, business and civil society, along with key individuals and groups, and specific sub-processes, within each systems view • methods for such scoping • illustrative case examples. Produce guides to a) all the potential contributions of different disciplines and stakeholders, focusing on generic issues rather than specifics b) all the potential ways of considering diverse unknowns including taxonomies, different approaches of disciplines and stakeholders, and unknowns that would be banished in discipline-based research c) the roles of government, business and civil society that can help teams understand where action is possible. **I2S as a Whole** Gather together and develop useful concepts, methods and case examples for managing the vast amount of information that is inevitably involved when the three domains are combined. Collect case examples to investigate the intersection between 'stakeholders' and 'policy makers and practitioners', especially limits on what is possible for scoping and how these can be overcome.	√	√	√	√

Framework question	I2S Development Drive tasks	I2S Development Drive involves compiling:			
		Concepts	Methods	Case examples	Guides
Boundary setting	**Domains 1–3** Collate published and unpublished concepts and methods for boundary setting, along with case examples that emphasise how and why decisions were made.	√	√	√	
	Domain 2 addition Develop boundary-setting methods to allow the most significant unknowns to be identified.				
	Domain 3 addition Collate case examples demonstrating how special advantages of teams (such as long-established relationships with particular policy makers) were taken into account.				
	I2S as a Whole Collate case examples relevant to interactions between the domains in boundary setting, such as: a) ensuring relatively equal coverage of each domain; b) congruence between how knowledge synthesis, unknowns and providing integrated research support were approached; and c) not allowing congruence to be too limiting, especially in restricting coverage of key aspects of the approach to the problem or the potential for change.				

233

Framework question	I2S Development Drive tasks	I2S Development Drive involves compiling:			
		Concepts	Methods	Case examples	Guides
Framing	**Domains 1–3** Draw together useful concepts and practical methods for framing, along with case examples of when it has worked well and when it has failed.	√	√	√	
	Domain 2 addition Develop new ways of framing unknowns that signal their importance and potential for achieving better outcomes on complex real-world problems.				
	Domain 3 addition Framing is also relevant to the findings of the integrated research. Collect case examples of competition between framings trying to influence policy or practice change.				
	I2S as a Whole Draw together case examples of the relationships between the frames used in the three domains—for example, when these were the same or different framings, as well as assessments of how well these worked. Collect case examples of accurate and inaccurate framings for the position of integrative applied research teams on controversial issues.				
Values	**Domains 1–3 and I2S as a Whole** Compile case examples that illustrate different experiences of bringing values into play and their consequences for the integrative applied research. Produce a guide to concepts and methods for understanding and responding to the various dimensions of values.			√	√
	Domain 3 and I2S as a Whole addition Compile case examples examining congruence in values across the three domains, as well as assessing integrity. The latter includes gauging independence from government, business and civil society pressures, as well as commitment to the provision of 'public value'.				

Framework question	I2S Development Drive tasks	I2S Development Drive involves compiling:			
		Concepts	Methods	Case examples	Guides
Harnessing and managing differences	**Domains 1–3** Gather together concepts and methods for understanding differences, as well as for harnessing and managing them, along with illustrative case examples.	√	√	√	
	I2S as a Whole Gather together case examples to: a) ascertain how the same differences play out across all three domains, b) examine how management strategies fare across the domains, and c) figure out when best to apply methods for managing differences (proactively or reactively).				
Iteration	**Domains 1–3** Compile case examples of how iterative processes between the six categories of concepts and methods played out.			√	
	I2S as a Whole Compile case examples of how iteration occurred across the three domains, particularly whether the processes were independent for each domain or if there were interactions between the iterative processes across the three domains.				
	Compile case examples of choices made and judgment exercised (that is, imperfection) in dealing with the six categories.				

235

| Framework question | I2S Development Drive tasks | I2S Development Drive involves compiling: | | | |
		Concepts	Methods	Case examples	Guides
3. How Methods	**Domains 1–3** Identify and catalogue the full range of methods that has been used for: a) knowledge synthesis, b) understanding and managing diverse unknowns, and c) providing integrated research support for policy and practice change, as well as their conceptual bases and case examples of their application. Update and improve existing compilations.	✓	✓	✓	
	Domain 2 addition Develop new methods for understanding and managing unknowns, including for reduction (beyond methods used in the disciplines), acceptance, surrender, exploitation and denial.				
	Draw together understandings of how stakeholders might use strategies like surrender, exploitation and denial in furthering their agendas, so that these can be taken into account in understanding and responding to complex real-world problems.				
	Pull together concepts, methods and cases that will assist in appreciating and dealing with the complexities involved in understanding and managing diverse unknowns (for example, that the same strategy can be adaptive or maladaptive depending on the circumstances).				
	Domain 3 addition This includes taking a broad view of communication (such as effectiveness at different stages of the policy cycle), identifying and assessing the value of brokering agencies, and developing rules of thumb for when methods for generating fresh thinking on complex problems are likely to be useful.				
	I2S as a Whole Collect methods (and underpinning concepts) that can be used across two or all three domains, along with illustrative case examples.				
	Identify which methods can productively be used together, as well as which methods are likely to be incompatible. Explore other issues affecting congruence. Compile case examples that illustrate the range of issues involved.				
	Further explore the nature and value of an overarching classification based on options for reciprocity and action-orientation.				

Framework question	I2S Development Drive tasks	I2S Development Drive involves compiling:			
		Concepts	Methods	Case examples	Guides
By whom and when	**Domains 1–3** Collect case examples of implementation of different options for who undertook: a) the knowledge synthesis, b) comprehensive consideration of diverse unknowns, and c) provision of integrated research support for policy and practice change, and when in the research process this occurred.			√	
	Domain 3 addition Take into account the options for policy and practice recipients and the timing issues that are relevant for them.				
	I2S as a Whole Collect case examples looking at the congruence of 'who' and 'when' across the three domains.				
4. Context Overall	**Domains 1–3** Collect case examples dealing with overall context relevant to: a) the knowledge synthesis, b) considering diverse unknowns, and c) the government, business and civil society arenas.			√	√
	Produce guides for how context can be taken into account.				
	I2S as a Whole Collect case examples of how: a) the requisite agility to deal with the inevitable unpredictability was fostered, b) interacting influences between the three domains were managed, and c) the inevitability of incongruence and the likely imperfection of solutions were taken into account.				
	Produce a guide for combining considerations of context in the three domains.				

237

Framework question	I2S Development Drive tasks	I2S Development Drive involves compiling:			
		Concepts	Methods	Case examples	Guides
Authorisation	**Domains 1–3** Gather case examples describing funding, endorsement and other forms of authorisation, along with any restrictions on knowledge synthesis, understanding and management of diverse unknowns and providing integrated research support for policy and practice change.			√	
	Domain 2 addition Examine whether provision of untied funding enhances the ability to explore unknowns in less traditional ways.				
	I2S as a Whole Gather case examples of how integrative applied research teams managed congruence in terms of different restrictions, different interests and other consequences of authorisation.				
Organisational barriers and facilitators	**Domains 1–3** Compile case examples describing the diversity and impact of organisational barriers and facilitators.			√	
	Domain 3 addition Examine the policy and practice organisations as well as the research organisations.				
	I2S as a Whole Compile case examples examining interactions and congruence in organisational barriers and facilitators within and between research bodies and policy and practice institutions.				

Framework question	I2S Development Drive tasks	I2S Development Drive involves compiling:			
		Concepts	Methods	Case examples	Guides
5. Outcomes	**Domains 1–3** Gather and analyse case examples of evaluation both to improve the list of assessment questions and to develop more detailed guidelines for reviewers.			√	
	Domain 3 addition Gather and review case examples that examine complexities arising from: a) opposition by vested interests, b) the requirement for multiple viewpoints to understand impact, and c) the inability to predict impact.				
	I2S as a Whole Compile case examples about, and assess the effectiveness of, peer-review processes in integrative applied research. Compile case examples illustrating whether the integrative applied research required prerequisite conditions, especially resources for project development, communication mechanisms, translation and conflict-resolution processes, 'database' development and funding mechanisms, from which exemplars can be highlighted and general rules proposed. Compile case examples about how imperfection was managed in the assessment process.				

Table 34.2 Summary of Guides to Relevant Knowledge from Outside I2S

Type of guide	Experts to be convened	Purpose for I2S
Systems approaches to complex real-world problems	Experts in systems thinking and in using systems approaches	Provide different systems approaches that can be used to consider the elements of a problem and their interrelationships, in terms of both knowledge and unknowns.
Systems approaches to the policy and practice arenas Separate guides for 1. government 2. business 3. civil society	Respectively: political scientists, business analysts, experts in civil society	Provide understanding of organisation structures, as well as theories that deliver insights into government, business and civil society processes, to inform how integrated research can provide support.
Combining different systems approaches	Experts in systems thinking and in combining systems approaches	Demonstrate which systems approaches can be combined productively and which cannot. This includes bringing together different approaches to the problem (which may be used for knowledge synthesis and dealing with unknowns), as well as merging systems approaches to the problem and those for the policy and practice arenas.
Scoping guide to knowledge	Discipline and stakeholder experts	Provide a general overview of the knowledge contributions different disciplines and stakeholders can make to understanding complex real-world problems.
Scoping guide to unknowns	Experts in thinking about unknowns and discipline and stakeholder experts interested in unknowns	Provide a more complete picture of unknowns, including 1. different taxonomies and other classification systems, and 2. an overview of different discipline and stakeholder perspectives in terms of: a) approach to unknowns and how these map onto taxonomies, b) the terrain they cover, c) additional considerations they highlight that cannot be covered by taxonomies, d) unknowns disciplines would normally banish from consideration, and e) unknowns at the intersection of disciplines.

Type of guide	Experts to be convened	Purpose for I2S
Scoping guide to supporting policy and practice change	Political scientists, public policy experts, business analysts and experts in civil society processes	Provide general overviews of possibilities for providing research support for policy and practice change, describing the roles of government, business and civil society (within particular systems views), as well as how to identify key individuals and sub-processes.
Values	Applied philosophers and other experts in thinking about values (such as those developing and using the concept of 'public value')	Provide an overview of the different dimensions of values, congruence between different values, how they can be taken into account, and the consequences for understanding and acting on the problem.
Overall context	Social scientists	Provide an overview of considerations relevant to gaining broad background understanding about specific complex real-world problems, relevant to: a) how the problem manifests and is understood, b) the unknowns considered to be pertinent, and c) the possibilities for acting on the problem and hence where integrated research support might best be targeted.
Guide to imperfection	Range of experts (for example, on adaptive management and on hindsight bias)	Provide an overview of ways of thinking about and managing imperfection. This includes positive strategies as well as those to avoid.

References

Aitken, C., Moore, D., Higgs, P., Kelsall, J. and Kerger, M. (2002). 'The impact of a police crackdown on a street drug scene: evidence from the street'. International Journal of *Drug Policy*, 13 (3): 189–98.

Aldred, J. and Jacobs, M. (2000). 'Citizens and wetlands: evaluating the Ely citizens' jury'. *Ecological Economics*, 34 (2): 217–32.

Althaus, C., Bridgman, P. and Davis, G. (2007). *The Australian Policy Handbook*. Fourth Edition. Crows Nest, NSW: Allen & Unwin.

Anderson, C. and Bammer, G. (2005). 'Measuring the global research environment: information science challenges for the 21st century'. *Sparking Synergies: Bringing Research and Practice Together. Proceedings of the 68th American Society of Information Science and Technology Annual Meeting, October 28 – November 2, 2005*. Charlotte, NC: <http://hdl.handle.net/10150/105639> (accessed 19 December 2011).

Attewell, R. G. (2008). 'Statistics: an essential tool for model citizens'. In: Bammer, G. and Smithson, M. (eds). *Uncertainty and Risk: Multidisciplinary perspectives*. London: Earthscan, 81–90.

Babor, T. F. (2009). 'Alcohol research and the alcoholic beverage industry: issues, concerns and conflicts of interest'. *Addiction*, 104 (Supplement 1): 34–47.

Badham, J. (2010). 'A compendium of modelling techniques'. *Integration Insights*, Number 12 (May). Canberra: The Australian National University; <http://i2s.anu.edu.au/sites/default/files/integration-insights/integration-insight_12.pdf>

Bammer, G. (1999). 'Provision of diamorphine (heroin) by prescription for drug dependency: issues and recommendations'. *CNS Drugs*, 11 (4): 253–62.

Bammer, G. (2005). 'Integration and Implementation Sciences: building a new specialization'. *Ecology and Society*, 10 (2): article 6; <http://www.ecologyandsociety.org/vol10/iss2/art6/>

Bammer, G. (2008). 'Enhancing research collaboration: three key management challenges'. *Research Policy*, 37: 875–87.

Bammer, G. (2012). *Strengthening Interdisciplinary Research: What it is, what it does, how it does it and how it is supported*. Report for the Australian Council of Learned Academies; <http://www.acola.org.au> and <http://i2s.anu.edu.au/publications/acola-interdisciplinarity-report> (accessed 19 July 2012).

Bammer, G. and LWA Integration Symposium Participants. (2005). 'Guiding principles for integration in natural resource management (NRM) as a contribution to sustainability'. *Australasian Journal of Environmental Management*, 12 (Supplement): 5–7.

Bammer, G. and Sengoz, A. (1994). *How would the controlled availability of heroin affect the illicit market in the Australian Capital Territory?* Feasibility Research into the Controlled Availability of Opioids Stage 2 Working Paper Number 10. Canberra: The Australian National University; <http://digitalcollections. anu.edu.au/handle/1885/41247> (accessed 30 July 2012).

Bammer, G. and Smithson, M. (eds). (2008). *Uncertainty and Risk: Multidisciplinary perspectives*. London: Earthscan.

Bammer, G. and The Goolabri Group. (2007). 'Improving the management of ignorance and uncertainty. A case illustrating integration in collaboration'. In: Shani, A. B., Mohrman, S. A., Pasmore, W. A., Stymne, B. and Adler, N. (eds). *Handbook of Collaborative Management Research*. Thousand Oaks, CA: Sage, 421–37.

Bammer, G., Tunnicliff, D. and Chadwick-Masters, J. (1994). *How could an influx of users be prevented if Canberra introduces a trial of controlled availability of heroin?* Feasibility Research into the Controlled Availability of Opioids Stage 2 Working Paper Number 9. Canberra: The Australian National University; <http://digitalcollections.anu.edu.au/handle/1885/41245> (accessed 30 July 2012).

Bammer, G., Dance, P., Stevens, A., Mugford, S., Ostini, R. and Crawford, D. (1996). 'Attitudes to a proposal for controlled availability of heroin in Australia: is it time for a trial?' *Addiction Research*, 4: 45–55.

Bammer, G., Dobler-Mikola, A., Fleming, P. M., Strang, J. and Uchtenhagen, A. (1999). 'The heroin prescribing debate—integrating science and politics'. *Science*, 284 (21 May): 1277–8.

Bammer, G., Curtis, A., Mobbs, C., Lane, R. and Dovers, S. (eds). (2005a). 'Australian case studies of integration in natural resource management (NRM)'. *Australasian Journal of Environmental Management*, 12 (Supplement).

Bammer, G., O'Connell, D., Roughley, A. and Syme, G. (eds). (2005b). 'New challenges for research practice: natural resource management in Australia'. *Journal of Research Practice*, 1 (2) (Special Issue); <http://jrp.icaap.org/index. php/jrp/issue/view/2> (accessed 3 January 2012).

Bammer, G., Ritter, A., Deane, P., Strazdins, L., McDonald, D., Berry, H. and van Kerkhoff, L. (2007). Improving research support for environmental policy making: lessons from the literature and issues for debate. Unpublished report prepared for the Global Environmental Change and Food Systems (GECAFS) project; <http://i2s.anu.edu.au/sites/default/files/projects/research-support-for-policy.pdf>

Bammer, G., Smithson, M. and The Goolabri Group. (2008). 'The nature of uncertainty'. In: Bammer, G. and Smithson, M. (eds). *Uncertainty and Risk: Multidisciplinary perspectives*. London: Earthscan, 289–303.

Bammer, G., with Michaux, A. and Sanson, A. (eds). (2010a). *Bridging the 'Know–Do' Gap: Knowledge brokering to improve child wellbeing*. Canberra: ANU E Press; <http://epress.anu.edu.au/titles/knowledge_citation>

Bammer, G., Strazdins, L., McDonald, D., Berry, H., Ritter, A., Deane, P. and van Kerkhoff, L. (2010b). 'Expanding the deliberations about the research–policy gap: useful lessons from the literature'. In: Bammer, G., with Michaux, A. and Sanson, A. (eds). *Bridging the 'Know–Do' Gap: Knowledge brokering to improve child wellbeing*. Canberra: ANU E Press, 135–55; <http://epress.anu.edu.au/knowledge_citation>

Belbin, M. (1993). *Team Roles at Work*. Oxford: Butterworth-Heinemann.

Bergman, M., Jahn, T., Knobloch, T., Krohn, W., Pohl, C. and Schramm, E. (2010). *Methoden transdisziplinaerer Forschung: Ein Ueberblick mit Anwendungsbeispielen*. Frankfurt: Campus Verlag. (English version: *Methods for Transdisciplinary Research: A primer for practice* published in 2012.)

Briscoe, J. (2010). 'Viewpoint—overreach and response: the politics of the WCD and its aftermath'. *Water Alternatives*, 3 (2): 399–415.

Brocklehurst, N. J., Hook, G., Bond, M. and Goodwin, S. (2005). 'Developing the public health practitioner work force in England: lessons from theory and practice'. *Public Health*, 119 (11): 995–1002.

Brownson, R. C., Royer, C., Ewing, R. and McBride, T. D. (2006). 'Researchers and policymakers: travelers in parallel universes'. *American Journal of Preventive Medicine*, 30 (2): 164–72.

Buckman, S. J. (2008). 'Uncertainty in the physical sciences: how big? How small? Is it actually there at all?'. In: Bammer, G. and Smithson, M. (eds). *Uncertainty and Risk: Multidisciplinary perspectives*. London: Earthscan, 71–80.

Campbell, A. and Scott, R. (eds). (2008). *The Blair Years. Extracts from the Alastair Campbell diaries*. London: Arrow Books.

Cardiff Council. (2005). *Reducing Cardiff's Ecological Footprint: A resource accounting tool for sustainable consumption*. Cardiff, Wales: Cardiff Council.

Chapman, S. (1998). *Over Our Dead Bodies. Port Arthur and Australia's fight for gun control*. Annandale, NSW: Pluto Press.

Chapman, S. (2007). *Public Health Advocacy and Tobacco Control: Making smoking history*. Oxford: Blackwell.

Checkland, P. (1984). *Systems Thinking, Systems Practice*. Chichester, UK: John Wiley and Sons.

Clark, W. C. (2007). 'Sustainability science: a room of its own'. *Proceedings of the National Academy of Sciences of the United States of America*, 104 (6): 1737–8.

Collins, A. and Flynn, A. (2005). 'A new perspective on the environmental impacts of planning: a case study of Cardiff's International Sports Village'. *Journal of Environmental Policy and Planning*, 7 (4): 277–302.

Collins, A. and Flynn, A. (2007). 'Engaging with the ecological footprint as a decision-making tool: process and responses'. *Local Environment: The International Journal of Justice and Sustainability*, 12 (3): 295–312.

Collins, A., Flynn, A., Wiedmann, T. and Barrett, J. (2006). 'The environmental impacts of consumption at a subnational level: the ecological footprint of Cardiff'. *Journal of Industrial Ecology*, 10 (3): 9–24.

Collins, F. S., Morgan, M. and Patrinos, A. (2003). 'The Human Genome Project: lessons from large-scale biology'. *Science*, 300: 286–90.

Committee on Facilitating Interdisciplinary Research, Committee on Science, Engineering, and Public Policy, National Academy of Sciences, National Academy of Engineering and Institute of Medicine of the National Academies. (2004). *Facilitating Interdisciplinary Research*. Washington, DC: National Academies Press; <http://www.nap.edu/catalog/11153.html> (accessed 3 January 2012).

Compton, A. H. (1956). *Atomic Quest. A personal narrative*. London: Oxford University Press.

Costanza, R., Darge, R., Degroot, R., Farber, S., Grasso, M., Hannon, B., Limburg, K., Naeem, S., Oneill, R. V., Paruelo, J., Raskin, R. G., Sutton, P. and Vandenbelt, M. (1997). 'The value of the world's ecosystem services and natural capital'. *Nature*, 387 (6630): 253–60.

Curthoys, A. (2008). 'Historians and disputes over uncertainty'. In: Bammer, G. and Smithson, M. (eds). *Uncertainty and Risk: Multidisciplinary perspectives*. London: Earthscan, 128–36.

Daily, G. C. (1999). 'Developing a scientific basis for managing Earth's life support systems'. *Conservation Ecology*, 3 (2): article 14; <http://www.ecologyandsociety.org/vol3/iss2/art14/> (accessed 3 January 2012).

Davis, R. M. and Pless, B. (2001). 'BMJ bans "accidents". Accidents are not unpredictable'. [Editorial]. *British Medical Journal*, 332: 1320–1.

De Bono, E. (1999). *Six Thinking Hats*. New York: Back Bay Books (Little, Brown and Company).

Edwards, M. (2004). *Social science research and public policy: narrowing the divide*. Occasional Paper 2/2004. Canberra: Academy of the Social Sciences in Australia; <http://www.assa.edu.au/publications/occasional_papers/2004_No2.php> (accessed 3 January 2012).

Falk-Krzesinski, H. J., Contractor, N., Fiore, S. M., Hall, K. L., Kane, C., Keyton, J., Klein, J. T., Spring, B., Stokols, D. and Trochim, W. (2011). 'Mapping a research agenda for the science of team science'. *Research Evaluation*, 20 (2): 145–58.

Fenna, A. (2004). *Australian Public Policy*. Frenchs Forest, NSW: Pearson Longman.

Fineberg, H. V. C. (2011). *Report of the Review Committee on the Functioning of the International Health Regulations (2005) in Relation to Pandemic (H1N1) 2009*. Geneva: World Health Organisation; <http://apps.who.int/gb/ebwha/pdf_files/WHA64/A64_10-en.pdf> (accessed 21 December 2011).

Fisher, R., Ury, W. and Patton, B. (1991). *Getting to Yes. Negotiating an agreement without giving in*. London: Random House Business Books.

Franco, L. A. (2006). 'Forms of conversation and problem structuring methods: a conceptual development'. *Journal of the Operational Research Society*, 57: 813–21.

Frodeman, R. (ed.), Klein, J. T. and Mitcham, C. (associate eds). (2010). *The Oxford Handbook of Interdisciplinarity*. Oxford: Oxford University Press.

Funtowicz, S. O. and Ravetz, J. R. (1993). 'Science for the post-normal age'. *Futures*, 25 (September): 739–55.

Gardner, H. (2006). *Changing Minds. The art and science of changing our own and other people's minds*. Boston, MA: Harvard Business School Press.

Gibbons, M., Limoges, C., Nowotny, H., Schwartzman, S., Scott, P. and Trow, M. (1994). *The New Production of Knowledge. The dynamics of science and research in contemporary societies.* Thousand Oaks, CA: Sage.

Gibson, B. (2003a). 'Beyond "two communities"'. In: Lin, V. and Gibson, B. (eds). *Evidence-Based Health Policy. Problems and possibilities.* Oxford: Oxford University Press, 18–30.

Gibson, B. (2003b). From transfer to transformation: rethinking the relationship between research and policy. PhD Thesis, The Australian National University, Canberra; <http://hdl.handle.net/1885/47083> (accessed 18 December, 2011).

Goleman, D. (1995). *Emotional Intelligence.* New York: Bantam.

Gray, B. (1989). *Collaboration: Finding common ground for multiparty problems.* San Francisco: Jossey-Bass.

Gregrich, R. J. (2003). 'A note to researchers: communicating science to policy makers and practitioners'. *Journal of Substance Abuse Treatment*, 25 (3): 233–7.

Grishin, S. (2008). 'Uncertainty as a creative force in visual art'. In: Bammer, G. and Smithson, M. (eds). *Uncertainty and Risk: Multidisciplinary perspectives.* London: Earthscan, 115–25.

Groueff, S. (1967). *Manhattan Project. The untold story of the making of the atomic bomb.* Boston: Little, Brown and Company.

Hackman, J. R. (ed.). (1990). *Groups That Work (And Those That Don't). Creating conditions for effective teamwork.* San Francisco: Jossey-Bass.

Hájek, A. (2008). 'A philosopher's guide to probability'. In: Bammer, G. and Smithson, M. (eds). *Uncertainty and Risk: Multidisciplinary perspectives.* London: Earthscan, 91–104.

Hartland, N. (1991). 'The political context'. *Feasibility Research into the Controlled Availability of Opioids. Volume 2.* Canberra: National Centre for Epidemiology and Population Health, The Australian National University, 163–89; <http://digitalcollections.anu.edu.au/handle/1885/41235> (accessed 30 July 2012).

Hartland, N., McDonald, D., Dance, P. and Bammer, G. (1992). 'Australian reports into drug use and the possibility of heroin maintenance'. *Drug and Alcohol Review*, 11: 175–82.

Hawks, D. (1992). 'Lying down with the lion: co-operating with the alcohol industry? The 1991 Leonard Ball Oration'. *Drug and Alcohol Review*, 11: 51–8.

Heyman, S. J. (2000). 'Health and social policy'. In: Berkman, L. F. and Kawachi, I. (eds). *Social Epidemiology*. Oxford: Oxford University Press, 368–82.

Hirsch Hadorn, G., Hoffmann-Riem, H., Biber-Klemm, S., Grossenbacher-Mansuy, W., Joye, D., Pohl, C., Wiesmann, U. and Zemp, E. (eds). (2008). *Handbook of Transdisciplinary Research*. New York: Springer Verlag.

Hough, L. (2002). 'A meeting of the minds. What happens when the Kennedy School's executive sessions unite practitioners and academics together?' *Harvard University John F. Kennedy School of Government Bulletin* (Spring): 32–7; <http://www.ksg.harvard.edu/ksgpress/bulletin/spring2002/features/meeting.html> (accessed 18 December 2011).

IUCN—World Conservation Union and the World Bank Group. (1997). *Large Dams: Learning from the past, looking at the future. Workshop proceedings.* Gland, Switzerland, and Washington, DC: IUCN—World Conservation Union and World Bank Group; <http://water.worldbank.org/water/publications/large-dams-learning-past-looking-future-workshop-proceedings-gland-switzerland-april-11> (accessed 3 January 2012).

Jones, J. S. (2008). 'Certainty as illusion: the nature and purpose of uncertainty in the law'. In: Bammer, G. and Smithson, M. (eds). *Uncertainty and Risk: Multidisciplinary perspectives*. London: Earthscan, 269–86.

Kasperson, R. E. (2008). 'Coping with deep uncertainty: challenges for environmental assessment and decision-making'. In: Bammer, G. and Smithson, M. (eds). *Uncertainty and Risk: Multidisciplinary perspectives*. London: Earthscan, 337–47.

Kerwin, A. (1993). 'None too solid: medical ignorance'. *Knowledge: Creation, Diffusion, Utilisation*, 15 (2): 166–85.

Khagram, S. (2004). *Dams and Development. Transnational struggles for water and power*. Ithaca, NY: Cornell University Press.

Kingdon, J. W. (2003). *Agendas, Alternatives, and Public Policies*. Second Edition. New York: Longman.

Klein, J. T. (1990). *Interdisciplinarity: History, theory and practice*. Detroit: Wayne State University Press.

Lakoff, G. (2004). *Don't Think of an Elephant! Know your values and frame the debate. The essential guide for progressives*. White River Junction, VT: Chelsea Green Publishing.

Lambright, W. H. (2002). *Managing 'Big Science': A case study of the human genome project*. New Ways to Manage Series. The PricewaterhouseCoopers Endowment for the Business of Government; <http://www.businessofgovernment.org/report/managing-big-science-case-study-human-genome-project> (accessed 6 December 2012).

Láng, B. (2010). 'Why don't we decipher an outdated cipher system? The Codex of Rohonc'. *Cryptologia*, 34: 115–44.

Larson, A. (1992). *Estimating the numbers of heroin users in the ACT*. Feasibility Research into the Controlled Availability of Opioids Stage 2 Working Paper Number 1. Canberra: The Australian National University; <http://digitalcollections.anu.edu.au/handle/1885/41238> (accessed 30 July 2012).

Larson, A. and Bammer, G. (1996). 'Why? Who? How? Estimating numbers of illicit drug users. Lessons from an ACT case study'. *Australian and New Zealand Journal of Public Health*, 20: 493–9.

Lawrence, G., Bammer, G. and Chapman, S. (2000). '"Sending the wrong signal": analysis of print media reportage of the ACT heroin prescription proposal, August 1997'. *Australian and New Zealand Journal of Public Health*, 24: 254–64.

Lindblom, C. E. (1959). 'The science of "muddling through"'. *Public Administration Review*, 19 (2): 79–88.

Lindblom, C. E. (1979). 'Still muddling, not yet through'. *Public Administration Review*, 39 (26): 517–26.

Lindblom, C. E. (1990). *Inquiry and Change. The troubled attempt to understand and shape society*. New Haven, CT: Yale University Press and Russell Sage Foundation.

Littlemore, R. (2010). 'Manufacturing doubt'. *New Scientist*, 206 (2760): 41.

Longford, S. (2008). 'Uncertainty in decision-making: intelligence as a solution'. In: Bammer, G. and Smithson, M. (eds). *Uncertainty and Risk: Multidisciplinary perspectives*. London: Earthscan, 219–30.

Mackey, J. (2008). 'Musical improvisation, creativity and uncertainty'. In: Bammer, G. and Smithson, M. (eds). *Uncertainty and Risk: Multidisciplinary perspectives*. London: Earthscan, 105–13.

Mandell, M. P. (ed.). (2001). *Getting Results through Collaboration. Networks and network structures for public policy and management*. Westport, CT: Quorum Books.

McCully, P. (2001). 'The use of a trilateral network: an activist's perspective on the formation of the World Commission on Dams'. *American University International Law Review*, 16 (6):1453-75.

McDonald, D., Bammer, G., Legge, D.G. and Sibthorpe, B.M. (1994). 'Service provision considerations for the evaluation of a heroin trial: a discussion paper'. In Issues for Designing and Evaluating a 'Heroin Trial': Three Discussion Papers. *Feasibility Research into the Controlled Availability of Opioids Stage 2 Working Paper Number 8*. Canberra: The Australian National University; <http://digitalcollections.anu.edu.au/bitstream/1885/41246/2/work8a.pdf> (accessed 30 July 2012).

McDonald, D., Bammer, G. and Deane, P. (2009). *Research Integration Using Dialogue Methods*. Canberra: ANU E-Press; <http://epress.anu.edu.au/dialogue_methods_citation>

McFadden, M., Lyon, R. and Pinsker, R. (2008). 'Uncertainty, terrorism and law enforcement'. In: Bammer, G. and Smithson, M. (eds). *Uncertainty and Risk: Multidisciplinary perspectives*. London: Earthscan, 261-8.

Michaelowa, A. and Koch, T. (2001). *Glossary of International Climate Policy Terms, Marrakesh Accords Edition*. Hamburg: Hamburgisches Welt-Wirtschafts-Archiv; <http://www.joanneum.at/encofor/publication/glossary_of_climate_policy.pdf> (accessed 4 January 2012).

Midgley, G. (2000). *Systemic Intervention: Philosophy, methodology, and practice*. New York: Kluwer Academic/Plenum Publishers.

Moore, D., Dray, A., Green, R., Hudson, S. L., Jenkinson, R., Siokou, C., Perez, P., Bammer, G., Maher, L. and Dietze, P. (2009). 'Extending drug ethno-epidemiology using agent-based modelling'. *Addiction*, 104: 1991–7.

Moore, M. (2008). 'Political practice: uncertainty, ethics and outcomes'. In: Bammer, G. and Smithson, M. (eds). *Uncertainty and Risk: Multidisciplinary perspectives*. London: Earthscan, 171–82.

Moore, M. H. (1995). *Creating Public Value. Strategic management in government*. Cambridge, MA: Harvard University Press.

Moore, M. H. and Hartmann, F. X. (1999). On the theory and practice of 'Executive Sessions'. Unpublished manuscipt; <http://www.hks.harvard.edu/var/ezp_site/storage/fckeditor/file/pdfs/centers-programs/programs/criminal-justice/exec_sessions_theory.pdf> (accessed 18 December 2011).

Mouzos, J. (1999). 'Firearm-related violence: the impact of the nationwide agreement on firearms'. *Trends and Issues in Crime and Criminal Justice*,

Number 116. Canberra: Australian Institute of Criminology; <http://aic.gov.au/en/publications/current%20series/tandi/101-120.aspx> (accessed 25 October 2011).

Murray, C. J. L., Salomon, J. A. and Mathers, C. (2000). 'A critical examination of summary measures of population health'. *Bulletin of the World Health Organization*, 78 (8): 981–94.

Myers, I. B. with Myers, P. B. [1980] (1993). *Gifts Differing. Understanding personality type*. Palo Alto, CA: CPP Books.

Nagel, E. and Newman, J. R. [1959] (1964). *Godel's Proof*. London: Routledge and Kegan Paul.

National Institutes of Health State-of-the-Science Panel. (2006). 'National Institutes of Health State-of-the-Science Conference statement: tobacco use: prevention, cessation, and control'. *Annals of Internal Medicine*, 145 (11): 839–44.

Neuman, W. L. (2003). *Social Research Methods. Qualitative and quantitative approaches*. Boston: Allyn and Bacon.

Newell, W. H. (ed.). (1998). *Interdisciplinarity. Essays from the literature*. New York: College Entrance Examination Board.

Nickerson, R. S. (1998). 'Confirmation bias: a ubiquitous phenomenon in many guises'. *Review of General Psychology*, 2 (2): 175–220.

Ostini, R., Bammer, G., Dance, P. R. and Goodin, R. E. (1993). 'The ethics of experimental heroin maintenance'. *Journal of Medical Ethics*, 19: 175–82.

O'Sullivan, K. (1994). *Understanding Ways. Communicating between cultures*. Sydney: Hale and Iremonger.

Passell, H. D., Tidwell, V. C., Conrad, S. H., Thomas, R. P. and Roach, J. (2003). *Cooperative Water Resources Modeling in the Middle Rio Grande Basin*. Albuquerque, NM: Sandia National Laboratories; <http://www.sandia.gov/water/docs/ID02_ModelingRioGrande.pdf> (accessed 3 January 2012).

Pickard, S. (2008). 'Uncertainty and religion: ten provisional theses'. In: Bammer, G. and Smithson, M. (eds). *Uncertainty and Risk: Multidisciplinary perspectives*. London: Earthscan, 55–69.

Plant, A. J. (2008). 'When action can't wait: investigating infectious disease outbreaks'. In: Bammer, G. and Smithson, M. (eds). *Uncertainty and Risk: Multidisciplinary perspectives*. London: Earthscan, 45–53.

Pohl, C. and Hirsch Hadorn, G. (2007a). 'Die Gestaltungsprinzipien für transdisziplinäre Forschung des td-net und ihre Bedeutung für die Evaluation'. In: Stoll-Kleemann, S. and Pohl, C. (eds). *Evaluation inter- und transdisziplinärer Forschung: Humanökologie und Nachhaltigkeitsforschung auf dem Prüfstand*. Muenchen: oekom, 173–93.

Pohl, C. and Hirsch Hadorn, G. (2007b). *Principles for Designing Transdisciplinary Research. Proposed by the Swiss Academies of Arts and Sciences*. Munich: oekom.

Pohl, C., van Kerkhoff, L., Hirsch Hadorn, G. and Bammer, G. (2008). 'Integration'. In: Hirsch Hadorn, G., Hoffmann-Riem, H., Biber-Klemm, S., Grossenbacher-Mansuy, W., Joye, D., Pohl, C., Wiesmann, U. and Zemp, E. (eds). *Handbook of Transdisciplinary Research*. Zurich: Springer, 411–26.

Quiggin, J. (2008). 'Economists and uncertainty'. In: Bammer, G. and Smithson, M. (eds). *Uncertainty and Risk: Multidisciplinary perspectives*. London: Earthscan, 196–203.

Ravetz, J. (2008). 'Preface'. In: Bammer, G. and Smithson, M. (eds). *Uncertainty and Risk: Multidisciplinary perspectives*. London: Earthscan, xiii–xvi.

Rayner, S. (2006). 'What drives environmental policy?'. *Global Environmental Change*, 16 (1): 4–6.

Reason, P. and Bradbury, H. (eds). (2001). *Handbook of Action Research: Participative inquiry and practice*. Thousand Oaks, CA: Sage.

Reed, J., Pearson, P., Douglas, B., Swinburne, S. and Wilding, H. (2002). 'Going home from hospital—an appreciative inquiry study'. *Health and Social Care in the Community*, 10 (1): 36–45.

Repko, A. F. (2008). *Interdisciplinary Research: Process and theory*. Los Angeles: Sage.

Rhodes, R. (1986). *The Making of the Atomic Bomb*. London: Simon and Schuster.

Ritter, A. (2008). 'Heroin: injected with uncertainty'. In: Bammer, G. and Smithson, M. (eds). *Uncertainty and Risk: Multidisciplinary perspectives*. London: Earthscan, 157–69.

Ritter, A. and Bammer, G. (2010). 'Models of policy-making and their relevance for drug research'. *Drug and Alcohol Review*, 29: 352–7.

Sabatier, P. A. (1988). 'An advocacy coalition framework of policy change and the role of policy-orientated learning therein'. *Policy Sciences*, 21 (2/3): 129–68.

Sabatier, P. A. and Weible, C. M. (2007). 'The advocacy coalition framework: innovations and clarifications'. In: Sabatier, P. A. (ed.). *Theories of the Policy Process*. Boulder, CO.: Westview, 189–220.

Sawer, M. (1990). *Sisters in Suits. Women and public policy in Australia*. Sydney: Allen and Unwin.

Scholz, R. W. (2011). *Environmental Literacy in Science and Society: From knowledge to decisions*. Cambridge: Cambridge University Press.

Scotton, R. B. (2000). 'Medibank: from conception to delivery and beyond'. *Medical Journal of Australia*, 173: 9–11; <http://www.mja.com.au/public/issues/173_01_030700/scotton1/scotton1.html> (accessed 3 January 2012).

Scudder, T. (2001). 'The World Commission on Dams and the need for a new development paradigm'. *Water Resources Development*, 17 (3): 329–41.

Senge, P. M. (1990). *The Fifth Discipline. The art and practice of the learning organisation*. London: Century Business.

Shergold, P. (2005). 'Book launch at annual symposium'. *Dialogue (Academy of the Social Sciences in Australia)*, 24 (3): 1–3; <http://www.assa.edu.au/publications/dialogue/2005_Vol24_No3.php> (accessed 6 December 2011).

Smeaton, D. (1997). Firearms and public policy. *Second National Outlook Symposium: Violent Crime, Property Crime and Public Policy*, 3–4 March, Canberra, ACT; <http://www.aic.gov.au/events/aic%20upcoming%20events/1997/outlook97.aspx> (accessed 25 October 2011).

Smithson, M. (1989). *Ignorance and Uncertainty. Emerging paradigms*. New York: Springer Verlag.

Smithson, M. (2008a). 'The many faces and masks of uncertainty'. In: Bammer, G. and Smithson, M. (eds). *Uncertainty and Risk: Multidisciplinary perspectives*. London: Earthscan, 13–25.

Smithson, M. (2008b). 'Psychology's ambivalent view of uncertainty'. In: Bammer, G. and Smithson, M. (eds). *Uncertainty and Risk: Multidisciplinary perspectives*. London: Earthscan, 205–17.

Smithson, M., Bammer, G. and The Goolabri Group. (2008). 'Coping and managing under uncertainty'. In: Bammer, G. and Smithson, M. (eds). *Uncertainty and Risk: Multidisciplinary perspectives*. London: Earthscan, 321–33.

Stankey, G. H., Clark, R. N. and Bormann, B. T. (2005). *Adaptive Management of Natural Resources: Theory, concepts, and management institutions*. General

Technical Report PNW-GTR-654. Portland, Oregon.: US Department of Agriculture, Forest Service, Pacific Northwest Research Station; <http://www.fs.fed.us/pnw/pubs/pnw_gtr654.pdf> (accessed 14 December 2011).

Stokols, D., Hall, K. L., Taylor, B. K., Moser, R. P. and Syme, S. L. (eds). (2008). 'The science of team science. Assessing the value of transdisciplinary research'. *American Journal of Preventive Medicine*, 35 (Supplement 2): S77–252.

Sulston, J. and Ferry, G. (2002). *The Common Thread. A story of science, politics, ethics and the human genome*. London: Bantam Press.

Tversky, A. and Kahneman, D. (1974). 'Judgment under uncertainty: heuristics and biases'. *Science*, 185 (4157): 1124–31.

Uren, T. (1994). *Straight Left*. Sydney: Random House.

Ury, W. (1993). *Getting Past No. Negotiating your way from confrontation to cooperation*. New York: Bantam Books.

Van Asselt, M. B. A., Rotmans, J. and Greeuw, S. C. H. (2001). *Puzzle-Solving for Policy. A provisional handbook for Integrated Assessment*. Maastricht: International Centre for Integrative Studies (ICIS).

Venter, J. C. (2007). *A Life Decoded. My genome: my life*. London: Penguin.

Wackernagel, M. and Rees, W. E. (1996). *Our Ecological Footprint: Reducing human impact on the earth*. Gabriola Island, British Columbia: New Society Publishers.

Walsh, R. A. and Sanson-Fisher, R. W. (1994). 'What universities do about tobacco industry research funding'. *Tobacco Control*, 3: 308–15.

Winer, M. and Ray, K. (1994). *Collaboration Handbook. Creating, sustaining and enjoying the journey*. Saint Paul, Minnesota: Amherst H. Wilder Foundation.

World Commission on Dams. (2000). *Dams and Development: A new framework for decision-making*. London: Earthscan; <http://hqweb.unep.org/dams/WCD/report/WCD_DAMS%20report.pdf> (accessed 5 December 2011).

Wright, T. S. A. (2006). 'Giving "teeth" to an environmental policy: a Delphi study at Dalhousie University'. *Journal of Cleaner Production*, 14 (9–11): 761–8.

Commentaries

35. Rationale and Key Themes

The invited commentaries that follow are designed to kick-start further conversations and debate as a first step in widespread discussion to progress thinking about the practicalities of undertaking more effective research on complex real-world problems. If there is to be a discipline of I2S (or even just a storehouse of concepts, methods, case studies and guides to relevant knowledge for researching complex real-world problems), it is going to require a large, committed group to carry the ideas forward—to reshape, rework and refine them. To do this effectively, group members will need to engage with each other, as well as to hear the views of distinguished senior scholars and leaders of research organisations. At this time, there is no obvious forum where that interaction can occur, especially not one where the full diversity of pertinent and important viewpoints can readily connect.

The choice of commentators was influenced by the desire to engage a broad range of individuals and networks. When issuing the invitation to contribute, I provided a brief rationale for the selection of that individual[1] and often suggested areas where their views would be particularly valuable,[2] although they were encouraged to cover any topics they thought would promote productive discussion. They were also invited to address one or more of the following questions.

1. If you had $1 million to spend, which of the proposals in this book would you fund to be further developed?

2. What is the book's greatest weakness and how could it be addressed?

3. Who do you think should be encouraged to be involved in the ongoing discussion about I2S?

4. How do you see yourself in relation to I2S?

I tried to make it clear that I was not looking for endorsement or a 'puff piece', but rather honest, constructive appraisal that would move thinking forward. Further, because the book does not discuss in detail related initiatives like transdisciplinarity or the science of team science, relevant commentators were also invited to discuss what is proposed here in light of their own work on these topics.[3]

---

1   Some invitees combined their efforts and others included co-workers as co-authors.

2   A footnote summarises the specific invitation to each commentator. While the person did not necessarily address these issues, I have included the information because it gives context for many of the commentaries. More information about my relationship with the contributors is provided in 'The book's origins and acknowledgments' section of the Preface.

3   Although proponents of most of the major approaches were invited to contribute, some of them were not able to do so, so that there is no representative of a number of these specific approaches.

About half of the invitees contributed and I am extremely grateful for their thoughtful insights. The commentary process occurred in two stages. The initial six commentators—Daniel Walker, Deborah O'Connell (and colleagues), Michael Smithson, Alison Ritter, Alice Roughley and Lawrence Cram—responded to the first full draft of the book produced in early 2010. Their inputs confirmed that the commentaries would be a strong addition to the book. I was pleased that some of the second group, who wrote their commentaries based on a book draft reworked in 2010–11, also responded to the original six contributions. I continued to edit the book to improve clarity during the second commentary phase. The commentators had an opportunity to review the final version of the book and to make amendments.[4]

Unsurprisingly the commentaries reflect the diversity of the respondents. Because there are no straightforward ways to group all the contributions, I decided to present them in the order they were received. Overall, the commentaries reflect excitement about the challenges the book tackles, agreement that this area of endeavour has a significant (albeit scattered) body of work to celebrate and build on, the feeling that the time is ripe, and willingness to engage in the contest of ideas in order to find productive ways to improve the research contribution to addressing complex real-world problems.

In the remainder of this chapter, I present five themes, each of which ran through several of the contributions. The first is the importance of keeping the development of I2S grounded in research practice—a topic on which there was agreement. The second crosscutting theme covers the challenges in one area of research practice—namely the third domain, '*Providing integrated research support for policy and practice change*', which provoked considerable discussion and a variety of views. The proposal that I2S should be a new discipline was also an area of debate and this intersected with input about the theoretical base of this endeavour. These are encompassed as the third theme. The fourth reports on suggestions about institutional arrangements, where there was accord about their importance, but not about ways forward. The final theme pulls together issues relevant to progressing the I2S Development Drive, particularly methods and areas to search, and major suggestions for further work, including ideas for how to spend $1 million.

It is impossible to write a synthesis that includes every nugget of insight contained in the commentaries. The main task now is to find ways to continue the exchange, so that all the gems can be considered. It would be particularly productive to expand the discussion forums to include other integrative applied research practitioners, as well as theorists in this and related areas, for the large-scale exchange of experiences and ideas.

---

4 Further changes—editing for clarity, rather than substantive—were made in light of the comments of the anonymous reviewers.

Keeping I2S Grounded in Research Practice

In the opening commentary, Daniel Walker argues that I2S will only be useful if there is a fertile interplay between theory and practice; if the frameworks, concepts and methods provide those undertaking integrative applied research with better approaches and tools *and* if the investigation-based experience of the research practitioners influences the building of new theory and the sharpening of that which already exists. In his proposal that philosophy could help build the theoretical base for I2S, Michael O'Rourke puts forward a similar proposition, as does Michael Smithson with his suggestion that decision science ('the bastard offspring of psychology, probability theory and behavioural economics') provides a useful model for the development of I2S, especially because it has a 'descriptive branch' (that is, practitioners) that actively debates with its 'prescriptive branch' (that is, theoreticians).

The point is strongly reinforced by the case studies that form the basis of some of the contributions—in particular, those by Deborah O'Connell and colleagues, Ted Lefroy, Budi Haryanto and Merritt Polk. Merritt Polk wrote her commentary when she was two years into her investigation, Deborah O'Connell when her team's program of work was four to five years old, and Ted Lefroy and Budi Haryanto reflected on completed investigations. These accounts provide a richness and level of detail that are essential complements to the theoretical framework. Some of them also describe the value of the structured approach provided by the I2S framework in making explicit their actions based on collective experience, intuition and serendipity, as well as giving them greater appreciation of what they did well and where there were gaps and areas for improvement. Fasihuddin, in his reflections on applying the I2S framework, echoes that view.

More particularly, the cases demonstrate how practical experience will aid the further development of I2S. Let me give three examples. One is that they illustrate different structural approaches to integrative applied research. Deborah O'Connell outlines how her team embedded disciplinary, multidisciplinary, interdisciplinary and transdisciplinary sub-projects, with important roles played by two classes of integrators: conceptual integrators, and data, model and platform integrators. In his project, Ted Lefroy set up specific teams for 'knowledge integration' and 'knowledge broking' to work with five 'knowledge discovery' teams. Merritt Polk describes the principles that govern the intense negotiation required to establish her transdisciplinary investigation. A second input comes from the description of specific concepts, methods and tactics, such as Merritt Polk alerting us to useful terms coined by others, specifically 'agonistic' interactions and 'optimal ambiguity', as well as Budi Haryanto's strategies for capturing media attention. The final example is reinforcement of the importance of 'people factors'. Ted Lefroy argues that the I2S framework needs to place much more emphasis on the importance of 'social cohesion, collaboration and personal and professional satisfaction'. His proposal is bolstered by results from a survey of the various participants in his project. The point is also made strongly by Deborah O'Connell, who further warns that '[i]t is easy to discuss "assembling a team"…as if it were as simple as going shopping; however, the reality…is quite different.'

There is clearly scope for fertile interchange between those developing the I2S framework and those undertaking various forms of integrative applied research. In the first instance this will involve reflections on completed or ongoing work, which can be at varying levels of detail, as the commentaries illustrate. Fasihuddin raises the acid test that I2S will face as it matures: will it be useful prospectively? While there are encouraging signs that I2S can help people reflect on accomplishments, will it add value in planning and executing new integrative applied research? Deborah O'Connell and Merritt Polk foreshadow that the guidance provided by the framework and the training of a cadre of researchers will make new investigations more efficient and effective, but that aim has still to be tested.

The Challenges of Providing Integrated Research Support for Policy and Practice Change

Three different but intersecting issues are raised in the commentaries: conducting research in highly political environments, differentiating between adoption and use, and the benefits and costs of close engagement between researchers and end users. Let us deal with each in turn.

The sorts of complex real-world problems integrative applied research and I2S set out to tackle are generally political and the challenge of conducting research in a highly contested environment is addressed in four of the commentaries (by Alison Ritter, Lawrence Cram, Howard Gadlin and Michelle Bennett, and Michael Wesley) and highlighted as an issue that needs more attention in two others (by David Brown and Simon Bronitt). Although these issues are relevant to all three arenas (government, business and civil society), most of the commentaries focused on the first. A major challenge is what Michael Wesley calls 'a crumbling divide between politics and policy', where 'the domain of objective policy analysis and actions has been dragged into that of values-based contestation and the contending of absolute knowledge claims'. Lawrence Cram puts it a little differently as 'the risk of cynical exploitation of the academy'. He suggests that while academics see competing evidence and ideas as 'an essential feature of the discovery, construction and reframing of knowledge', partisan politics eschews these niceties. These commentators recognise that (again, quoting Michael Wesley) 'politics intrudes on both sides of the I2S equation': first in a political contest over how to define and attack the problem and later in interpreting the proposed solution. Although the commentaries are similar in defining the challenge, they come to different conclusions.

Michael Wesley urges an expansion of the I2S framework to grapple more specifically with these issues. Lawrence Cram suggests a partial way forward in a 'gate-keeping and filtering' role for I2S specialists so that research teams avoid spending valuable effort on 'wrongly stated and prioritised problems, or on unworthy causes'. Alison Ritter argues that the I2S approach 'dissolves' what she refers to as the 'researcher–advocacy delineation/impasse', not only by making implementation 'core business' as the third domain, but also by the process of engaging all stakeholders and identifying beneficiaries at the start, dealing with values and value congruence, as well as boundaries and scoping, and by paying specific attention to unknowns. Further, being part of a discipline provides access not only to concepts and methods for undertaking these tasks, but also to peer review and the ability to differentiate scholarly from political criticism. Howard Gadlin and Michelle Bennett strongly disagree. They take particular issue with Alison Ritter's suggestion that the researcher–advocacy dilemma is dissolved, arguing that it is not and ought not be, as it 'provides the creative tensions necessary for democratic policy decision-making processes'.

Alice Roughley and Ian Elsum take a different tack. Alice Roughley maintains that supporting policy and practice change should provide the overarching rationale for the whole framework and points out that discussion of how researchers might recommend a particular course of action for policy or practice change is missing. Ian Elsum embellishes this point by presenting useful lessons from the work that has been undertaken on innovation and applied research in distinguishing between adoption and use—namely:

> Adoption—the willingness and ability to take research results and convert them into something that is useable more broadly—and use by others apart from the adopter must be considered separately as they are distinct processes: the factors causing a person or organisation to adopt research results and incorporate them into an artefact, service or advice will differ in many important ways from those factors pertinent to a person or organisation deciding to use the artefact, service or advice.

He also describes the challenges researchers face when they find themselves in situations that are inherently chaotic and defy ordering, and where less-than-perfect solutions are acceptable, as long as they are workable.

Other commentators contend that I2S needs to pay more attention to the relationships with policy makers and practitioners (who are often referred to as 'end users'). There is a strong push by Ted Lefroy and Linda Neuhauser for greater recognition to be given to the benefits for eventual research implementation of close engagement and co-production of knowledge between researchers and end users. Merritt Polk and Christian Pohl take this as a given in the transdisciplinary research they describe. Simon Bronitt presents a different angle in arguing for the embedding of end users in research projects to overcome three challenges for bridging the cultural divide between the research and the policy and practice worlds: 'understanding the intrinsic difficulty of doing good research', 'accepting equivocal research findings' and 'government preference for consultancy-driven policy'. He also worries about 'New Public Management' and narrow models of accountability, which operate 'as a straitjacket for the research as well as the policy and practice communities'.

Still others—in particular, Catherine Lyall and Alice Roughley—raise cautions. Catherine Lyall submits that it may be difficult to maintain impartiality and confidentiality, avoid being immersed in stakeholder concerns and overcome impatience at the time taken to achieve research results. She is also concerned about outcomes if end users have a role in evaluating the research, particularly if they do not understand research goals, norms and methods. In her mind, the danger is that integrative applied research is consigned to short-term problem solving and a service role, unable to compete effectively against 'problem portable knowledge'. Although Alice Roughley generally supports an engaged approach, she points to lessons from social impact assessment, which reinforce the risks of cooption.

The broad issue of research implementation is not only pertinent to integrative applied research and I2S, but is also a topic of conversation, analysis and investigation in its own right in several applied areas: certainly in those that I know moderately well (medicine and other health, the environment, and policing and security). It is striking that the relatively small number of commentaries in this book, written largely independently, have advanced many of the key arguments and debating points. As they demonstrate, there is still a long way to go to achieve consensus and a clear way forward.

I2S as a Discipline and the Need for a Stronger Theoretical Base

There are two primary sets of arguments in this theme: concerns about proposing the formation of a new I2S discipline and suggestions about the work that is required to establish such a discipline. In addition, there are several comments about the immature state of I2S at this stage—well summarised by Linda Neuhauser, who maintains that to be a discipline I2S needs 'a stronger theoretical foundation, better-defined methods and rigorous testing in multiple contexts'. Daniel Walker takes this further, contending that additional work is required to demonstrate a convincing case that I2S is 'a legitimate, viable and useful discipline', and Alison Ritter asks whether I2S 'must be dealt with as a whole discipline or whether researchers and practitioners can cherry-pick the components that are most helpful or useful to them at that point in time'.

Some oppose the notion of an I2S discipline. Ted Lefroy suggests that it is 'further complicating an already challenging area by attempting to define it as a discipline with an unfriendly name with an inaccessible acronym'.[5] Christian Pohl recalls a highly charged reaction when the idea was first presented at a conference, wondering '[w]hat deep convictions had been disturbed by the idea of a specialisation in collaborative research processes for policy-relevant research?'. Marcel Bursztyn and Maria Beatriz Maury argue that there are major differences from disciplines, especially that '[i]nterdisciplinary programs… are multiform and nonlinear spaces of integration. Shaped largely in reaction to problem-oriented demands, these programs have, by definition, a complex identity'.

Later, they state:

> … we strongly caution against turning interdisciplinarity into a discipline. Interdisciplinarity is a process; it can constitute specific fields, and even lead to the formation of epistemic communities with their own identities. But there will be no integration if the processes of institutionalisation follow the previous practices of creating university departments. We do not oppose formal interdisciplinary arrangements, but we see these as opening a space where complex problems can be addressed by teams comprising researchers with varied backgrounds.

Others also express unease based on the history of established disciplines. In particular, Daniel Walker and Ian Elsum echo my concerns about I2S becoming self-referential rather than engaged (with Ian Elsum providing examples of ways other than forming a discipline to share knowledge and learning), while Howard Gadlin and Michelle Bennett worry about 'the elitist assumption that those who know the most know the best'.

---

5   Ted Lefroy argues strongly against both the I2S acronym, which he sees as a 'barrier to communication', and moving away from the use of the term interdisciplinarity to the more specific nomenclature proposed. On the latter point, he contends: 'Interdisciplinary research is awkward enough as an umbrella term, but most researchers and many research users can understand what is meant: people from different disciplines working together. Sure, it can and does involve more than that, but the more we get involved in subtleties the more inaccessible we make what is an enabling practice.'

Some suggest that a discipline is the wrong construct. In particular, Michael O'Rourke, Michael Wesley and Julie Thompson Klein suggest that I2S is bigger than, and/or different from, a discipline, respectively referring to it as 'an umbrella area covering a number of more or less loosely connected disciplines' ('as biological science is to microbiology and evolutionary biology'), a potential 'metadiscipline' and an 'interdiscipline'. Julie Thompson Klein adds that this term does not 'acknowledge the "interprofessional" dimensions of practice', but 'at least takes into account the relevance of not only disciplines but also interdisciplinary fields and networks as well as the interfaces of disciplinary, interdisciplinary and professional spheres'.

Howard Gadlin and Michelle Bennett express disquiet about the idea of setting out to create a discipline rather than letting it emerge naturally. They point out what they see as a flaw arising from the construction—namely a fundamental incommensurability at the heart of the three domains, which they argue makes it impossible for I2S to be a discipline. In particular, they contend:

> We do not doubt that one can develop processes for setting policy or making crucial decisions that involve people from the three domains (science, advocacy and policy), but we believe that the challenge in doing this is very different from the challenge of integrating multiple scientific disciplines and methodologies into an inter- or trans-disciplinary field. I2S is an attempt to bring together components that are incommensurable and we believe that any approach for dealing with incommensurability must be based on acknowledging and maintaining the distinctiveness.

Alison Ritter and Michael O'Rourke would like to see justification for the selection of the three domains and the five questions that are used to address them. Daniel Walker raises a connected issue in asking for I2S to be mapped against the areas that cover associated terrains, such as multi-, inter- and trans-disciplinary research, action research, planning and management, and the science of team science. He suggests that it will be helpful in achieving clarity about where the contest of ideas will play out. Christian Pohl starts to do exactly this in his comparison of transdisciplinarity with I2S, proposing that, among many similarities, unknowns and the importance of theory are useful points of differentiation.

Glenn Withers addresses a more fundamental concern relevant to integrative applied research rather than I2S. He argues that any attempt to modify interdisciplinarity must be 'clear and precise on what the counterpart, "disciplinarity", is'. He goes on to say:

> The point is important because the fact is that disciplinary boundaries, their subjects and methods are dynamic and blurred, partly from

internal evolution as knowledge advances and sometimes because of the tensions emanating from the reasons interdisciplinarity is sought. One possibility is that disciplines are indeed dynamically interdisciplinary—but that interdisciplinarity emerges from a micro-evolution, bottom-up approach and often implicitly rather than explicitly. As weaknesses or opportunities for innovation emerge in present research within disciplines, researchers seek to adjust assumptions, methods and topics to embrace these…Sometimes intellectual curiosity seeks a more 'big bang' answer. Correspondingly in the Bammer project interdisciplinarity is top down rather than merely incrementalist. It wants overview, taxonomy, method and impact all at once as its overarching ambition. This is no mean ambition. Such a macro-approach can give context and connection in ways that iterative research evolution may not, except by serendipity. The ideal might be in the end for the macro-approach to have micro-foundations, and thus blend the incremental with the bigger picture.

Let us now move on to suggestions about the work that would be required to establish I2S as a discipline, focusing on the commentaries provided by Lawrence Cram, Michael Smithson and Michael O'Rourke.

Lawrence Cram considers where I2S 'fits', suggesting that it is located at the intersection of the human and the design sciences (also known as 'the sciences of the artificial'): 'I2S is a human science since it entails interpersonal and inter-group interactions, and a science of the artificial since it leads to the creation of symbols, objects, services and environments by and for humans.'

He also suggests that as well as having much to learn from the design sciences, the evolution in sociology in understanding relationships between publics and academics—especially in 'public, policy, professional and critical sociologies'—has useful lessons for I2S.

Michael Smithson also reflects on lessons that other disciplines can provide. In particular, he points out the limitations in using statistics as an analogy for I2S and, as discussed earlier, submits that the decision sciences provide a useful template for the further development of I2S. He overlaps with Glenn Withers in suggesting that the development of I2S 'would include histories of relations among disciplines and subject areas. These histories influence the current relations among the disciplines concerned, and thereby affect the potential for integrative applied research that involves those disciplines.' He describes a number of additional tasks that are included in the last theme.

Third, Michael O'Rourke recommends engaging philosophy to explore whether I2S has a 'secure conceptual foundation'. He goes on to say that '[a] good disciplinary theory should satisfy two desiderata: a) supply a systematic conceptual foundation for the discipline that unifies its questions, methods and confirmation standards, and b) frame the disciplinary problem space in ways that are productive of new questions and insights.

He also foreshadows the contributions philosophy could make to analysing major I2S concepts:

> We can use the standard, three-part distinction of philosophy into epistemology, metaphysics and axiology to help classify these. Within epistemology some concepts will concern more local aspects of integrative applied research practice, such as the relationship among the six identified ways of dealing with unknowns, while others will concern topics of exogenous interest to philosophers, such as the prospects for reasonable disagreement in integrative applied research…Many issues of theoretical interest will fall under the banner of metaphysics, including those related to the disparate scales that figure into integration and implementation, the character of emergent phenomena in complex systems, and the ontological status of various boundary objects used to effect synthesis and integration. With respect to axiology…'dealing with values'…will be an important topic for philosophical theory. Ethical considerations will come into play across the trajectory of integration and implementation, as will issues of advocacy, bias and cultural variation. Philosophical attention to these topics and many others will be an important part of theoretical development of an enterprise such as I2S.

He also considers how the principal I2S concepts might be melded together into a foundation for a discipline, undertaking preliminary analysis on the ideas of 'synthesis' and 'integration'. He proposes that the current distinction could be improved by re-conceptualising where stakeholders fit using three classifications: disciplinary, translational and professional.

To conclude, let us return to the hesitation about an I2S discipline. It is particularly worth noting that this does not signify satisfaction with the status quo, but rather questioning if establishing a new discipline is the best way to overcome the fragmentation and marginalisation that beset integrative applied research. There is widespread support for strengthening the practice of integrative applied research through more structure, more formal arrangements and defining 'epistemic communities' or 'communities of practice'. As Julie Thompson Klein says, positing I2S as a discipline 'underscores the need for a robust structure that is more than an add-on to existing ones'.

Institutional Factors

As the conclusion to the previous theme highlights, enhancing the research contribution to tackling complex real-world problems in a way that is embedded in the academic mainstream remains an ongoing challenge. One option is to organise the research so that it fits with existing institutional structures and reward systems, which is part of the intent of proposing an I2S discipline. Another is to change the institutional structures and reward systems. And, of course, combining elements of these two strategies also has potential. In this theme, I have identified the countries the commentators work in because, although there are general pervasive concerns, they play out differently in specific country contexts.

Based on her empirical research in the United Kingdom, Catherine Lyall lays out many of the key institutional constraints: difficulties in agreeing on quality and hence undertaking effective evaluation; inability to identify suitable peers to act as reviewers; inconsistency and lack of follow-through in funding priorities; challenges in developing effective teamwork when members have different restrictions on their contributions depending on their home departments and organisations; and risks for building a career. While the details vary, Duane Nellis describes the same categories of problems in the United States. Marcel Bursztyn and Maria Beatriz Maury from Brazil and Alison Ritter, Deborah O'Connell and colleagues and Glenn Withers from Australia make some of the same points, with Deborah O'Connell adding the challenge of finding appropriate journals to publish in. The focus on publishing in highly ranked journals as primary measures of quality and prestige is a particular concern and described for the United Kingdom (Catherine Lyall), the United States (David Brown) and Australia (Deborah O'Connell and colleagues, Alison Ritter and Michael Wesley).[6]

So how can we advance? Do we need to move outside universities? Both Alice Roughley in Australia and David Brown in the United States submit that the best work is currently happening in other institutions, including think tanks and consulting firms. David Brown goes on to say that the evolution of I2S 'will depend substantially on how and with whom it defines its bases of legitimacy and standards of accountability', adding: 'Legitimacy can be grounded in normative, legal, technical, political, cognitive or associational terms with a wide range of stakeholders; accountability refers to answering expectations established with more specific stakeholders, such as those affected by or affecting particular research or practice programs'; and concluding with: 'it will be important to develop ideas about indicators of I2S performance as a basis for assessing its

---

6   Catherine Lyall, Alison Ritter and Glenn Withers see hope in the development of new assessment criteria based on impact.

impacts and enabling its accountability to immediate stakeholders, for building its legitimacy with wider publics, and for catalysing ongoing learning in the field. These raise clear challenges for how universities currently operate.

Glenn Withers from Australia proposes 'creating the new university', arguing that universities are enduring and useful, but significant reform is needed because 'there is nothing in the disciplinary research enterprise that ensures comprehensive coverage of the knowledge needs of human kind'. Both Glenn Withers and Ian Elsum (also from Australia) point to the important links between research and teaching, with Ian Elsum arguing not only that existing research organisations have a responsibility to foster integrative applied research, but also that '[u]niversities have a particular responsibility because students, both graduate and undergraduate, must experience learning across disciplines as well as within the specialisations of traditional disciplines'. Marcel Bursztyn and Maria Beatriz Maury add to this by highlighting the challenge of building new models of research and teaching at the same time as implementing them.

Others suggest changes that are less radical than those Glenn Withers proposes, building on current developments within existing structures. From his vantage point as a highly sympathetic university president, Duane Nellis provides insights into how change happens and the importance of having successful programs and projects to build on. The available expertise has to match the desire to do things differently:

> Facilitating strategies and mechanisms for interdisciplinarity and environments for I2S will require alternative administrative structures and leadership throughout every level of the university, with appropriate investment, infrastructural support and reward structures. Certainly, central and college-level advocacy and support are crucial, but without interdisciplinarity and facilitation of I2S percolating at the faculty level, such efforts will not work in the environment of a complex public research university…

New funding can help lubricate reform and being able to piggyback on other initiatives is helpful. Both he and Catherine Lyall point to the importance of advocacy at all levels.

Duane Nellis is looking to establish a 'School of Interdisciplinary Studies', which is in line with Lawrence Cram's proposition that in Australia

> [t]he normal pathway for an emergent discipline in the modern university is to acquire initial formal recognition through formation as a 'centre' or 'institute' or 'network' either within or between existing academic disciplinary units. If the centre prospers in an academic sense, through growth in educational and/or research attention, the university

will likely find ways to support growing independence. Colonisation of affiliated disciplines can occur and will support rapid growth; legitimacy in an academic sense requires emergence of similar disciplinary foci in several universities.

An associated point of leverage is to concentrate on sympathetic areas of activity. Linda Neuhauser from the United States proposes public health as the 'platform on which to build and test the I2S concepts', as public health is home to researchers from many disciplines and provides compelling examples of how research linked to practice can result in improved wellbeing for the community at large. She suggests:

> Public health is one of the most interdisciplinary disciplines both within and outside the university. Schools of public health include faculty trained in medicine, sociology, public policy, business, psychology, anthropology, biology, communication, education, economics, law, environmental science, architecture, city planning, government and many other fields, and joint appointments with other disciplinary schools are common. In addition, many public health academics not only have expertise in research, but also in practice with government, communities, policy institutes, and/or the private sector…Because public health problems intersect biological, behavioural, environmental and other domains, they are inherently complex to understand and to address.

Glenn Withers submits that the environmental sciences are where initiatives relevant to integrative applied research and I2S are currently playing out and that they are a litmus test for whether universities can adapt to new research forms.

Taking a different perspective, Holly Falk-Krzesinski proposes that the new and growing cadre of research development professionals provides a group of potential I2S specialists and that they would both benefit from and contribute to the further development of I2S. Such professionals are increasingly being employed in US universities to catalyse and facilitate team-based research. Initially their role was to help produce funding applications, but they are now often embedded as integral members of the team. Holly Falk-Krzesinski particularly highlights their strengths in working with stakeholders, dealing with unknowns and engaging with policy makers and practitioners, adding:

> Trained as a class of I2S specialists, research development professionals could help funders and stakeholders navigate the limitations academicians bring to partnerships. Moreover, they could provide professional development and training for faculty and university

leadership in basic I2S concepts and methods to enable them to gain a better understanding of considering unknowns in their research and the most effective mechanisms for extending their findings.

Nevertheless, their designation as 'servant leaders' who do not initiate or head research programs provides a reminder of a concern raised by Catherine Lyall that these skills are often relegated to a service role and therefore not valued. Ted Lefroy from Australia provides a complementary perspective, reporting that conceiving knowledge integration (as well as spatial analysis and social research) in a service role in his project was a mistake as it under-represented 'the primary research contribution of these teams to the collaboration. This distinction influenced relationships between teams and presented obstacles to progress that had some negative implications evident throughout the course of the project.'

Regardless of the merits of Holly Falk-Krzesinski's proposal, fleshing out specialist roles and competencies can provide a helpful focus for discussion, as Christian Pohl points out, and leads to the question Daniel Walker raises: 'what new dynamics (for better and for worse) will such specialists introduce into the practice of integration and implementation?'

Finally, in a different take on institutionalisation, Julie Thompson Klein challenges us to join the modern era and establish a 'prominent virtual presence'. She sees this as a critical component of the large-scale and widespread engagement required to overcome current marginalisation and fragmentation.

As these commentaries illustrate, there is an important discussion to be had about how much and exactly how we need to change the research (and teaching) landscape. Whatever changes are made, there are unlikely to be perfect solutions—a point well illustrated by Deborah O'Connell and colleagues. The organisation in which they work, Australia's CSIRO, moved to a matrix structure to make it easier for those with specialist skills to contribute to various flagship projects tackling major national priorities; but for the on-the-ground research program manager, the flexible structure still does not translate easily into the formation of viable productive teams. It is important, therefore, to ground discussion about requisite institutional changes in experience: building on successes, overcoming problems and always keeping in mind realistic targets given that perfection is impossible.

Moving the I2S Development Drive Forward

The point of the I2S Development Drive is to build a storehouse of concepts, methods and cases, as well as guides to relevant knowledge from outside I2S.

This involves finding, gathering, organising and classifying, making accessible and encouraging use. While the Development Drive was conceived as a way of building the I2S discipline, the idea of strengthening and systematising research practice for investigating complex real-world problems has support, even among those who eschew the notion of a disciplinary base. Julie Thompson Klein summarises the issues:

> [R]esources are under-utilised, cross-fertilisations foreshortened and progress in establishing an identifiable field stalled by fragmentation and marginalisation. The fragility and vulnerability of local projects and programs mirror this problem at the level of individuals and teams. Ill-informed definitions, shallow practices and inappropriate criteria for evaluation also prevail.

She adds later: 'the price of waiting is high, impeding progress at a critical moment in the host of problems in need of integrative applied research.'

David Brown also describes the significance of moving beyond immediate processes and particular problems to thinking 'about the long-term, large-scale implications…for developing a new field', and Christian Pohl notes the 'magnitude of the scientific endeavour we are talking about—one that requires big money, a lot of brain power and the engagement of a wide range of scholars'.

There were many helpful suggestions for how to proceed, which form the basis of this final theme. I deal first with specific suggestions for how the search could be undertaken and areas where relevant materials are likely to be found. I do not reiterate the importance of learning from cases or summarise the resources developed by many of the contributors themselves. These must also be gathered in the I2S Development Drive. I then move on to bigger-picture issues, especially how contributors would spend $1 million and other large-scale ideas for moving I2S forward.

Let us begin with how to undertake the I2S Development Drive. Julie Thompson Klein reminds us about the boom in advanced database search tools that can assist in finding relevant concepts, methods and case studies. These can help tackle the problem of the 'scatter' of relevant materials throughout the published and grey literatures and can provide outcomes better than the simple Google and Wikipedia searches many resort to. Her encouragement to establish a 'prominent virtual presence' is necessary not only for institutionalisation of I2S, but also to find useful undocumented materials for the Development Drive. Christian Pohl adds to this, proposing that theory should guide priorities for 'what empty spaces in the storehouse's shelves are the most relevant to fill with concepts, methods, case examples and guides'.

If we now move on to what needs to be collected and areas that may provide useful materials: one important aspect is gathering practical theories about different ways of thinking about integration and implementation (this is different from the theory underpinning I2S discussed above). David Brown suggests that the following fields will be helpful: 'ecology preservation, peace building or rights-based development', as well as '[e]xisting research and theory about bringing together diverse groups for joint action, such as public–private partnerships'. Linda Neuhauser points to applicable models from public health, such as 'Stokol's use of analytical, organisational and geographic dimensions' and 'Sussman and colleagues' emphasis on cyclical phases of interdisciplinary and implementation activity'. Christian Pohl notes the lively debate about theory within transdisciplinarity, especially regarding concepts for the co-production of knowledge and the inclusion of stakeholders.

While the focus of these commentators is on theory, others have suggested areas useful for methods and case studies as well. Alice Roughley points to the 'large literature on community engagement, participatory research methods and research adoption', as well as practical experiences that can be learnt from professionals 'working in areas such as human relations, evaluation, risk analysis, Indigenous health, natural resource management, and social and environmental impact assessment', as well as 'community, social and international development and social geography'. In advancing his argument to increase attention to social cohesion, Ted Lefroy proposes that '[l]eadership, project management and internal communication methods all contribute to this and are areas in which we could all learn'.

Howard Gadlin and Michelle Bennett highlight 'a considerable amount of theorising, thinking and activity directed towards creating decision-making processes for controversial, multi-party issues and conflicts that require cooperation and collaboration among groups of people quite disparate in values, perspective, culture, power and just about every dimension of identity you can list'. They specifically point to lessons from academia (such as the work of the German philosopher Jürgen Habermas) and from various government and non-government organisations, as well as from the fields of collaborative governance and negotiated rule making. In addition, although they use it to bolster their arguments about problems with an I2S discipline because of incommensurability, Howard Gadlin and Michelle Bennett's descriptions of the US National Institutes of Health Consensus Development Program and the recommendations of the US Bipartisan Policy Committee (presented in Box 53.1) can also be seen as providing ideas for dealing with conflicts of interest and bias in I2S.

Linda Neuhauser points to other lessons from the US National Institutes of Health, suggesting that evaluations of transdisciplinary research they have funded could also provide valuable concepts, methods and cases. Michael Smithson recommends

> accounts of stakeholder perspectives and responses to research processes and outputs, and how researchers and stakeholders understand and manage unknowns. Both of these sub-areas could be built up initially by borrowing heavily from relevant disciplines and research areas (for example, political and social sciences re stakeholders and decision sciences re management of unknowns), but there would still be considerable work to be done by descriptive I2S scholars and researchers.

He then goes on to provide a number of useful suggestions for expanding ways of considering unknowns.

There are also a number of proposals for areas that need strengthening, without specific suggestions for where the I2S Development Drive might look. These include recommendations from David Brown and Alice Roughley for more work on 'recognising and dealing with value differences' and the 'credibility of actors'. Ian Elsum gives high priority to '[d]evelopment of strategies for modularising a complex problem so that work on sub-problems can be reintegrated into the whole without distortion'.

The proposals for major further work and ideas for how to spend $1 million are summarised in Table 35.1. Not surprisingly, many of them reprise ideas discussed in the previous four themes: gathering case studies, strengthening the theoretical core, codifying taxonomies of knowledge, linking methods and problems, and strengthening institutional arrangements, including opportunities to gather together the community of scholars dedicated to these issues.

Table 35.1 Proposals for Further Major Work, Including Ideas for How to Spend $1 Million

'My Big-Science project would seek to: i) further articulate a foundational methodological and, better still, theoretical core to I2S, ii) position that core in the context of other relevant disciplines/discourses and demonstrate uniqueness, and iii) demonstrate the operational value of that postulated core theory and methods in the practice of integration and implementation across a range of domains.' (Daniel Walker)
'...I would invest in three things. First, commission systematic reviews of applied interdisciplinary research from each of the major fields in which it is practised...Second, convene an international Congress of Interdisciplinary Research at which these would be presented along with other invited papers and an open call. Third, publish, in addition to the proceedings, an analysis of selected case studies to facilitate the exchange of practical experience across these fields.' This builds on an earlier recommendation: '... I would add evaluations of selected case studies from the perspectives of the three major parties involved— that is: the funders with their interest in return on investment, the users from the perspective of the relevance of the research, and researchers who typically place value on the rigour of research outputs and the contribution they make to their professional development...Summative evaluation is a luxury few interdisciplinary research projects experience, partly due to the time delay in the adoption process, and a great deal could be learned by carefully scoped and well-resourced evaluations'. (Ted Lefroy)
'A descriptive branch of I2S would produce or accumulate careful accounts of integrative applied research and its near kin. It would develop frameworks and theories for understanding how and why this kind of research gets done. Descriptive I2S also would have an evaluative component, generating and guiding debates about the strengths, weaknesses, successes and failures of relevant research practices. This evaluative component would provide a conduit of exchange between descriptive I2S and prescriptive I2S.' (Michael Smithson) Other tasks Michael Smithson raises have been discussed earlier, including 'histories of relations among disciplines and subject areas' and more on understanding stakeholders and on unknowns. In reviewing the array of necessary activities, he concludes that the type of labour and time-intensive research needed (historiography, ethnography and survey methods), along with time for reflection, mean that the maturing of I2S could not be a rapid process.

'What might be the most productive nudges towards both more "muddle through" and genuine "big bang" interdisciplinarity in research? Step one might be projects that codify taxonomies of knowledge, so that the way in which each discipline treats the logical development of theory, the assembly and examination of evidence and the consideration of values in assessment of evidence would be a start. All rational knowledge generation, as opposed to intuition and experience as sources of knowledge for action, must incorporate these elements. But the language and techniques by which these components are expressed are many and various. They can be assembled, explicated and evaluated for what they contribute.' (Glenn Withers)

'If I had $1 million to spend it would be on the methodology that assigns methods to problem types, funding the (daring) scholars who explore the methods and tools in co-production processes.' (Christian Pohl)

'A comprehensive research endeavour is required to establish whether the outcomes are different when the entire I2S toolkit is used versus selected components.' (Alison Ritter)

'Perhaps if I was in a philanthropic mood and had $1 million to spend, I would focus on these issues of recognition, reward and evaluation, and, specifically, I would launch a new international journal of I2S to help establish proof-of-concept and build academic credibility.' (Catherine Lyall)

'The challenge for researchers, research institutions and research funders is to foster a community of reflective practitioners of this new approach. The initial step should be support for organisational centres and networks and recognition and reward for researchers who contribute to the advancement of integrative applied research.' (Ian Elsum)

'I suggest finding support for: 1) several meetings of people interested in I2S to discuss selected Drive issues and refine a two-year work plan; 2) synthesis of available information about I2S in several discrete areas; and 3) experimental training of I2S in a university or field setting.' (Linda Neuhauser)

These suggestions ram home the magnitude of the work required to effectively build on what we know, reinforcing why the I2S Development Drive is at the scale of a Big-Science project. It is important to remember that the Drive seeks to boost multiplicity in approaches, along with an array of options for concepts and methods; or, in Julie Thompson Klein's words, 'a systematic approach that is greater than any single method or theory. Systematic does not mean universalist...The Drive...begins by accepting, not minimising or erasing, the diversity of formts of research on real-world problems.'

36. An I2S Discipline: Legitimate, viable, useful?

Daniel Walker[1]

I have a research background in the dynamics of resource use at a variety of scales and play a leadership role in my organisation in developing the research capability needed to address issues of climate, biodiversity decline, water and food security, and energy transitions. Based on this experience, I see a manifest need for increasingly effective engagement by researchers in integration and implementation across a range of public policy domains. We do have strong understanding of many of the ways in which we use our natural resources and interact with the environment and therefore of consequent drivers of unsustainability. Nevertheless, with our tightly coupled global system undergoing often exponential change, every useful action or decision to address these issues, no matter how good, contains the seeds of the next problem. Cross-sectoral sustainability dynamics therefore result in policy conundrums for government, industry and community that are increasingly obvious. Organising and conducting the research needed to inform effective public policy on such 'wicked' problems is challenging. My organisation has recognised this and is seeking to develop the integrated sustainability science insights that policy makers need in order to assess not only what a decision can achieve but also the problems it may cause. In doing so, it is clear that disciplinary science is powerful in solving problems but often does not adequately meet implementation needs and is rarely well placed to anticipate the full spectrum of consequent issues or address unknowns. Integrative applied research is therefore critical in enhancing our contribution to changing policy and practice in the way we use resources.

As a consequence, researchers are increasingly expected to play a significant role in integration and implementation. Effective integration and implementation is unlikely to happen by accident. Equally, many of the challenges in integration and implementation in domains as diverse as biodiversity conservation, resource use transitions and public health policy will have much in common. This makes the prospect of a rigorous and collective approach to integrative applied research and an underpinning 'I2S' appealing. So, as someone whose research has always been at the boundaries of disciplines, who has always worked in applied domains and who has played roles in research leadership and management and

---

1 Daniel Walker was invited to contribute as a 'research leader whose organisation grapples with complex real-world problems requiring research integration and implementation. Your comments on whether the ideas in this book could enhance your organisation's ability to undertake such research would be very pertinent.'

continues to wrestle with the role of research in addressing sustainability issues, the challenge articulated in this book resonates with me. And yet in reading the draft, I have had a number of questions about the concept of I2S. Does it make sense to talk of I2S as a disciple? Is I2S viable as a discipline? Would I2S be a useful discipline?

Is I2S Really a Potential Discipline?

In the most generic sense a discipline is a field of study. This book makes a compelling case for the common ground in integration and implementation across a range of domains and, therefore, the opportunity for a field of study to transcend those boundaries. The analogy with statistics, in this sense, works well.

Nevertheless, most of the discussion in the book focuses on the practice of integration and implementation, on integration and implementation as praxis rather than study. This is appropriate given the need for better integration and implementation in practice. Nevertheless, the study of the phenomena of integration and implementation (as opposed to practising integration and implementation) will provide the basis for I2S as a discipline and this is contingent on the prospect of an emergent set of axioms and theory.

So it is both meaningful and useful to propose I2S as a potential discipline—the subject matter and questions exist—but I2S will need to develop a theoretical and methodological core if it is ultimately to be called a discipline. Moreover, as discussed below, I2S will need to be able to demonstrate that the effective practice of I2S is at least in principle contingent on reference to underpinning theory—in other words, that I2S is a matter of science (in the sense of the systematic application of knowledge) as well as art (in the sense of the application of experience and creativity). The development and application of any discipline require both.

Is I2S Viable as a Discipline?

I2S is naturally and appropriately the domain of systems thinkers. I call myself a systems thinker, as are almost all the people I work with. We distinguish ourselves from those who take a reductionist scientific approach and argue the merits of systems perspectives for many questions. Nevertheless, I do recognise that a natural tendency to seek to be too all-encompassing to enable tractable research is a real problem in systems-based approaches. To be viable as a discipline, I2S needs to not only generate a core set of methods and theories but also be sufficiently distinct from other disciplines in terms both of theory and methods and of subject matter.

The preliminary boundaries of I2S articulated in this book encompass core concerns for many other disciplines (such as the many manifestations of planning and management as meta-disciplines), emergent fields of study (such as the 'science of team science') and domains of practice in integration (multi-, inter- and trans-disciplinary research approaches, for example, as well as action research). This book articulates the important points of difference with discussion around multi- and trans-disciplinary research but does not yet map I2S in the full firmament of other relevant approaches. Clearly, the contest of ideas is not only healthy but is fundamental to innovation. Nevertheless, addressing the place of I2S will be critical in assessing its viability; it will only be viable if it achieves an adequate 'share of voice' both in theoretical and methodological dialogue and in practice, and will only do that if it articulates a real point of difference. It would be better still if a new discipline of I2S succeeded in subsuming subordinate or related constructs and helped rationalise the terminology in overlapping areas of inquiry. Only time will tell.

Would I2S be a Useful Discipline?

Integration and implementation are matters of process and practice. The value of I2S as a discipline is therefore contingent on its ability to understand these phenomena systematically, to provide a theoretical basis for improved practice and to thereby improve practice. The question then is, to what extent is effective integration and implementation constrained by inadequate theory and methods? This will be a core issue in establishing I2S as a field of study, so at this stage I can only speculate, as follows.

Effective statistical analysis is clearly contingent on theory and methods (theory drives practice and practice tests theory), which is why the analogy between I2S and statistics is beguiling; however, statistics as a discipline is only one analogy and others suggest different conclusions. Leadership is a legitimate field of study (I wasn't surprised that a quick Google search brought up a *Journal of Leadership Studies*), but I suspect that the impact of leadership studies on leadership in practice is substantially more limited than the impact of statistics as a discipline on applied statistical analyses. Arguably, leadership is more art than science. Indeed, there is a growing industry in leadership development, coaching and training but, observationally, this industry draws on experienced practitioners more than theoreticians. If the balance between 'art' and 'science' in I2S is more akin to leadership than statistical analysis, is it useful to think of and develop I2S as a discipline?

So what might we expect of the dynamic relationship between I2S theory and methods and integration and implementation practice? Figure 32.1 neatly captures the relationship between a core of 'theory and methods', 'methodological development with respect to a sector' and 'application in a specific sector'. The acid test of the utility of I2S as a discipline will be the relative effort expended on each of these methodological layers and how tightly coupled they are. If the relative effort decreases substantially from 'application in a specific sector' through 'methodological development with respect to a sector' to 'theory and methods', and information flows only in this one direction then, notwithstanding the deep importance of integration and implementation in practice, I2S has little useful contribution to make as a discipline. If relative effort is more balanced and information flows strongly in both directions then I2S will be a demonstrably useful discipline. (If information flows dominantly from 'theory and methods' through 'methodological development with respect to a sector' to 'application in a specific sector' then the discipline would run the risk of being a self-referential dogma. This seems hard to conceive of in relation to I2S.)

I2S Researchers and I2S Practitioners

The case for I2S is based on the need for better integration and implementation in research across a broad range of research and policy or practice domains and the view that it will not happen, or will not happen effectively, without specialist attention. So, is I2S an inevitable consequence of this need?

The alternative perspective is that existing disciplines in applied domains need to be more competent in integration and implementation. In other words, that there is an increasing para-professional requirement of researchers to be engaged in integration and implementation and therefore for disciplines to be engaged in addressing their interface with other disciplines and with the world of implementation as well as their core areas of inquiry.

Of course, setting these two views up as being mutually exclusive is rhetorical rather than realistic. In practice, it seems unlikely that anyone would argue the case for integration and implementation practice being the exclusive domain of a cadre of I2S specialists. Equally, while we might increasingly expect many scientists to be paying attention to matters of integration and implementation to ensure the relevance of their research, it is easy to see how they would benefit from interfacing with serious and specialised theory and practice in I2S. This might also unwind a growing proliferation of different terms for talking about the same phenomena and practices—a regular Tower of Babel—in linking science and society.

So the case for I2S as a discipline centres on the interplay between theory and practice in integration and implementation; however, there is something of a paradox in conceiving of a new discipline to help achieve integration across disciplines and between disciplines and application that is needed because of the tendency of disciplines to become self-referential. In short, the consequences of applying a core tool of institutionalised research ('the discipline') to addressing a problem that that tool has created are worth paying attention to. An I2S research community could make effective contributions to increasing collective competence in integration and implementation but only if it avoids becoming self-referential.

Having thought about some of the issues that need to be addressed in furthering the case for scholarly investigation of integration and implementation challenges, it is also worth briefly canvassing questions around the development of a growing pool of specialist I2S practitioners. Is it feasible and appropriate to delegate the substantial challenges of integrating disciplines and research into practice to a cadre of I2S specialists? What are the potential costs of doing so in terms of the broader reintegration that is required? Integration and implementation effort across the full range of stakeholders (within disciplines and in the implementation space) in complex public policy issues is, empirically, extremely challenging. But what new dynamics (for better and for worse) will such specialists introduce into the practice of integration and implementation?

Moving Forwards

This book provides foundational arguments for I2S as a legitimate, viable and useful discipline. Nevertheless, in my view, further consideration is needed in relation to each of these questions, as outlined above. My Big-Science project would seek to: i) further articulate a foundational methodological and, better still, theoretical core to I2S, ii) position that core in the context of other relevant disciplines/discourses and demonstrate uniqueness; and iii) demonstrate the operational value of that postulated core theory and methods in the practice of integration and implementation across a range of domains.

I don't know whether articulation of core theory and methods should take a grounded approach—starting from review of a diversity of case studies—or be built from first principles and then 'tested' against existing case studies. I have no doubt though that the final step of testing the operational value of that core content needs to take an empirical and comparative approach with new projects across multiple domains. Given the large number of integrated applied research projects being funded across many domains this is eminently achievable and would certainly constitute 'big science'.

Contributed February 2010

Brief Biography

Dr Daniel Walker is a Deputy Chief of CSIRO's Division of Ecosystems Science. The division comprises some 500 staff with expertise in ecology, agricultural and forestry systems sciences, social and economic sciences, environmental biotechnology and urban infrastructure and engineering at 18 laboratories across Australia. He plays a leadership role in systems-oriented research on the environmental, economic and social dimensions of sustainable production and consumption in Australia's urban centres, agricultural, forestry and rangelands landscapes as well as management of our conservation estate. He is also an Editor-in-Chief of the international journal *Agricultural Systems*. He joined CSIRO in Townsville in 1994 and worked on regional sustainability and development issues in northern Australia including work with the sugar industry and regional planning and management in Australia's savannahs. He moved to Canberra in 2004 and is a graduate of the Australian Rural Leadership Program. Before joining CSIRO, he worked on research to better integrate local knowledge systems into research, and development and evaluation programs in agroforestry in the developing world. This included substantial work in Sri Lanka, Thailand and Nepal.

37. Integration and Implementation Research: Would CSIRO contribute to, and benefit from, a more formalised I2S approach?

Deborah O'Connell, with Damien Farine, Michael O'Connor and Michael Dunlop[1]

This commentary is focused squarely on one of the challenges put to the commentators—namely *'How do you see yourself in relation to I2S?'*. It is based on the personal experiences, observations and reflections of the lead author after 20 years of working in integrated assessment projects in the water, energy and sustainability domains. I have applied the framework proposed by the book to the actual operation of a current project, which is developing and using integration methods in the absence of a formalised I2S disciplinary approach. Within this project, a core team provides much of the integration—and in writing this commentary it became clear that the views expressed are so closely linked with the original and ongoing ideas of team members that I have acknowledged their contributions in the authorship.

Our experience is in line with one of the book's premises—namely that there are thousands of projects around the world tackling complex social and environmental problems that are developing their own approaches to integration and implementation. We argue strongly in favour of the benefit of a more structured approach and the development of specific disciplinary expertise around integration and implementation science, particularly in the light of the urgency of the sustainability issues the world faces. In our organisation, CSIRO, we also note an increasing trend to assembling research teams based on short-term (from months to three years) projects—increasingly focused on 'integrated' research. Such teams are expected to tackle complex problems rapidly; they have frequent turnover in membership and are often geographically dispersed. The researchers are expected to join different teams and to address different problems in parallel or in quick succession. This is a very challenging set of circumstances, and we argue in this commentary that I2S methods and specialists could assist with the delivery of such research.

1   Deborah O'Connell was invited as a senior researcher 'who grapples with complex real-world problems requiring research integration and implementation. Your comments on whether the ideas in this book could enhance your ability to undertake such research would be very pertinent.' She invited colleagues to co-author the chapter.

We begin this commentary with a brief description of our parent organisation and how research is evolving. Our research is an example of a broader trend within CSIRO, so we then move on to the 'Sustainable Biomass Production' project, describing it using the I2S framework. We show how this demonstrates that we did some things well, but could have improved others. We particularly examine the roles played by different team members. Finally we return to an organisation-wide focus and explore some challenges and opportunities for I2S.

CSIRO Mission and Structure

The Commonwealth Scientific and Industrial Research Organisation (CSIRO) is Australia's major research and development organisation, with a staff of 6000 and an annual budget of approximately AUD$1 billion, of which AUD$600 million is provided by the Government directly and the remainder is external funding. CSIRO is spread across 56 sites in major cities and regional areas of Australia. In recent years, CSIRO has explicitly recognised its critical role in integration and implementation, especially citing the importance of cross-disciplinary research and the adoption of science into meaningful policy in addressing major issues of national significance. A large proportion of the overall resources have been redirected to CSIRO 'Flagships', which focus on major national priorities such as health, water, climate change, energy, mineral exploration, food and sustainable agriculture.[2]

CSIRO has conducted a major restructure in order to more effectively deliver such research. The organisation has adopted a matrix structure, with scientists housed according to disciplinary expertise in 'divisions' (such as Entomology, Plant Industry, Land and Water) and then assigned to temporary project teams within the flagships and other themes. The organisational design principles and matrix structure are described elsewhere.[3] The new organisational structure was intended to improve flexibility and responsiveness, allowing the formation of multidisciplinary teams to respond rapidly and with enormous capacity.[4]

The national research priorities in food and water security, sustainable agriculture, climate change and greenhouse gas abatement are urgent, high profile and highly politicised. They require synthesis across a large number of complex, linked social and natural systems. Even partial answers require contributions from multiple people, several disciplines, explicit through to tacit

---

2 For more information, see: <http://www.csiro.au/org/AboutNationalResearchFlagships.html> (accessed 13 February 2012).

3 For example, Mann and Marshall (2007).

4 Dr Catherine Livingstone, former CSIRO Board Chairman, quoted in *Solve* Issue 9 (CSIRO, November 2006), <www.solve.csiro.au/1106/article1.htm> (accessed 4 December 2012).

knowledge, various types of modelling approaches, a range of epistemologies, and sometimes different cultures and political systems. Because available data and measured data are almost always very sparse, tackling the priorities requires science conducted within the context of significant uncertainties and unknowns about the past and the present—let alone the future. Thus, we argue that the I2S ideas and framework are of great relevance to CSIRO, especially within flagships.

There are many examples of projects or whole programs of research within CSIRO that have had demonstrated policy or practice impact on climate change, water management or agriculture, to name a few. So, does the organisation need a formalised disciplinary I2S approach? How useful would the proposed 'storehouse' of I2S learnings be? Do we need theory and methods about integration per se to achieve our research goals at project, flagship, organisational and national or international levels? Would systematically applying the elements of a systems approach, scoping, boundary setting, framing, assessing values, and harnessing and managing differences make any material difference to the ease with which we conduct our research, the quality of the results or the level of adoption and influence in policy and practice?

In this team's experience, despite the success of achieving policy and practice goals at project through to organisational levels, much of this work is at a mono-disciplinary or sometimes multidisciplinary mode. The further along the multi- to inter-disciplinary continuum goals the research is positioned, the more patchy is the performance at project through to organisational levels. Individual scientists in CSIRO with different disciplinary backgrounds and focal scales see quite different solutions to natural resource problems. Frequently, the broader integrative 'systems thinkers' amongst us find it difficult to reduce large and complex problems—for example, sustainability issues—into tractable pieces of research that are meaningful and useable.

We contend that much of the integration science at the project level is very dependent upon the personal skills expertise and experience of individual researchers. Therefore we suggest that CSIRO as an organisation could greatly benefit from a more systematic approach to I2S. We illustrate this with our own research on the potential for biofuels and bioenergy in Australia, which is a current project in the Energy Transformed Flagship. Our reflections are based not on formal project evaluation, but on our experience.

Project Application: The 'Sustainable Bioenergy' example

The CSIRO Flagship Response: Bioenergy research

The CSIRO Energy Transformed Flagship set up a series of projects in 2007 to investigate the potential for biofuels and bioelectricity to form part of Australia's future renewable energy mix. These were underpinned by one of the projects, entitled 'Sustainable Biomass Production in Australia: Can biomass contribute to low emission energy without compromising food-, water- and bio-security?'.

The research inherently requires a high level of integration. Biofuel value chains cross from biomass (primary) production, through to biofuel processing and conversion, to distribution and retail, and finally combustion in different types of engines and transport sectors (for example, passenger, freight or aviation). Assessing the potential for biofuels therefore includes synthesis across many disciplines including forestry, waste management and agriculture, economics, process engineering, chemistry and carbon accounting. Many different areas of policy are relevant across different segments of the value chain, and jurisdiction for these is usually held by different State and Australian governments.[5]

The project therefore provides a relevant example for assessing the role (or not) of I2S as a formal discipline in achieving research goals in the area of sustainability. In the next section, we provide some background to how we have worked in an operational sense, before we then evaluate how applying and further developing some of the I2S framework suggested in the book may help.

Setting Up a Team

We evolved from the start of the project in 2006 into realising that we would require multi-, inter- and trans-disciplinary approaches in order to address the issues of sustainable bioenergy in Australia. We assembled a project team comprising researchers with expertise in forestry, agronomy and farming systems, ecology, economics, soil science and hydrology, spatial modelling, life-cycle analysis, climate change and policy analysis. Knowledge gaps were filled by fostering collaborations and working closely with colleagues (in related projects) with expertise in process engineering and biotechnology.

It is easy to discuss 'assembling a team' (as is done by CSIRO management as well as the example put forward in Chapter 31) as if it were as simple as

---

5   O'Connell et al. (2009).

going shopping; however, the reality of the situation in CSIRO, as well as when dealing with multi-agency collaboration or when recruitment is not the modus operandi, is quite different. In our case, a block of strategic funding allowed us to build critical mass in a team—although it was a slow (and still ongoing) process. Within the matrix structure of CSIRO, different divisions originally 'offered' staff with 'unallocated' time to the project. They were spread across eight different dispersed CSIRO sites and, while they had the required disciplinary backgrounds, few had any experience in the science of biofuels. Many had never met each other. Most of the original participants only had a small proportion of their time 'free'—most of it was still allocated to existing projects on other subjects, and therefore the bioenergy project was given only 10 to 20 per cent of their time.

Several of the team identify their skill base as 'system analysts', giving us a strong foundational advantage when setting up this project. Parts of the I2S framework were used, but these were on the basis of collective experience, intuition and the serendipity of team composition and dynamics rather than any formal approach. Within the domain of 'synthesis of disciplinary and stakeholder knowledge', four of the six elements were innate steps in the approach developed by our project team: 'taking a systems view' (including identifying drivers, levers, scale), 'scoping', 'framing' (expressed as a nested set of research questions) and 'boundary setting'. Thus, an explicit and central part of our project methods addressed these elements. We did not, however, explicitly recognise other elements ('taking values into account' and 'harnessing and managing differences') or other domains ('policy and practice' and 'dealing with unknowns'). The benefit of reviewing this book has already shown us how we could have thought through these elements more clearly, as well as how we might benefit from setting up such a practice in the future within this project and others.

We have tried to stabilise the team by constant negotiation within the team and with the multitude of line managers in the matrix, consolidating roles and responsibilities, career pathways and time commitments to this project. We now have a core of 10–12 (and draw on other specialised expertise outside of this) people who have more than a half-time commitment to this project. Those who remain in the team are able and willing to see the world through the lens of another discipline—which is not a universal skill or desire. Through this process of negotiation as well as broader organisational streamlining, the team is now distributed across four geographic sites (instead of the original eight), which facilitates communication, tool building, workload management and delivery of our science outputs. We have developed a strong team culture and a rapidly increasing level of competence in applying our skill sets to this particular project.

Our Approach to the Three I2S Domains

In order to 'frame' the problem and 'set the boundaries', as well as make the project tractable with the resources we had, we developed a hierarchical set of nested research questions. These fell along a continuum ranging from those that rely on a single discipline through to multidisciplinary, pluridisciplinary, interdisciplinary and transdisciplinary questions (as illustrated in Figure 37.1).

A program of work required to answer the full set of questions was scoped. The full program would require $25 million or more to implement. We have operated with an approximate budget of $2 million per year, largely funded from the Energy Transformed Flagship. The full program of work was therefore cut down to a set of tasks, according to tractability and priority, and each was clearly mapped to the set of resulting research questions. The advantage of viewing the full system and the full scope of work first is that it provided us with the opportunity to plot our critical research pathway with the totality in mind, as well as the opportunity to grow the project through collaboration and as more resources became available, knowing that we were contributing to a holistic research agenda.

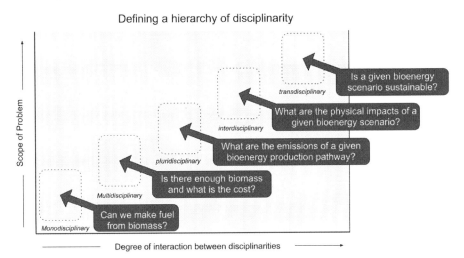

Figure 37.1 A Hierarchy of Questions Requiring Different Levels of Synthesis and Disciplinarity to Address

Source: Adapted from Farine and O'Connor (2010).

As the project has evolved, an iterative approach to assessing the size and sustainability of a future bioenergy industry has, as in Europe and the United States, followed a trajectory starting from simple analyses to increasingly more complex ones. Each step of analysis reduced the level of uncertainty and unknowns, and thus provided confidence to move to the next, more sophisticated iteration. We started with analysis of simple national or State-level statistics and models to assess the theoretical and technical potential for use of biomass. We then progressed to more complex, spatially explicit methods assessing the environmental and economic potentials, and are now working towards the regional-scale implementation potential.

In tandem with our increasingly complex and more detailed assessments, we are moving along a continuum of employing more complex and robust analytical tools to support the analysis. The integration and development of analytical tools are only possible, however, after the conceptual integration has been progressed through discussion, negotiation of meaning and triangulation of our methods via different types of analyses. We are still in progress with this; we are not funded at levels to begin major software engineering exercises nor is this appropriate at this stage of the research. We still have some way to go to bridge the gap between our supply-based resource-assessment approaches and the demand-based economic approaches,[6] to reach a true integrated assessment such as some of those conducted in Europe.[7] This is the frontier of our current research effort, and it will probably take several more years of research and increased funding to provide reliable assessments of implementation potential at regional and national scales, taking the full range of technologies and sustainability issues into account. So, our success at this level of integration is yet to be determined.

Our focus (as evident from Figure 37.1) was on the 'Synthesis of disciplinary and stakeholder knowledge' part of the I2S domains or storehouse. We believe that this has been a strength within the project. It is attributable to the tacit knowledge and experience of key researchers in the team and the roles that they have taken (outlined further in the next section). This was (and still is) an evolving iterative process, and we believe it could have been greatly expedited by the systematic application of the I2S framework proposed in this book.

We paid less methodological attention to the other two domains of the I2S approach. We did not have a formal approach, for example, to the domain 'Providing integrated research support for policy and practice change', but through the participation of some key researchers with a great deal of experience in this area, we have had some impact in implementation. A CSIRO-wide process of mapping projects to impact pathways is currently being conducted, and will help to formalise and further develop this domain. Four years into the project, we are still grappling with the 'Understanding and managing diverse unknowns' I2S domain and could clearly benefit from learning from the experience of others.

---

6   For example, CSIRO and Future Fuels Forum (2008).
7   For example, European Environment Agency (2006).

Roles Within the Team

Integration has been developed and supported by a number of researchers within this team. In the parlance of this book, the I2S model has evolved from one person (the team leader) taking the integration role in a synthesis of existing knowledge from a number of domain experts in a publication at the start of this project.[8] The current mode of operation is that integration is conducted by a core group within the team, with everyone in the team involved in delivering into an integrated science product. The roles taken by various team members do not reflect management structure, seniority or the amount of time committed to the project; rather, they grew from the natural expertise, dynamics, personalities, relationships and aspirations of the researchers. We believe that the active management and alignment of a team of researchers to their natural strengths and aspirations in integration have actually been a surrogate for some of the formalised I2S methods, but that this process has been somewhat serendipitous as well as inefficient, and could be enhanced by the use of more structured methods. We expand more on this by discussing the roles of researchers within the I2S framework.

Disciplinary and Multidisciplinary Researchers

These members of the team conduct research within their own discipline. The contribution to the integration agenda varies. These are mainly early to mid-career researchers who ensure that the science is credible within the frame of reference of their own discipline, that it uses the latest knowledge or most applicable methods, and that the results contribute back to their own disciplinary knowledge where possible. Their contribution to I2S is therefore in providing the knowledge and data for integrated analysis, as well as testing the sense and applicability of the results. As the team culture has grown, many of the disciplinary researchers have become fluent in their understanding of other disciplines or at least in the areas of each discipline that are challenging to integrate. For example, the synthesis of production data from different forms of biomass production (agriculture, forestry and waste) with economics has required close collaboration between the relevant researchers, without any of them having to develop new tools or methods. This is a good example of multidisciplinary research. Importantly, the institutional, and often personal, driver for delivery of scientific outputs by these researchers is into their own disciplinary domains.

---

8   O'Connell et al. (2007a).

Interdisciplinary Researchers

The interdisciplinary researchers fall into two categories.

1. Conceptual integrators. These scientists, who include the project leader, generally operate outside any single discipline. Their contribution is in ensuring that the integrative applied research is conceptually consistent in terms of its construction and analytical methods. They may be skilled at using a number of analytical tools, applying new techniques, and understanding and translating the languages, approaches and methods of different disciplines. They can rapidly construct arguments, develop new ideas and understand the role of the analytical tools at the disposal of the team, and how they could be used. They broker the relationships within the broader team; manage creative tension and conflict; and help push boundaries especially up and down scales, as well as across disciplines and sectors. In order to achieve this, they need a broad range of knowledge at a range of scales. For example, there is large variation in global estimates of bioenergy potential that have been produced by various international research groups. The differences between the estimates hinge largely on completely different modelling approaches, as well as on embedded assumptions in different models. Some of these differences are disciplinary—for example, different crop or tree productivity models. More challenging, however, are the assumptions about the critical unknowns—for example, the future impact of climate change, population, global food security and the efficacy of the full range of alternative renewable energy technologies. In order to produce such estimates for Australia, or even sensibly evaluate the estimates of others, a breadth of knowledge across these areas is necessary.

2. The data, model and platform integrators. As the team moves beyond the multidisciplinary stage to an interdisciplinary stage, the team requires I2S specialists who can drive data, model and platform integration. For example, in our team, we have had to create models and data for the carbon accounting from various forms of biomass production (each using their own types of models and data of varying form and reliability), going to various biofuel or bioenergy production pathways through to different types of combustion engine technology (for example, internal combustion engines, electric vehicles, airplane turbines). The ability to combine data and ideas from different theoretical constructs, in a way that is rigorous and technically defensible within any of the disciplines contributing to the integrated analysis, is a difficult, time-consuming and specialist task. Success and efficiency rely on a robust conceptual integration being in place.

Implementation Specialists: Impact in policy and practice

Experienced 'tribal elders' who have established reputations as leaders in their disciplinary fields and have had substantial impact through their careers in either policy or practice have been particularly valuable. Renowned researchers in sustainable forest management (with a demonstrated integration pathway to forest policy), agriculture (with influence on the agricultural practices of farmers) and institutional economics have had a role in the team with relatively minor time commitment, but with a large impact on our approach. They understand different pathways to impact in policy and practice arenas, and have the networks, experience and credibility to position the research. These researchers participate at a project level and provide significant guidance. Their participation frequently comes from their desire to solve sustainability issues beyond the boundaries of their discipline, as well as a sense of mentorship of younger scientists.

People in research management positions also have the potential to be extremely useful as implementation specialists; however, in the period of massive organisational change during which this project has operated, there has been a very high degree of transience in the management structure, which has reduced the efficacy of this pathway.

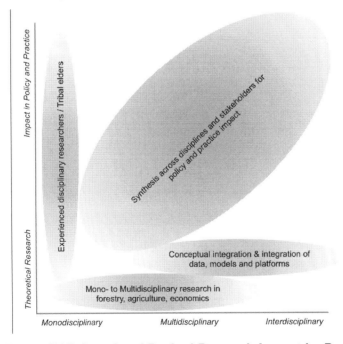

Figure 37.2 Actual and Desired Research Impact by Research Style

Source: Authors' illustration.

In Figure 37.2, we plot two of the domains of I2S: along the x-axis is shown the synthesis of knowledge across disciplines, and the y-axis shows impact on policy or practice (frequently achieved through a transdisciplinary approach of working with the beneficiaries of the research). In blue, we show where, to date, we have naturally placed ourselves in this space and, in green, where we aspire to be through more effective I2S development.

Research Outputs and Impact

During the four years of operation of the project, we have built a new area of integrated research, drawing on a body of previous work done within CSIRO and elsewhere. In Figure 37.3, we present a view of the sorts of outputs along with the number produced (compared with our estimates of the expectations of a project with this level of resourcing and this number of research and support scientists). We track subjective rating of the integration success of these against the axes shown in Figure 37.2.

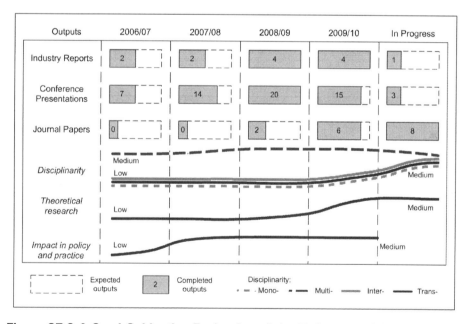

Figure 37.3 A Semi-Subjective Evaluation of the Trajectory of Outputs and Impacts over the Four Years of the Sustainable Biomass Production Project

Source: Authors' illustration.

We began the project in 2006–07 with industry reports that were 'position statements'—gathering what was known and pointing to critical knowledge gaps.[9] This work was very multidisciplinary in nature and largely based on synthesis of existing knowledge. We were commissioned to design a research and development program (by a research funding body) to address the critical knowledge gaps.[10] These outputs led to recognition for our synthesis of a set of complicated issues—but no new science was conducted. Based on this, through 2006–07 to the present we have developed new knowledge. Through this time we have had a very high level of requests for conference and keynote presentations for 'in-progress' research. We had relatively high impact (when viewed with respect to our level of resourcing) in terms of media coverage, inputs into government submission and inquiry processes, and emerging policy positions that use some of our research outputs.

Through this trajectory of progress, our ability to produce monodisciplinary conference and journal papers (for example, on the amount of waste wood that could be used for biofuels)[11] has increased, as has our ability to feed these into interdisciplinary analyses and publications. We have recently produced one transdisciplinary report.[12] We have some way to go before we can produce truly integrated assessments that reconcile the conceptual differences in supply and demand-based approaches at regional through to national scales, as well as reliable assessments of sustainability in natural and global economic systems that are prone to sudden, unpredictable and irreversible threshold changes. These 'wicked' problems, and the integration approaches required to start addressing them, are common to many domains of sustainability research and I2S would provide some of the tools and structures for cross-team and cross-project diffusion of approaches.

Reflections

Our subjective evaluation of our own progress is that we have achieved some success with our integration science agenda within a bioenergy project (at least consistent with our level of resourcing). We ascribe much of this to serendipity arising from the actual team members, experience and intuition as surrogates for the lack of formal methods and approaches. The approach brought to the project by the system analysts in the team, as well as the 'tribal elders'—who have had experience in taking science from theory through to policy and practice implementation—has been fundamental. Our ability to provide integrated

---

9   Batten and O'Connell (2007); Haritos (2007); O'Connell et al. (2007a).
10   O'Connell et al. (2007b).
11   For example Taylor et al. (2009)
12   Braid et al. (2010).

science has been facilitated by the flagships approach and the use of strategic internal funding to build the capacity to the point where the CSIRO bioenergy research (comprising not only the project described here but several related projects) has gone from very little capacity in 2004 to a recognised reputation for integration in a complex area of resource and technology assessment, sustainability analysis and energy policy.

We contend that our work at a project level could have been (and still could be) greatly enhanced by the formal development and application of I2S as a discipline—through the systematic methodological approaches put forward in this book and ongoing opportunities and forums to draw on the experience and methods of others. There are, however, some challenges within the CSIRO and broader external research environments that are critical to the success of integrated assessment research, which may or may not be addressed by I2S per se. These are discussed in the following sections.

Building Effective Teams for Integrated Research and Cross-Team Learning

The utopian ideal of 'virtual' teams for integrated assessment, meeting and working by video link, with short-term team structures coming together around specific projects, is put forward by CSIRO and is also mooted in Chapter 31. Our belief is that this is a very risky approach to integration science—and that the more this becomes the modus operandi, the more important formal I2S methods and training will be in order for it to be successful.

Commencing and continuing integrated research require a stable project team, with good team processes and sound project leadership. These factors are necessary to move beyond the whacking together of various disparate data sets, and for moving towards the process of negotiation of meaning—which in turn underpins the development of a shared understanding and language between the practitioners from different disciplines. Increasingly in CSIRO, tasks and teams are established rapidly and according to short-term opportunity and availability. As Mann and Marshall[13] clearly recognise, sometimes productive relationships follow, but often attention to teamwork and relationship building is perfunctory or ignored completely. They contend that leadership skills and team processes for conflict resolution, brainstorming, team learning and creative dialogue have a direct impact on such factors as trust, which in turn is necessary to enable the free flow of knowledge in a research team and consequently sound team performance.

---

13   Mann and Marshall (2007).

We have had four years with a relatively stable team and funding in a new area of research and expertise. We estimate that a shared understanding was achieved after the first year, trust and a common language after the second, and only from the third year onwards has significant integration of concepts been achievable. Furthermore, we found geographic distribution to be the most challenging aspect of our integration activities. It is workable when a distant team member has a specific and independent task to deliver but is very problematic for the project when close work is required among multiple team members.

There are many project teams that work effectively (especially in the 'implementation' aspect of I2S) and may not need interdisciplinary, stable, longer-term teams or I2S methods and specialists; however, the further along the 'synthesis' and 'interdisciplinary' continuum a team is working, the more important the general team and leadership factors become, and the more formalised I2S methods, tools and specialists may be able to contribute to effective research and delivery. The I2S methods and tools themselves can help to specify an appropriate level of team building and stability, project leadership management, and input of I2S methods or specialists required to solve a particular research question. This could be done very effectively during the project development phase, ensuring that projects set reasonable expectations and resources for specified degrees of integration.[14]

We are now, as a team, called on frequently to collaborate with other 'cognate' teams (for example, undertaking broader carbon modelling). This collaboration is usually not founded on the benefit of common language, tools or team building, and remains challenging. Our experience is that cross-team learning has relied entirely on the personal relationships between team members; there is generally no formal mechanism in place within CSIRO to facilitate this type of activity. We consider that a formalised set of I2S methods, in combination with more formal and consistent mechanisms for cross-team learning in CSIRO, will greatly enhance our ability to more efficiently and consistently deliver science in an integrated and cross-disciplinary fashion.

These issues are dealt with briefly in Chapter 26, Box 26.1, and may indeed form part of the 'storehouse' of methods and approaches in integration research.

Publishing

The issue of publishing integration research is well recognised. Finding appropriate journals for some types of integrated research publications can be problematic. In addition, authorship of the products of integrated research can be challenging because it is difficult to tease apart the original contributors of

---

14   For example, Farine and O'Connor (2010).

concepts and ideas that are tightly linked. This commentary is a case in point: although the lead author reviewed the book and drafted much of the 'personal perspective', it is difficult to separate these perspectives from the original ideas and contributions of many in the team (particularly the 'core integration' group).

Better development and recognition of the I2S discipline and implementation of processes in this book (for example, identifying the goals of integration versus goals of the project and goals of the components) will assist this process. In the absence of a formal discipline, many of us have experienced (with our early forays into integration) the fact that benchmarks for academic quality acquired in disciplinary training do not translate to our new work. Despite conducting what we assess as difficult and novel work, this lack of benchmarks makes the academic quality of our work difficult to judge personally and by peers, research clients and colleagues.

This is exacerbated by systems such as the Australian Department of Innovation, Industry, Science and Research metrics applied to universities. The publications are ascribed a certain number of points according to level—for example, journals, book chapters, conference proceedings. The rules prescribe that the points assigned to each type of publication are divided by the number of authors of the paper. So, for example, a journal paper might be worth one point to a single author, but only 0.1 points if there are 10 authors. This has the potential to undermine the motivation for publishing multi-authored integration research papers, and may lead to some undesirable outcomes for I2S research and publication.

Conclusion

We conclude that culture and body of knowledge about integration have been evolving within various parts of CSIRO, but more formal development of the I2S specialisation and recognition of the skills and community of practice will greatly assist the integration mission essential for so many of the complex problems CSIRO finds itself addressing. In particular it will help its scientists to

- assess the level of resources and I2S input required to address particular research questions; not every project requires a specialist approach and many already have what they need to deliver and implement integrated science
- for those research problems that do require integrated assessment teams, I2S can help with team leadership, membership and research methods and processes that are less prone to patchy experience and tacit knowledge, thus greatly improving the chances of achieving the significant national research goals sought by flagships

- share knowledge, experience, methods and tools within and across project teams in a more formalised, transferable manner, thus improving the efficiency of building teams and training early career staff
- provide formal recognition of those of us who are already working as, or evolving into, integration specialists; within the current matrix structure they are currently placed back to disciplinary groups, which do not provide an adequate home or 'community of practice' for integration
- create demand among discipline-based project leaders for specialist skills to help integrate knowledge across scales and dimensions, and develop a culture of asking research questions from an integrated perspective
- help internal and external recognition of I2S specialists by providing more outlets for the publication of their integration contributions as scientific outputs as well as their theory and methods.

Finally, there must be clear and explicit recognition that *people* are central to the success of integration. This can easily be lost in the wave of organisational change, managerialism and business-focused dogma. Much of this discussion has focused on skills and research processes, and how they could be enhanced by the formal development of I2S. At least part of the 'integration' agenda must, however, acknowledge the critical human elements of a team—different mother tongues, cultures, world views ('conservative' versus 'liberal'), psychologies ('risk taker' versus 'risk averse'), personalities (introverts versus extroverts; 'big picture' versus 'details'), behaviours and roles ('openers' versus 'finishers'; 'leadership' or 'followship')—and be responsive to the changing mix of these elements as the team membership is revised and the members themselves change their own work modes/behaviours over time.

Formalised I2S development will not replace the 'meeting of the minds' necessary to deliver effective integration. Nor will it suffice or flourish in an organisation where a matrix structure fragments people across project areas or physical locations. It will not replace the imperative for allocating sufficient money, time and priority to supporting its scientists, developing healthy teams, providing a productive and safe working environment, and ensuring robust leadership and management processes. If the prerequisites of healthy teams, robust leadership and sufficient resourcing are met, however, it has the potential to greatly enhance our response to increasingly urgent issues that require an integrated research approach. I2S, whether formally accepted as a new discipline or not, can help to provide science leaders, teams, individuals and the organisation as a whole with: 1) innovative theoretical constructs for cross-disciplinary science, 2) greater efficiencies for intra- and across-team approaches, 3) tools and methods, and 4) most importantly, better outcomes in terms of impact and usefulness of our science.

Contributed February 2010

Acknowledgments

We thank the others in the team who have participated (perhaps unwittingly) in developing or implementing our approach, and therefore featuring anonymously in this article. These include John Raison, Barrie May, Andrew Braid, Joely Taylor, Alexander Herr, Luis Rodriguez, Tim Grant, Tom Jovanovic, Debbie Crawford, David Batten, Mick Poole, Perry Poulton, Peter Thorburn, Peter Campbell, Franzi Poldy, Nick Abel, Roy Chamberlain, Brian Keating, Cameron Begley, Victoria Haritos. We thank Roy Chamberlain for review.

References

Batten, D. and O'Connell, D. (2007). *Biofuels in Australia—Some economic and policy considerations.* Canberra: Rural Industries Research and Development Corporation, RIRDC Publication No 07/177.

Braid, A., O'Connell, D. and Handberg, K. (2010). *Bioenergy sustainability— where to from here?* Report to the Victorian Department of Sustainability and Environment. Canberra: CSIRO.

CSIRO and Future Fuels Forum. (2008). *Fuel for Thought—The future of transport fuels: challenges and opportunities.* Canberra: CSIRO.

European Environment Agency. (2006). *How much bioenergy can Europe produce without harming the environment?* EEA Report Number 7/2006. Luxembourg: Office for Official Publications of the European Communities; <www.eea. europa.eu/publications/eea_report_2006_7> (accessed 6 August 2012).

Farine, D. R. and O'Connor, M. H. (2010). Disciplinarity in research: the role of semantics and ontologies in addressing sustainability and other global-scale issues. Unpublished manuscipt.

Haritos, V. S. (2007). *Biobased Product in Australia—Opportunities for Australian agricultural industries.* Canberra: Rural Industries Research and Development Corporation, RIRDC Publication No 07/176.

Mann, L. and Marshall, R. J. (2007). 'Teams in CSIRO: reorganising for national research imperatives'. *Innovation: Management, Policy and Practice,* 9: 136–45.

O'Connell, D., Batten, D., O'Connor, M., May, B., Raison, J., Keating, B., Beer, T., Braid, A., Haritos, V., Begley, C., Poole, M., Poulton, P., Graham, S., Dunlop,

M., Grant, T., Campbell, P. and Lamb, D. (2007a). *Biofuels in Australia—Issues and prospects*. Canberra: Rural Industries Research and Development Corporation, RIRDC Publication No 07/071.

O'Connell, D., Haritos, V., Graham, S., Farine, D., O'Connor, M., Batten, D., May, B., Raison, J., Braid, A., Dunlop, M., Beer, T., Begley, C., Braid, A., Poole, M. and Lamb, D. (2007b). *Bioenergy, bioproducts and energy—A framework for research and development*. Canberra: Rural Industries Research and Development Corporation, RIRDC Publication No 07/178.

O'Connell, D., Braid, A., Raison, J., Handberg, K., Cowie, A., Rodriguez, L. and George, B. (2009). *Sustainable Production of Bioenergy—A review of global bioenergy sustainability frameworks and assessment systems*. Canberra: Rural Industries Research and Development Corporation, RIRDC Publication No 09/167.

Taylor, J. A., Herr, A. and Siggins, A. W. (2009). 'The influence of distance from landfill and population density on degree of wood residue recycling in Australia'. *Biomass and Bioenergy*, 33: 1474.

Brief Biography

Dr Deborah O'Connell is a researcher at CSIRO Material Sciences and Engineering (CMSE) and the Energy Transformed Flagship. Her research has focused on developing and applying integrated assessment frameworks and systems analysis approaches in the domains of water and energy. For the past five years she has worked in the area of biomass and bioenergy, leading an interdisciplinary team of 20 scientists across forestry, agriculture, waste management, process and chemical engineering, energy technologies, policy analysis, economics, life-cycle analysis and sustainability science. The reports and papers produced by this team and ongoing interactions with government, industry and interest group stakeholders have set the agenda for biofuels and bioenergy research in Australia. Deborah has given many conference presentations, had steady engagement with print, radio and TV media, and has been on numerous steering committees, discussion panels and other industry forums.

38. I2S: Prescriptive, descriptive or both?

Michael Smithson[1]

The primary rationale Bammer presents for envisioning I2S as a discipline is that it needs a storehouse of ideas, a network of specialists and its own organs for evaluating and disseminating new developments. Even if we accept this rationale, the notion of I2S-as-discipline still has some problems. I will attempt to address some of them by taking up Bammer's fruitful analogy between statistics and I2S. I will argue that statistics is not a sufficient template, at least not for I2S at this stage in its development. Alternative templates can be found, and investigations of these lead to the notion that I2S needs both a descriptive and a prescriptive branch.

Templates for I2S as a Discipline

I2S as a discipline is the key metaphor in the framework Gabriele Bammer develops in this book. More specifically, Bammer envisions I2S as a discipline akin to statistics. As statistics supports quantitative data analysis, so I2S would support 'integrative applied research'. Like statisticians, I2S experts would work on a wide variety of social and environmental problems. I2S methods would be applied by specialists in other disciplines much as statistical methods are. Nevertheless, like statistics, I2S would have its own professional journals and conferences, and new developments in it would be evaluated by I2S specialists and published in I2S outlets.

Why base the template for I2S on statistics? Why wouldn't disciplines like chemistry, architecture or history do instead? What about professions such as medicine, engineering or law? These all fail primarily on two criteria. First, other disciplines do not often engage with the *subject matter* of these disciplines or professions. Second, they do not often apply *methods* from these disciplines or professions.

Are there other disciplines, professions or even cross-disciplinary areas that satisfy these two criteria? Two disciplines come readily to mind—namely philosophy and mathematics, both with much longer pedigrees than statistics.

---

1   Michael Smithson was invited as a senior researcher 'who has outstanding expertise in unknowns, and who also has broad knowledge about research'.

Let us consider philosophy first. As with statistics, many disciplines and professions claim to possess or use a philosophy. Even those that don't make such claims depend on an implicit philosophical foundation of some kind; however, they seldom make explicit use of philosophical methods or perspectives, nor do their specialists consult philosophers as they do statisticians. There are few 'philosopher' experts in these disciplines who play the same kind of role as statistical experts. Why not? Is it because the philosophical issues facing most disciplines don't require specialists to deal with? Or have philosophers been unable to 'sell' their expertise on practical grounds?

I suspect it is both. Most disciplines proceed on a philosophical consensus about their ontology and epistemology unless they are mired in a crisis that threatens their foundations. There is little practical philosophical work to be done in the course of normal science or arts practice. Much the same holds true for professions. In cases where members of a profession perceive a need for such work, as in the recent surge of interest in ethics by professional business managers, they bring in philosophical expertise with the aim of integrating the resultant knowledge into normal professional practice.

Turning to mathematics, we find a closer analogy with statistics. Many disciplines and professions use mathematical methods, they consult with mathematicians, and there are numerous examples of 'pure' mathematics finding applications in practical problems (number theory applied to cryptography, to name just one). And of course, new developments in mathematics are assessed by mathematicians and not specialists from other disciplines. Unlike philosophy, mathematics has been successfully sold to other disciplines.

What distinguishes mathematics and statistics from philosophy that could account for the greater and wider practical impacts of the former two disciplines? Could I2S learn anything from the answer to this question? Unfortunately, the answer appears to boil down to a phenomenon that is not well understood: the widespread 'mathematisation' of a variety of disciplines during the 19th and 20th centuries. I say that this is not understood because we have no entirely sufficient account for why mathematics works so well in so many areas. Even the success of statistics can be accounted for by mathematisation. The earliest statistical associations (circa 1830–60) were devoted to the collection of neutral, routine and quantifiable knowledge about society, and one of their avowed aims was to exclude opinions. Probability, meanwhile, remained a branch of mathematics. Probabilistic inference from samples to populations did not enter into this area until the late 19th and early 20th centuries. The spread of statistics gained momentum when probability theory was imported into it, enabling both the founding of inferential statistics and the randomised, controlled experimental designs. Statistics was transformed from merely rearranging information already in hand to making inferences about and estimates of unknown quantities.

Alas, none of the foregoing yields clues about a 'magic selling point' for I2S. Mathematisation is unlikely to play the same role there, although some mathematics (for example, complexity theory) may well prove useful in I2S. There might be other transdisciplinary conceptual or methodological developments that would provide this kind of selling point for I2S, but they have yet to emerge.

Comparisons with other disciplines yield a potentially more productive question: what distinguishes philosophy, mathematics and statistics from disciplines like chemistry, architecture, history and music that makes the former more attractive templates for I2S than the latter? To begin with, a discipline is partly defined by its subject and partly by its methods. Some are defined more by one than the other. Disciplines such as chemistry, architecture and history are defined chiefly by their subject matter. Indeed, these three have their origins partly in specific crafts. The subject matter of philosophy, mathematics or statistics is more universal than the subjects of craft-based disciplines, and these three disciplines also are chiefly defined by their methods. Their subjects differ from those of chemistry, architecture and history in another crucial respect: they are primarily prescriptive, and their methods embody those prescriptions. These are 'how-to-think' disciplines. Thus, in Bammer's vision, I2S is cast as a prescriptive 'how-to' discipline to be defined mainly by its methods.

There are considerable obstacles to be overcome before this vision can be realised. I will briefly discuss two of these. First, I2S is a long way from having a basis for 'gold standard' methods or even a methodological consensus. Statistics and mathematics can support claims of well-founded methods, which enable them to be strongly prescriptive and consensual as well. This is not to say that there are no foundational problems or disputes in these disciplines; of course there are; however, their foundations are not nearly as contestable or undecided as those in most of the concerns to be addressed by I2S. Therefore, I2S as a discipline will need to orient itself towards enabling extensive and productive discourses regarding its foundations.

Second, statistics and mathematics have well-established training and educational programs and a host of specialists who have graduated from those programs. It will be some time before I2S will possess such programs or experts. Meanwhile, I2S will need to orient itself to draw on relevant sources of expertise, insights or learning. Both of these obstacles suggest that 'how-to' disciplines such as statistics and mathematics may not provide an adequate template for I2S in its nascent stages (although they might eventually suffice for a mature I2S discipline).

There is a third possible template for I2S, but it is not a discipline. Instead it is an area I shall call 'decision science': the bastard offspring of psychology, probability theory and behavioural economics. Its subject matter, decision making, is a ubiquitous human activity and so, like statistics, it has very wide applicability in other disciplines and areas. It is also a 'how-to' subject. Like I2S, decision science is young. Its foundations are contestable, and there are deep disagreements among decision scientists about fundamentals. Decision scientists are in the process of building storehouses of knowledge, ideas, educational programs and resources with prescriptive goals in mind.

I shall offer decision science as an alternative template for I2S because it has a feature not found in statistics, mathematics or even philosophy: a descriptive branch that actively debates with its prescriptive branch. Statisticians and mathematicians are not seriously interested in how non-specialists do statistics or mathematics. Decision scientists, however, are interested in studying how novices and area experts alike make decisions. They evaluate and compare these practices with the prescriptions of formal decisional frameworks. Decision science journals and conferences typically include a mix of prescriptive and descriptive material, and each kind is expected to connect with the other. Contemporary debates about rationality (the 'how-to' of decision making under uncertainty) are being shaped by these exchanges between proponents of formal frameworks and students of decisional 'heuristics' used by human decision makers.

It is noteworthy that the earliest versions of decision science (in the 1950s and 1960s) were strongly prescriptive. Formal decision methods were grounded in subjective expected utility theory, whose foundations included Bayesian probability theory. Perspectives such as neo-classical economics were built on an assumption that humans acted as subjective expected utility decision makers in economic activities; however, the 1970s and 1980s saw an accumulation of evidence that human decision makers do not adhere to the prescriptions of subjective expected utility. Researchers raised the possibility that some aspects of non-adherence were not 'irrational', and the ensuing debates led to reconsiderations of subjective expected utility and eventually the foundations of rationality itself. In retrospect, the early prescriptive stance of decision scientists was premature.

At this stage in its development, then, it seems ill advised for I2S to aspire to be solely prescriptive. It needs an active *descriptive* branch that can exchange findings and ideas with its prescriptive branch. What might this descriptive branch look like, what would it need to undertake and what methods would it require?

Descriptive I2S

A descriptive branch of I2S would produce or accumulate careful accounts of integrative applied research and its near kin. It would develop frameworks and theories for understanding how and why this kind of research gets done. Descriptive I2S also would have an evaluative component, generating and guiding debates about the strengths, weaknesses, successes and failures of relevant research practices. This evaluative component would provide a conduit of exchange between descriptive I2S and prescriptive I2S. Indeed, all of these points are raised in the first two chapters of this book, indicating compatibility between this notion of descriptive I2S and Bammer's vision of I2S as a discipline.

Descriptive I2S would need to encompass more than the study of specific attempts at integrative applied research. Its purview would include histories of relations among disciplines and subject areas. These histories influence the current relations among the disciplines concerned, and thereby affect the potential for integrative applied research that involves those disciplines. Here are some examples of such relations.

- Division of subject area: Organic and inorganic chemistry form a paradigmatic example. The division between sociology and anthropology ('society' versus 'culture') is a messier and more contested example.

- Division of labour: Analytical philosophy (how should we think?) and cognitive psychology (how do we think?) form an example. The professional and scientific wings of some disciplines (for example, medicine and psychology) display another kind of division of labour.

- Level of analysis: Examples are molecular biology → chemistry → physics, and sociology → psychology (again, a messier and more contested instance).

- Borrowing and lending: Engineering borrows from physics; medicine from biology; and geography from several disciplines. Mathematics lends to numerous other disciplines; however, there are also plenty of cases of duplication or reinvention, sometimes within the same discipline.

- Competition: Psychology competes directly with psychiatry as a profession, and with most of the other social sciences as a discipline.

- Cooperation and constructive disputation: Psychology, neuroscience and economics have recently collaborated to generate neuroeconomics.

How would studying relationships among disciplines help I2S? On the one hand, it requires no special effort to know whether to turn to an organic or an inorganic chemist; however, many relationships between disciplines are messy, contested and poorly understood. In the case of newly emerging areas and disciplines, those relations also are fluid. Little is known about how effective

Disciplining Interdisciplinarity

or ineffective relationships among disciplines emerge. Knowledge about those relationships will be of practical value to I2S specialists because the potential for interdisciplinary collaboration and integration will hinge on matters such as whether the disciplines concerned are in a turf war with one another.

Descriptive I2S also would have to include two additional sub-areas: accounts of stakeholder perspectives and responses to research processes and outputs, and how researchers and stakeholders understand and manage unknowns. Both of these sub-areas could be built up initially by borrowing heavily from relevant disciplines and research areas (for example, political and social sciences re stakeholders and decision sciences re management of unknowns), but there would still be considerable work to be done by descriptive I2S scholars and researchers.

I will limit discussion of this last point to the issue of unknowns. There is a wealth of research on how people judge and deal with unknowns, most of which has occurred in psychology and behavioural economics. This literature could be mined for insights relevant to I2S. Consider judgments regarding the likelihood of novel (heretofore unobserved) events, or even just events that are contrary to predictions. An empirical literature on the psychology of probability judgments has unearthed a tendency for people to underestimate the likelihood of such events and to be overconfident of their predictions.

Another example with a theory-constructing component is the link between problem framing and attitudes towards unknowns. Orientations towards risks associated with unknowns can be influenced by framing. A large literature on Prospect Theory[2] tells us that framing a problem in terms of prospective gains will make people risk averse whereas framing it in terms of losses will make them more risk tolerant. Another psychological perspective, regulatory focus,[3] claims that framing goals in terms of preventing outcomes will tend to induce risk aversion, whereas framing them in terms of achieving outcomes will tend to induce risk tolerance.

These are examples of ready-made productive research and theory that descriptive I2S can use, but there are important limitations in the research literature on unknowns. Chief among these is a general restriction of unknowns to 'uncertainty'—usually probabilistic uncertainty. Research on other kinds of unknowns such as vagueness or bias is scarce. A second major limitation is that most research on judgment and decision making under uncertainty is framed by an implicit assumption that unknowns always are unwanted and deleterious. This is far from universally true. People have motivations for not knowing some things, and uses for unknowns. Unknowns also underpin specific forms of

---

2   Kahneman and Tversky (1979).
3   Higgins (1998).

social capital such as privacy and trust.[4] Almost no research has been done on these issues, and references to 'positive' functions of unknowns are scattered throughout several unconnected literatures.

An example of the kind of work that could complement the largely psychological research and theorising in the decision sciences is Gross's monograph on surprise.[5] Gross begins his book by declaring: 'Ignorance and surprise belong together.'[6] Events are surprising to us only if we are ignorant of them in some respect prior to their occurrence. Surprise therefore signifies ignorance. Like various kinds of unknowns, surprise often is framed negatively. The major exceptions are the concepts of 'serendipity' and learning from mistakes.[7] That the generation of new knowledge brings with it new unknowns and surprises is not a new insight.[8] Nevertheless, the notion that accelerating the rate of new knowledge production also might increase the frequency and even profundity of ensuing surprises has not been fully appreciated until relatively recently. A 'knowledge society' is also a 'surprise society'. Gross develops a framework integrating concepts of surprise, knowledge and unknowns and applies it to complex environmental issues.

Let us turn now to the scope outlined by Bammer in Section 3 for the consideration of unknowns by I2S. Two purposes for the inclusion of understanding and managing diverse unknowns are raising awareness of the inability to eliminate unknowns and awareness of the limitations of discipline-based approaches to unknowns. These are unobjectionable, but we should add 'consideration of which unknowns should or should not be eliminated'. This makes another a subject for descriptive I2S—namely the possibility of disagreements among researchers and/or stakeholders about how unknowns should be dealt with.

Bammer also lists four reasons unknowns are unlimited: 1) change is constant, so new unknowns will continue to arise; 2) research always uncovers new unknowns; 3) some things are unknowable; and 4) techniques to research some unknowns have not yet been developed. I would recommend adding a fifth reason unknowns are unlimited: 5) people have motivations for creating and maintaining some unknowns. In connection with reason two, for instance, *researchers* are the ones who uncover unknowns, not '*research*', and researchers are motivated to do so. Likewise, an example of intentional maintenance of unknowns in recent times is the suppression or prevention of certain kinds of biotechnological research.

---

4   Smithson (2008).
5   Gross (2010).
6   Gross (2010, p. 1).
7   For example, Wildavsky (1995).
8   See, for instance, Fleck (1935).

Finally, let us briefly consider the question of methods for descriptive I2S. Obvious candidates for the core methods include historiography, ethnography and survey methods. This list raises at least one concern. These are labour and time-intensive methods, unlikely to yield the rapid returns called for in Chapters 1 and 2 even with a massive injection of funds for descriptive I2S research. A large volume of such research also will require considerable time for scholars to derive theories and frameworks from it. Decision science has been able to make rapid progress partly because it is able to employ experimentation, simulation and mathematical methods, all of which tend to take less time and labour than methods such as historiography and ethnography. This issue is not fatal to the development of descriptive I2S, but should serve as a warning against optimistic estimates of how long it will take for the discipline to mature.

Summing Up

Because I2S has neither the kind of well-founded agreed-upon base that is enjoyed by mature disciplines such as statistics nor a readily identifiable network of experts, I have argued that statistics is not an adequate model for the discipline of I2S. Instead, I have presented decision science as an alternative template, chiefly because it is a young area that deals with similar problems by growing a descriptive branch that exchanges findings and ideas with its prescriptive branch. The resulting recommendation is that I2S develop its own descriptive branch, and the second half of this commentary is an attempt to adumbrate the shape and scope of descriptive I2S. Descriptive I2S, in turn, emerges as an area that will take some time and considerable effort to develop, both because of the complexity of its subject matter and because of its methodological requirements.

In closing, it is noteworthy that descriptive I2S might provide the same kind of 'insurance' that descriptive work in decision science has yielded for that area—namely insurance against wholesale failures in the prescriptive branch. The early developments in expected utility theory were followed by a growing realisation that humans not are subjective expected utility agents most of the time, and subjective expected utility theory is applicable only to well-structured decisional contexts where there is ample time for computations. These revelations posed a great threat to the field. Had decision scientists continued relying solely on subjective expected utility, they would have found their field relegated to a very small corner in the realm of decision making. Instead, they derived new concepts such as bounded rationality and adaptive heuristics from their descriptive research storehouse, and have since set about refashioning their prescriptive frameworks to encompass contexts where subjective expected utility cannot apply. I2S could find itself in a similar quandary, because it is possible that no overarching prescriptive framework for I2S can be found.

Descriptive I2S will render this new discipline robust enough to survive such an eventuality, and it will also provide the raw materials for constructing such a framework if it can be found.

Contributed February 2010

References

Fleck, L. [1935] (1979). *Genesis and Development of a Scientific Fact*. Chicago: University of Chicago Press.

Gross, M. (2010). *Ignorance and Surprise: Science, society, and ecological design*. Cambridge, MA: MIT Press.

Higgins, E. T. (1998). 'Promotion and prevention: regulatory focus as a motivational principle'. *Advances in Experimental Social Psychology*, 30: 1–46.

Kahneman, D. and Tversky, A. (1979). 'Prospect theory: an analysis of decision under risk'. *Econometria*, 47: 263–91.

Smithson, M. (2008). 'Social theories of ignorance'. In: Proctor, R. and Schiebinger, L. (eds). *Agnotology: The making and unmaking of ignorance*. Stanford, CA: Stanford University Press, 209-229.

Wildavsky, A. (1995). *But is it True? A citizen's guide to environmental health and safety issues*. Cambridge, MA: Harvard University Press.

Brief Biography

Michael Smithson is Professor in the Department of Psychology at The Australian National University and received his PhD from the University of Oregon. He is the author of *Confidence Intervals* (2003), *Statistics with Confidence* (2000), *Ignorance and Uncertainty* (1989) and *Fuzzy Set Analysis for the Behavioral and Social Sciences* (1987), co-author of *Fuzzy Set Theory: Applications in the social sciences* (2006), and co-editor of *Uncertainty and Risk: Multidisciplinary perspectives* (2008) and *Resolving Social Dilemmas: Dynamic, structural, and intergroup aspects* (1999). His other publications include more than 120 refereed journal articles and book chapters. His primary research interests are in judgment and decision making under uncertainty, social dilemmas, statistical methods for the social sciences, and applications of fuzzy set theory to the social sciences.

39. I2S Needs Theory as Well as a Toolkit

Alison Ritter[1]

I feel closely connected with Integration and Implementation Sciences (I2S), having been both an observer and a recipient of its early development and subsequent evolution to this point. Working with Gabriele Bammer since 1996, I have been strongly engaged with and influenced by her work—and my research in the area of drug policy attests to this. The Drug Policy Modelling Program (DPMP) is a program of research and practice aimed at improving Australian illicit drug policy. Research is conducted to address gaps in the evidence base, provide tools for policy makers to better use research evidence and to study how policy actually gets made. As one of five Chief Investigators for DPMP, Gabriele has focused on the ways in which I2S can inform the various components of DPMP. To a large extent, the DPMP work is involved in the third domain of I2S: policy and practice change. In addition, we have concentrated on synthesis of knowledge. Various types of knowledge synthesis have been used: working in multidisciplinary teams to bring different disciplines to bear on the problem at hand; strong engagement with stakeholders—both government decision makers and active drug users—in defining and scoping particular research questions; and the use of participatory computer modelling. In this commentary, I discuss two aspects of I2S: 1) the focus on practice rather than theory, and 2) the role of researchers as advocates for change.

Focus on Practice Rather than Theory

I strongly concur with the challenges of working at integration and implementation; somehow integrative applied research is seen as non-mainstream, unusual, and it does sit uncomfortably on occasion with the academic community. For example, I2S suggests to me that the most important outcomes are good processes with stakeholders that lead to policy or practice change. This is not the kind of metric used by universities, which is most commonly publication in a high-impact peer-reviewed international journal.

---

1 Alison Ritter was invited as 'leader of an innovative research program that has been influenced by, and fostered the development of, I2S. Your observations on this history will be very pertinent. Even more important, however, will be your remarks on how you think I2S might assist DPMP [Drug Policy Modelling Program] (and its subsequent manifestations) in future, as well as which concepts and methods would have been useful in the development of DPMP to this stage, had they been available.'

An important feature of I2S is that it offers a systematic approach to practice that goes beyond 'intuition' (Chapter 31). There is little doubt that a systematic specialist skill set is required for this fledgling discipline. Integrative applied researchers have been working from their own intuition until now. I2S provides a systematic, structured approach to integrative research practices. How will researchers receive I2S? Unfortunately, it is possible that those researchers already operating (with intuition) in this manner may actually dismiss it as 'obvious' or 'trite'. Those who do not have innate integrative applied research skills may find it overwhelming, as it requires a good dose of reflective practice on behalf of the researcher. Within the DPMP multidisciplinary team, there have been mixed reactions: some researchers understand it immediately; others see it as an overly structured approach to something they are doing anyway; and others have commented that components of the approach appear in other literatures (for example, management literature, operations research literature and the systems literature). These sets of reactions are unlikely to be unique. Thus, I suspect that one of the paradoxes for I2S is that those people—researchers and practitioners—who understand the intent, approach and benefits of I2S are likely to be those people who intuitively work in this particular way. Those who do not intuitively work at the edge of integration and implementation may find I2S challenging. A key test for I2S is therefore to distinguish itself in its uniqueness and to demonstrate the benefits of this particular approach over and above existing approaches. In this context, I believe the theoretical underpinnings of I2S are essential.

The book provides a practice-based, accessible toolkit; however, I am disconcerted by the absence of theory. Perhaps I2S is an approach to practice and not a theory, but then a strong rationale is lacking. That is, how will the practice of I2S make a difference to solving complex social problems? What would happen if you did not engage in synthesis, managing unknowns and focusing on change? How were these three domains chosen, if not derived from some theory about integrative applied research? The grand vision, the passion and the significant conceptual advance that Gabriele Bammer offers us with this approach seem hidden behind a tightly constructed set of domains, systematic questions and a storehouse.

In I2S becoming a discipline it is critical for it to demonstrate value. For example, in relation to uncertainty (Domain 2) it remains to be demonstrated how considering and managing diverse unknowns and all of the complexity that entails would produce better integration or implementation for any one specific project or more generally in terms of a body of knowledge. There is little doubt that managing uncertainty is a major challenge for all sciences and what I2S offers is a comprehensive way of thinking about how to approach this from multiple perspectives. In this sense, managing unknowns as a stand-alone component of I2S has enormous value. So this then raises the question about whether I2S must be dealt with as a whole discipline or whether researchers and practitioners can cherry-pick the components that are most helpful or useful to them at that point in time. A comprehensive research endeavour is required to establish whether the outcomes are different when the entire I2S toolkit is used versus selected components.

There appear to be two audiences for I2S: those who will engage with the theory of integrative applied research; and those who are, or want to, practise it. This book is clearly written for the latter; however, the former audience also deserves attention. This audience of thinkers, leaders, and ideas people are the ones who will carry the proposed discipline of I2S forward in academic circles. This is unlikely to be done by the practitioners. I would prefer a stronger vision of I2S; a description of the logical arguments and processes used to derive the central tenets, three domains and five elements; and how I2S supersedes what has come before.

Role of Scholars as Advocates for Change

The relevance of research to public policy is receiving more and more attention.[2] This greater focus on the direct, instrumental use of research to improve society is demonstrated in the focus on dissemination, 'bridging the gap' and translational research.[3] But the divide between the world of research (scholarship) and the world of policy is vast. Research generates new knowledge; the way in which that knowledge is disseminated, translated and taken up to address complex social problems is not necessarily obvious. Indeed, it is not even crafted as a core ingredient in the research process—despite more recent attempts by research funding bodies to address dissemination and impact, as noted above.

This divide is played out in terms of researcher stance: the neutral, dispassionate conveyor of 'fact' versus the passionate advocate. For the former, the role of a researcher is to provide objective, independent evidence. For the latter, evidence is presented in a way to achieve the desired outcome—using analogy and metaphor; framing the issues in the media; engagement in political lobbying; and building coalitions of support. This dichotomy has been noted by a number of commentators.[4] One resolution is to argue that the proper role of researchers is not to operate as advocates at all, and that advocacy can be taken up by others, but should not pollute the integrity, independence and objectivity of either the research itself or the individual researcher. Others, such as Chapman,[5]

2 For example, Brownson et al. (2006); Edwards (2005); Nutley et al. (2007).
3 For example, Hanney et al. (2003); Lomas (1997); Stone et al. (2001).
4 For example, Chapman (2001).
5 Chapman (2007).

have argued for ethical advocacy—advocacy that does not undermine research integrity but is effective in influencing policy or public opinion. This still leaves an impasse between passive delivery of scientific evidence and convincing persuasion.

I believe that I2S provides a significant new solution to this impasse. While the book suggests three strategies—communication, advocacy and engagement (Chapter 20)—that align with effective dissemination to generate impact and change, I2S itself actually transforms this impasse. Put simply, by making 'integrated research support for policy and practice change' the third domain, I2S places the dilemma at the front and centre and implies that rather than divorcing policy and practice change from the scientific endeavour, I2S integrates it as core business. Thus I2S is premised on public relevance and accountability beyond the research world. But I would argue that the I2S contribution is actually much larger than the simple inclusion of this domain. The solution to the impasse provided by I2S is in the process or way of working, which dissolves the researcher–advocacy delineation/impasse.

I2S suggests to me that the issue at stake is not the stance of the researcher; rather, it is inherent in the process of working within the I2S framework. Working within the I2S framework means

- participatory processes that are inclusive of stakeholders from the start and explicitly identify the beneficiaries of the work
- dealing with values, value congruence, boundaries and scoping
- dealing with unknowns within the research process
- being a member of a scholarly discipline.

Each of these aspects in and of itself resolves the research–advocacy dilemma. Some brief comments on each of these are made in the context of a case example: research on the legal status of cannabis (legalisation, decriminalisation or prohibition). Such a sensitive and potentially politically charged project conducted within the I2S frame would commence with inclusion of stakeholders including groups advocating for law reform as well as those advocating for prohibition. These participatory processes have the potential to both explicate the value stance and decrease the likelihood of the research results being dismissed by the communities of practice to which they pertain. If lawmakers are to be one of the beneficiaries of the work, then their identification from the start, including the types of research questions that will inform them, will lead to uptake and dissemination without explicit advocacy. The research team will have discussed values inherent within the team, implied within the research approach and will have ensured congruence. The definition of the scope and boundaries to the research (for example, including population health effects of changing the legal status of cannabis) will ensure that the research results are considered within the appropriate frame of reference as defined by the scoping exercise. This leaves, then, little opportunity for manipulation of the findings, taking them out of context or making assumptions not bounded by the approach.

Dealing with unknowns is a crucial element in managing the research–advocacy divide. One reason much advocacy is problematic is the potential to misuse or misinterpret the limitations inherent in any piece of research. An explicit and comprehensive approach to uncertainty within the research process significantly ameliorates the likelihood that this will occur. One uncertainty in the cannabis example is the extent to which a change in the legal status of cannabis will change the likelihood of cannabis use by young people (does its illegality actually deter use, and will law reform result in greater numbers of cannabis users?). Addressing the uncertainties around this within the research project provides a level of rigour unusual in research of this type.

Finally, being a member of a scholarly discipline is vital to ensure research integrity. As noted in Chapter 26, 'there is also a broader issue about integrative applied research being true to itself and not becoming an uncritical handmaiden to policy makers and practitioners'. In a sensitive area such as cannabis law reform, ensuring the integrity of the research is absolutely essential. I2S offers a disciplinary home for such research, which provides access to peer review, comprehensive tools and methodological approaches, differentiating scholarly criticism from political criticism.

Conclusion

In conclusion, I2S has an enormous amount to offer over and above a toolkit. For example, it provides a way to transform the researcher–advocacy divide; however, it would be strengthened with presentation of a strong theoretical underpinning. In addition, it requires significant time and willingness to work within the I2S approach. Whether a research team can afford to do all of the things implied by I2S whilst actually engaging in the research may be problematic.

I2S positioned within the academy gives greater strength to research integrity when juxtaposed against making change happen in the real world. But it is not clear whether universities will actually appreciate and encompass this unique and groundbreaking approach that has the potential to challenge traditional ways of thinking and doing research.

Contributed April 2010, revised May 2011

References

Brownson, R. C., Royer, C., Ewing, R. and McBride, T. D. (2006). 'Researchers and policymakers: travelers in parallel universes'. *American Journal of Preventive Medicine*, 30 (2): 164–72.

Chapman, S. (2001). 'Advocacy in public health: roles and challenges'. *International Journal of Epidemiology*, 30: 1226–32.

Chapman, S. (2007). *Public Health Advocacy and Tobacco Control: Making smoking history*. Oxford: Blackwell.

Edwards, M. (2005). 'Social science research and public policy: narrowing the divide'. *Australian Journal of Public Administration*, 64 (1): 68–74.

Hanney, S., Gonzalez-Block, M., Buxton, M. and Kogan, M. (2003). 'The utilisation of health research in policy-making: concepts, examples and methods of assessment'. *Health Research Policy and Systems*, 1 (2) (online).

Lomas, J. (1997). *Improving research dissemination and uptake in the health sector: beyond the sound of one hand clapping*. Policy Commentary C97-1. Hamilton, Ontario: McMaster University Center for Health Economics and Policy Analysis.

Nutley, S., Walter, I. and Davies, H. (2007). *Using Evidence: How research can inform public services*. Bristol: The Policy Press.

Stone, D., Maxwell, S. and Keating, M. (2001). *Bridging Research and Policy*. Warwick, UK: UK Department for International Development, Radcliffe House, Warwick University.

Brief Biography

Alison Ritter is a Professor at the National Drug and Alcohol Research Centre, at the University of New South Wales in Sydney, Australia, and is the Director of a major drug policy research program, the Drug Policy Modelling Program (<www.dpmp.unsw.edu.au>). The goal of the work is to advance illicit drug policy through improving the evidence base, developing new policy decision-making tools and understanding policy processes. The program crosses multiple disciplines and engages scholars from psychology, criminology, public policy, mathematics and medicine, to name a few. The focus is on translating research into policy. She is widely published, and is the Vice-President of the Alcohol and other Drug Council of Australia, and President of the International Society for the Study of Drug Policy.

40. Implementing Integration in Research and Practice

Alice Roughley[1]

The I2S Framework

This book establishes a sound theoretical framework for an I2S discipline. This framework is well supported by the recently published book of dialogue methods.[2] These methods will be central to the practice of I2S specialists who will work between professions, policy sectors, research methodologies, values and academic disciplines. The absolute brilliance of the book is that with the foundational research into dialogue methods it tackles the most critical integration methodology issue—that of analysing data generated through different disciplines and stakeholder perspectives/values.

Section four of the book introduces the third domain of the I2S framework: integrated research support for policy and practice change. As an integrator working in a policy context, I struggled most with the fit of this section in the framework. If I2S is to research real-world problems, supporting policy and practice change is the overarching component of the framework, the glue for managing the integral processes of engagement, negotiation, participation and research adoption. Yet this section does not deal with the issue of recommending particular courses of action to policy and government.

Instead this section discusses knowledge about policy and knowledge about scoping, managing engagement and influencing. The management/process component is an identified leg of the framework, as it should be, but the theoretical discussion on policy and practice change should constitute part of the introduction to the book as it sits across the framework as the context for integrated research into real-world problems.

The large literature on community engagement, participatory research methods and research adoption could be consulted and incorporated into the integration management/process chapters to illustrate that integrated research into real-world problems will usually be research and *development* if evidence-based,

---

1   Alice Roughley was invited as a scholar and practitioner 'who has extensive experience in research integration and implementation. I would particularly welcome your comments on the value of the book's ideas in supporting policy and practice change.'
2   McDonald et al. (2009).

directed action on the issue is the desired outcome. The development component demands knowledge of engagement, research adoption and negotiation processes. Perhaps this section could be called 'Managing integration processes in the real world'.

The New Discipline

Establishing a new discipline is no small challenge. New disciplines are generally born of a seemingly insurmountable social problem. Eclectic disciplines and endeavours that sit across traditional disciplines are often marginal. Think for instance about social work, social development, and so on. Their research methodologies are described as 'soft'. The findings of qualitative studies are frequently dismissed as not being 'scientific'. Purist and positivist disciplines are accepted as the norm and this preconception is difficult to disarm in the context of the academy. The epistemological polarisation is very real, leaving a significant void that I2S can surely occupy. The cleavage is the space where we need to find not only theory and methods but also reason with respect to the reality that some of the world's greatest challenges can only be understood by looking through multiple lenses.

The analogy Gabriele Bammer draws with statistics is significant in demonstrating how I2S can operate and make a significant intellectual contribution. It lends weight to the case for the new discipline. A 'discipline', according to the *Penguin New English Dictionary*, is 'a field of study'. The *Macquarie Dictionary* defines a 'discipline' as 'a branch of instruction or learning'. This book establishes the theoretical framework for a discipline and invites collaboration in the next steps: building a knowledge base and training program from that framework. This is an alluring prospect for those of us who are excited about integration.

Integrationists will surely be people who think creatively, people who see the big picture, understand systems and want to connect disparate parts of pictures. In my view, work remains to be done to take I2S beyond a field of study and to illustrate what the I2S field of practice will look like. Placing the hypothetical view of the future that opens Chapter 31 at the beginning of the book would have been useful for me, to illustrate the vision of how I2S graduates might operate and contribute. Further examples of how integrationists might operate in a policy or practice change context, in addition to the research integration focus, will no doubt be further elaborated as I2S develops.

I2S specialists will, no doubt, have an interest in a wide range of social and political systems. When I, as an integrationist working in and between policy, research, teaching/practice, think about establishing I2S as a discipline, I think about theory, tools, knowledge, skills and practitioners. Further careful thought will be needed to establish a comprehensive curriculum for I2S.

Analysis and Actors

In my experience, the biggest challenge in practising integration is analysing data and information that are generated in disciplines at various points in the epistemological spectrum. Sense-making of local knowledge emanating from a social-action process and social and physical sciences inevitably involves a deal of 'expert judgment' and risks being labelled 'unscientific'. Fields of endeavour such as environmental and social impact assessments illustrate well the difficulty of weighting diverse data sources. The desired outcome of policy makers (who are often the research/study funding source) can also influence the analysis process. Factors in the integration context including values, power and credibility of actors are worthy of more detailed consideration in the book.

This has been the most tortured aspect of social-impact assessment, a methodology that is supposed to provide decision makers with options for action and their pros and cons, including mitigation strategies laid out for the cons. Social-impact assessment specialists have tended to be coopted by the agency funding the research and development and either make a case for the option the decision maker seeks or do not weight the data. In part, this is because there have been so few articulated and accepted methods for weighting multidisciplinary and stakeholder data. The result is often much contention over the findings based on the different perspectives and values of stakeholders. What we learn from social-impact assessment is that the more independent the research and development is and the more transparent the findings and the processes to generate them, the more credible and acceptable will be the results. The overview of relevant dialogue methods for integration and their suggested application is an immense advance in addressing this problem.

Managing the integrated research/study often demands a high level of interpersonal skill, not only knowledge of dialogue methods. The integrator is tasked with negotiating across value systems as well as political imperatives. There is often a researcher/policy/community cleavage. Training in interpersonal communications, including negotiating skills, will need to be core skills for I2S specialists. The I2S course entry criteria may need to be carefully determined with issues such as these in mind.

Why would someone enrol in I2S? Is there an employment future for graduates? Where might those opportunities be and how will the merits of I2S be promoted in such a way that employment opportunities will be created? It may seem trite to comment on the need for a business case in this commentary but the world of academia is very much a business these days.

Indeed, the academy has resisted interdisciplinarity. Much current integrative work occurs in practice, both private and public. Professions working in areas such as human relations, evaluation, risk analysis, Indigenous health, natural resource management, and social and environmental impact assessment generally sit outside academia, while practitioners work with academic theory and specialists. Disciplines including community, social and international development and social geography (note they are all social science disciplines and often marginal in universities) often produce practitioners who establish private practices. Many of these people are practising I2S, even though they are not always writing and publishing a process analysis of their work. They deserve greater recognition in the book. They may be the people who enrol in the course. They will contribute to the development of I2S with their prior knowledge and experience and specialist skills. They will bring to the discipline many items for the storeroom.

Continued Collaboration

This book sets out a truly ambitious and worthwhile project. With engagement and collaboration among integrationists and those with an interest in integration, the bringing together of people, tools and skills has potential for a discipline to emerge that is desperately needed if we are to address the complex problems of this world. This book presents both a sound theoretical basis for I2S and the challenge of further developing the three domains: synthesis of disciplinary and stakeholder knowledge, understanding and managing diverse unknowns and providing integrated research support for policy and practice change.

There is much work to be done in each domain to establish a curriculum and teaching/training program, a blend of theory and practical learning. The I2S storehouse will need to have plenty of tunnels as many of the tools will move between rooms, as will the integrationists. The prospect of such a course is very exciting. The collaboration that will make this a reality will be immensely rewarding. I am enthusiastic to be engaged in this pursuit.

Contributed April 2010

Reference

McDonald, D., Bammer, G. and Deane, P. (2009). *Research Integration Using Dialogue Methods*. Canberra: ANU E Press; <http://epress.anu.edu.au/dialogue_methods_citation> (accessed 6 August 2012).

Brief Biography

Dr Alice Roughley currently works in the heritage area of the Australian Government Department of Sustainability, Environment, Water, Population and Communities. She has been involved in a range of agencies and projects to build bridges across disciplines and between community, research and policy stakeholders. In her capacity as a part-time private consultant, she specialises in strategic planning and participatory evaluation. She has managed two highly integrated research and development portfolios, one for Land & Water Australia, the other for the Desert Knowledge Cooperative Research Centre. She holds a masters degree in Social Impact Assessment and a PhD in integrated local area planning, and has extensive experience in community development and as a social policy practitioner.

41. Building I2S into an Academic Program

Lawrence Cram[1]

A century after Kipling's 'The Sons of Martha' and a half-century after Snow's *The Two Cultures and the Scientific Revolution*, vast publics remain unaware of the scale of their reliance on knowledge-based technical practice.[2] That Kipling and Snow caricatured their unaware publics as élites added piquancy to the situation. Snow's position was particularly clear: '(literary) intellectuals are natural Luddites', he wrote. The passing of the half-century since *The Two Cultures* has seen technology-based practice address many of society's seemingly intractable challenges. Nonetheless, many publics (élite and otherwise) have become less aware of, and increasingly hostile towards, their reliance on science and knowledge-based technology.

A different but related cultural dichotomy motivates Gabriele's book. In one corner stand academic researchers, with knowledge and informed practices—always hard-won and often highly qualified. In the opposite corner stand officials and activists, with problems—always hard and often highly complex. The Integration and Implementation Sciences (I2S) stand between them, not to referee but rather to broker marriages. This commentary examines this positioning of I2S from the perspective of a university research manager.

Why Integration and Implementation Sciences?

The following observations are, I believe, the foundational propositions set out in Gabriele's monograph.

1a.   There are people with responsibilities and/or strivings to change aspects of human affairs. Call these people the primary participants.

1b.   Primary participants often characterise their agendas as addressing or solving important problems of human society.

---

1   Lawrence Cram was invited as a university leader 'who has a longstanding interest in "integration" to tackle complex real-world problems. Your observations on whether the ideas in the book are workable in a university such as the ANU will be very pertinent.'
2   Kipling (1907); Snow (1959).

2a. There is an activity known as academic research that has something to offer primary participants, but the primary participants do not know enough about it.

2b. Academic research is organised into disciplines, and more than one discipline has something to offer.

3a. Assembling disciplinary-based academic research so that it offers what is optimally useful to primary participants is an activity known as Integration and Implementation Sciences (I2S). I2S connects academic research to people aiming to change human affairs.

3b. I2S has not yet been reduced to a mature and systematic practice. An initial systematic practice is being assembled from available knowledge and methods in I2S, and practitioners are being educated in that practice.

3c. The initial practice could be enriched and improved by further systematic academic research in I2S, stimulated by deliberate and large-scale seed funding.

The significance of I2S is evident from the importance and richness of these propositions. The problematic features of I2S also begin to emerge.

Propositions (1a) and (1b) invite questions about the motivation and legitimacy of primary participants and their agendas. Mass media attention, political action, commercial interests, righteous indignation and wrong but honest beliefs all play out for people having an interest in creating the perception of a 'problem to be solved'. In practice, the problem may be fictitious or of lesser priority, or one where the solution is evident but unpalatable, or where doing nothing should be the preferred option. How might an I2S specialist prevent wasteful engagement between primary participants and academic researchers on wrongly stated and prioritised problems or on unworthy causes? Conversely, how does the I2S specialist coopt academic researchers for worthy causes? How does the I2S specialist exercise the evident responsibilities for gatekeeping and filtering?

Propositions (2a) and (2b) could be read as an indictment of the academic enterprise for its inability to communicate directly with broader audiences, reinforcing the stereotype of scholarly experts as intense and inaccessible specialists; however, this reading would underestimate the challenges that primary participants face in *integrating* academic knowledge, even when individual academic actors communicate clearly (which is not always the case). The propositions also hint at the risk of cynical exploitation of the academy. It is recognised that academic expert witnesses can be found on either side of most important issues. Academics accept this tentative uncertainty as an essential feature of the discovery, construction and reframing of knowledge. Primary participants, however, may not wish to grapple with uncertainty or recognise alternative perspectives, but instead coopt selected academic perspectives to their causes.

Propositions (3a)–(3c) invite the question 'Why is the need for I2S emerging only now?'. Perhaps a plausible explanation is found in (hotly contested) Cultural Theory. According to Cultural Theory, adherents to the putative high-group/low-grid[3] way will attach urgent importance to taking action on emerging crises. Since the power to take such action is perceived to be greater now than in the past (and may well be greater in some cases), these adherents have greater opportunities. A persistent and heightened sense of increasing complexity and ongoing crisis stimulate an increasing number and breadth of primary participants. A new profession arises to capture the efficiencies that arise through the division of labour, as academic researchers are unable to serve the growing need. A new discipline, I2S, arises to support the new profession.

The opportunities and needs for I2S will only intensify in the future. Once authors such as Gabriele point out what to look for as I2S, it can be seen in action in many parts of society. Scholarly work *on* I2S (theory building, codifying practice, and so on) will then be inevitable, and is bound to arise in many different disciplinary contexts until the character of I2S becomes better understood and refined.

I2S, Human Sciences and the Sciences of the Artificial

The history of ideas provides an account of the development of three categories of systematic knowledge and theory building: natural sciences, human sciences and the sciences of the artificial.[4] Distinctive epistemologies related to deep differences in the nature of theories and the objects of research arise among these sciences or understandings.

Research in the natural sciences is a quest for law-based explanations.[5] Encompassing astronomy and the earth sciences, physics, the materials sciences, and biology, it is characterised by systematic observation, critical

---

3   From Douglas (1970): a 'high-group' way of life is about a high degree of collective control, whereas a 'low-group' one emphasises individual self-sufficiency. A 'high-grid' way of life has conspicuous and durable forms of stratification in roles and authority, whereas 'low-grid' has a more egalitarian ordering.

4   Gregor (2009) and references therein.

5   Kuhn (1996).

experimentation, hypothesis formation and falsification. Research settings and problems in the natural sciences are reproducible, and progress is made through puzzle solving that confronts well-characterised anomalies.

Research in the human sciences is the quest for 'understanding of human and historical life'.[6] Encompassing the social sciences and the humanities, human sciences research entails an array of theories and methods that are more diverse and contested than in natural sciences research. This fluidity springs from the internalised, first-person capacity of humans for deliberated or unbidden stances and actions, fundamentally distinct from the reproducibility found in the natural sciences. Research in the human sciences is characterised by new and deeper hermeneutic reinterpretation, often arising from shifts in research settings and problems due to changes in social and political systems.

Research in the sciences of the artificial—the design sciences—is concerned 'not with how things are, but with how they might be'.[7] Research in the science of the artificial encompasses artefacts that may be symbols, material objects, activities and organised services, and complex environments for living and learning.[8] Research methods differ from those of research in the natural or human sciences in a number of ways, owing to the 'malignant' or 'wicked' nature of design science problems and puzzles. The account of 'Dilemmas in a general theory of planning' by Rittel and Webbers[9] identifies the following characteristics

1. problem understanding and problem resolution are concomitant

2. work on a problem terminates when time, money or patience is exhausted

3. there are no true or false answers

4. there is no way to trace all the waves through all the lives affected by a solution

5. every implemented solution has consequences that cannot be undone

6. judgment determines which solution should be pursued and implemented

7. part of the art is not knowing too early which solution to apply

8. every problem is a symptom of another problem

9. explanations are logically arbitrary and hypotheses not subject to crucial tests

10. practitioners are personally liable for the consequences of their actions.

---

6 Dilthey (1988).
7 Simon (1996).
8 Buchanan (1992).
9 Rittel and Webbers (1973).

Given these characteristics, and the nature of I2S as described by Gabriele, the 'science' in I2S is not natural science. Rather, it lies at the intersection of human science and design science. I2S is a human science since it entails interpersonal and inter-group interactions, and a science of the artificial since it leads to the creation of symbols, objects, services and environments by and for humans. The appearance of 'design' as part of the toolkit for I2S practitioners will draw on knowledge and understandings that oftentimes will be unfamiliar to the natural science and human science researchers who are coopted or 'called upon' into their projects. Indeed, not only coopted researchers but also the primary participants—the people with responsibilities or strivings for change—may be unfamiliar with a design science perspective on their activities.

Just as the natural and human sciences resolve into disciplinary specialisations, so too do the design sciences resolve in to specialisations—such as graphic design relating to symbols and industrial design relating to material objects. Design science specialisations relating to systems and environments also exist (engineering and urban planning, for example) and appear to be ripe for enrichment—a situation directly important for I2S as a field of academic inquiry. Of particular interest to I2S are refractions such as political science (normally viewed as a human science) contributing to the design of public policy, and environmental and economic sciences (normally viewed as natural and human sciences, respectively) contributing to development programs.

The course of sociology as a discipline over the past few decades offers insights into pathways for I2S. Burawoy's[10] description of public, policy, professional and critical sociologies raises many topics of direct interest to academic (that is, critical) consideration of I2S. Traditional and organic public sociologies entail relationships between publics and academics, which are reminiscent of the relationships that are the primary focus of I2S—the difference being that I2S is not in itself a longstanding discipline like sociology. The value of distinguishing between public and policy sociologies is evident, and perhaps a useful distinction that is not yet a part of I2S. It is axiomatic that I2S practice with a client group (that is, policy work) and with a public could have quite different complexions.

The normal pathway for an emergent discipline in the modern university is to acquire initial formal recognition through formation as a 'centre' or 'institute' or 'network' either within or between existing academic disciplinary units. If the centre prospers in an academic sense, through growth in educational and/ or research attention, the university will likely find ways to support growing independence. Colonisation of affiliated disciplines can occur and will support rapid growth; legitimacy in an academic sense requires emergence of similar

---

10   Burawoy (2005).

disciplinary foci in several universities. I2S exhibits many of these features, and we may be witnessing the appearance of a new discipline: I2S as described by Gabriele, or something quite like it.

Contributed June 2011

References

Buchanan, R. (1992). 'Wicked problems in design thinking'. *Design Issues*, 8 (2): 5–21.

Burawoy, M. (2005). 'For public sociology'. *American Sociological Review*, 70: 4–28.

Dilthey, W. (Translator Betanzos, R. J.). (1988). *Introduction to the Human Sciences*. Detroit: Wayne State University Press.

Douglas, M. (1970). *Natural Symbols: Explorations in cosmology*. New York: Pantheon.

Gregor, S. (2009). 'Building theory in the science of the artificial'. *Proceedings of the 4th International Conference on Design Science Research in Information Systems and Technology*. New York: Association for Computing Machinery.

Kipling, R. (1907). 'The Sons of Martha'. [Poem]; <http://www.online-literature. com/donne/920/> (accessed 6 August 2012).

Kuhn, T. (1996). *The Structure of Scientific Revolutions*. Third Edition. Chicago: University of Chicago Press.

Rittel, H. W. J. and Webbers, M. M. (1973). 'Dilemmas in a general theory of planning'. *Policy Sciences*, 4: 155–69.

Simon, H. (1996). *The Sciences of the Artificial*. Third Edition. Cambridge, MA: MIT Press.

Snow, C. P. (1959). *The Two Cultures and the Scientific Revolution*. Cambridge: Cambridge University Press.

Brief Biography

Professor Lawrence Cram is Deputy Vice-Chancellor (Research) at The Australian National University (ANU). His career spans research and teaching in engineering, mathematics, astronomy, physics and computing. He has extensive experience in public sector research management and public policy. He worked for three years as Executive Director in the Australian Research Council and has been involved in the successful commercialisation of research at CSIRO, the University of Sydney and ANU. He has long been interested in higher education, particularly in relation to the identification and enhancement of the affordances that arise between universities and their scholarly communities. He is a Fellow of Engineers Australia, the Australian Institute of Physics and the Royal Astronomical Society.

42. The Institutional Challenges of Changing the Academic Landscape

Catherine Lyall[1]

Disciplines confer many advantages, not least by placing boundaries around bodies of knowledge, which facilitates efficient teaching and provides guidance about adequate concepts and methodologies. Quality can often be more readily tested against disciplinary criteria. Set against this, the changing dynamics of the natural, social and political worlds mean that research funders are increasingly called upon to generate innovative solutions to multidimensional, policy-related problems on a regional, national or global scale. As complex problems of, for example, climate change or healthy ageing become more pressing, the ability of funders to deliver solutions to such challenges increasingly requires integration across disciplines as well as reaching out from academia to the policy, private and third sectors. Interesting and meaningful work happens at these boundaries and in the gaps between disciplines, and Lawrence Cram is undoubtedly right when he states in his commentary that 'the opportunities and needs for I2S will only intensify in the future'.

In addition to the obvious barriers to communication among different specialties and different stakeholders, I2S can, however, expect to encounter institutional barriers: departmental structures, management systems and career pathways that are most often based on well-established disciplines. These challenges need to be recognised and managed if individual researchers and centres are to build effective and successful I2S programs. The book's greatest weakness, certainly from a UK perspective, is that this issue is not adequately addressed, and I outline the key issues in this commentary.

In our own work,[2] we draw distinctions between long-term, interdisciplinary involvement for 'academic' reasons (for example, to enable a discipline to move into new areas of research) and the shorter-term, situational interest where the primary aim is problem oriented, and discipline-related outputs are less central to project design. We are also increasingly distinguishing between two levels of interdisciplinary integration: 'first order' (primarily ontological and epistemological factors) and 'second order' (primarily research management aspects). First order relates to the intellectual challenges faced at the start of an interdisciplinary project: how to manage complexity, to set constructive

---

1 Catherine Lyall was invited because of her 'significant contributions to the development of thinking about interdisciplinary research'.
2 For example, Lyall et al. (2011b).

boundaries on the project, what to include and what to exclude, how the main components of the project relate to one another—and to do this without resorting to the given boundaries of the contributing disciplines. These early decisions exemplify the really tough aspects of interdisciplinary research design, analysis and reporting: different research cultures determine different methodologies and underlying ontologies and these early decisions are what form the core of the integrative method. So often, as Gabriele laments, relevant insights about these first-order decisions regarding which disciplines to include languish undocumented in people's heads, dissipating 'creative effort by reinventing methodological wheels' (Chapter 31).

Related to these first-order decisions is the fundamental issue of evaluation. Evaluation plays a critical role in blocking or facilitating integrative applied research. Peer review must be the cornerstone of quality assessment, but discipline-based criteria can be insufficient for evaluation of work that steps beyond disciplines. Current review processes are a serious hindrance for integrative applied research and the lack of agreed indicators of quality may be one reason a question mark often hangs over the academic value of such work. The choice of evaluators, their disciplinary and interdisciplinary backgrounds, and their roles in the evaluation process need careful consideration. The process of finding suitable peers to review interdisciplinary work is a frequently cited challenge for those managing the evaluation process and often a source of deep frustration for researchers. The problem is acute for proposals attempting a novel interdisciplinary project where there may not be a recognised set of peers who are individually qualified to referee it. Moreover, the criteria appropriate to evaluation of academically oriented interdisciplinary research may often be different from problem-focused projects and programs. Improved evaluation protocols are vital to achieving a more stable and consistent role for integrative applied research and for improving its intellectual status in academia. In the United Kingdom, recent research[3] has recommended the establishment of an interdisciplinary reviewers' college, greater shared administrative resources for interdisciplinary investments among the Research Councils, and an 'Interdisciplinary Portal' to coordinate and consolidate access to information about funding, training and other support dedicated to interdisciplinarity and its evaluation.

Fundamental Tensions

Gabriele acknowledges the persistent institutional factors that can discourage interdisciplinary research—for example, a lack of opportunities to publish

---

3   Lyall et al. (2011a).

in high-ranking, refereed journals and discrimination by referees against interdisciplinary proposals and publications. As a leader of a collaborative centre in Scotland noted:[4] 'there is a fundamental tension between interdisciplinary institutes or centres and the university internal management system'—which needs to be recognised. Interdisciplinary interactions are clearly transforming the natural sciences and the social scientists who work with them but there can be real challenges in forging synergies across seemingly distant disciplines as well as between those that are more proximate. In particular, the context within which integrative applied research arises can vary across several dimensions and it is important to be aware of institutional constraints that may weigh differentially on team members in different departments or different universities. In contrast with discipline-based departments, interdisciplinary collaborations may run counter to institutional allocations of credit, finances, indirect costs or other resources.

Maintaining Integrity

In countries, such as the United Kingdom, where there is a governmental drive to increase knowledge exchange and the impact of research on both policy and practice, including commercial development, there is an increasing desire to engage potential users and other stakeholders in research projects. Including stakeholders in the research project is often regarded as conducive to interdisciplinary research for its own sake but also, significantly, in terms of promoting research uptake. Such stakeholders may include policy makers, local authorities, industry, professional groups (for example, educators, health professionals), civil society groups or citizens more generally. A key challenge may be how to maintain impartiality and avoid becoming completely immersed in stakeholder concerns. Where the research is intimately linked with stakeholder issues this may lead to conflicts (such as confidentiality issues) or impatience on the part of the research partner to achieve results. Involving potential research users in the evaluation of integrative applied research (either at the proposal stage or in the assessment of outputs) may also pose difficulties if those non-academic colleagues do not fully understand research goals, norms and methods.

A focus on stakeholder engagement may bring political pressures that challenge independent researchers' neutral competence and may fuel the arguments of those who see interdisciplinary research as irrevocably consigned to a short-term, problem-solving mode[5] or those who believe that 'problem-based knowledge is insufficiently abstract to survive in competition with problem-

---

4   Meagher and Lyall (2005a, p. 20).
5   Petts et al. (2006).

portable knowledge'.[6] Some regret that the 'persistent linking of the concepts of interdisciplinarity and "real world problems" has associated an interdisciplinary approach with instrumental, or applied research', and warn that uncritical advocacy of interdisciplinarity can oversimplify the different traditions and contributions made by different disciplines.[7]

Problem-focused research is thus sometimes seen as undermining academic research, taking its evolution in a direction with which many academics are uncomfortable. Pursuit of multifaceted problems beyond the scope of any one discipline is often seen by discipline-based researchers as at best irrelevant and at worst threatening, so that the barriers to integrative applied research are correspondingly greater. Alternatively, a research unit (or individual researcher) risks being reduced to a service role where staff provide specific, well-defined inputs (for example, data sets, tools) to another domain without the need for significant interdisciplinary interaction or contribution to advance their own core knowledge. Active researchers may migrate away from such collaborations if they are not seen to benefit their own research and careers.

The Role of Funders

We know that funding is a major driver for behaviour change among researchers, so national and international research funders could be key advocates for I2S. But, while it is evident that the relationship between disciplines is strongly influenced by national funding agencies, lack of organisational memory in these bodies can be an issue when the staff involved in championing cross-council or cross-disciplinary initiatives move on to new areas. Our experience as evaluators shows that there is a need to minimise the learning curve at the start of projects and programs,[8] and Gabriele rightly points to the importance of organisational learning and lesson sharing. In the United Kingdom as elsewhere, Research Councils have developed effective systems to run research programs within their core areas but may require additional assistance to capture occasional 'idiosyncratic' experiences—such as running interdisciplinary initiatives. Moreover, at either a funding-body level or the level of an institution, such initiatives can be vulnerable and regarded as dispensable when money is tight. Gabriele commends the benefits of relatively untied funding but this seems less likely in times of austerity here in the United Kingdom and the pessimist in me fears retrenchment to the hierarchy of disciplines.

---

6   Abbott (2001, p. 135).
7   Petts et al. (2006).
8   Lyall et al. (2011a).

Career Pathways

Integrative applied researchers will need to plan their personal development more carefully than colleagues with more conservative career paths. They may consequently need better mentoring so that they both respond to sponsors' requirements and think strategically about their own personal research and publication strategy. Gabriele points to the dangers of such researchers being marginalised within the academic mainstream: finding an appropriate scholarly community to counter the potential feeling of intellectual homelessness can be one of the keys to success. Significantly, in the early stages of establishing I2S as a discipline, there is a clear risk that young researchers will struggle at the start of their academic career. In a study we conducted of an interdisciplinary capacity-building scheme for the United Kingdom,[9] one professor was highly complimentary about the calibre of interdisciplinary PhD students produced by the scheme. Yet, when asked if he, personally, would hire someone with that background, he acknowledged that he would have to give priority to individuals seen to be able to teach introductory courses in his department's 'home' discipline. So young researchers will continue to straddle domains until they become established integrative applied researchers; the feedback we got from supervisors in that same study was that, although they felt comfortable in their interdisciplinarity now that they had achieved a certain status, their advice to early career researchers was not to pursue an interdisciplinary path until they had achieved tenure. As an aside, Gabriele notes that current education relevant to complex real-world problems is idiosyncratic. This is something that we recognise and have tried to address with our Interdisciplinary Masterclasses in the United Kingdom,[10] but this workshop-based, advanced training that we have developed at various levels, from PhD student to research leaders, is a drop in the ocean. I2S needs to be underpinned by sustained, systematic training throughout the researcher's life.

A key risk, especially but not exclusively for someone starting out in their career, may be lack of institutional advancement. The institutions of academia have long been geared towards disciplines and mono-disciplinary work, whether these institutions take the form of departments, faculties, universities, professional societies or journals. As I2S scholars, we know the disadvantages of promotion or selection criteria that are oriented towards evaluation of worth as measured by contribution to a single discipline. In preceding commentaries, Deborah O'Connell and colleagues have highlighted the challenges of publishing and Alison Ritter has drawn attention to the use of inappropriate metrics. A survey by the National Academies[11] captured this sort of risk across multiple

---

9   Meagher and Lyall (2005b).
10   See Lyall and Meagher (2012).
11   National Academies (2005, pp. 264–5).

US universities: promotion criteria were the highest ranked impediment to interdisciplinary research, as ranked both by individuals and by university provosts.

Although Gabriele does discuss some of these organisational barriers, I think—with the fervour of the true evangelist—she does tend to downplay the importance of academic reward structures. But these may change over time. In the United Kingdom, the new national Research Excellence Framework (REF) introduces for the first time an explicit element to assess the 'impact' arising from excellent research, alongside the 'outputs' and 'environment' elements.[12] The assessment of impact will be based on expert review of case studies submitted by universities; these case studies may include any social, economic or cultural impact or benefit beyond academia that has taken place during the assessment period, which was underpinned by excellent research produced by the submitting institution within a given time frame. Although these proposals initially caused considerable alarm among certain sectors of the UK academy, this approach may yet prove beneficial to those academics who pursue a less traditional form of scholarship—one more oriented towards I2S.

Universities are already beginning to employ individuals who can act at the interface between researchers and non-academic stakeholders; however, these emerging roles are not unproblematic in a research setting. The ambiguous, hybrid and often temporary nature of such university positions can be challenging for the post-holders who perform these 'blended' functions, occupying as they do a liminal space between academics and administrators.[13] As the Shergold quotation opening Chapter 17 emphasises, the policy world is rarely a comfortable home for the disciplinary purist.

Conclusion

Developing a new discipline is a major undertaking and not without risks. In offering her 'Big Science' manifesto for I2S, Gabriele's approach is fittingly ambitious but perhaps also overly optimistic, especially when institutional barriers are taken into account.

Disciplines exist because, in the past at least, they made knowledge manageable. They also bestow considerable benefits in terms of peer recognition, access to resources, clear training pathways and professional kudos. Some interdisciplinary fields have reached the point where they are recognised as disciplines in their own right with a shared epistemological base and associated esteem measures,

---

12   REF2014 website: <http://www.hefce.ac.uk/research/ref/> (accessed 16 February 2012).
13   Knight and Lightowler (2010); Whitchurch (2009).

resulting in stable systemic communities within which researchers concentrate their experience into a particular world view. So, in developing the new 'discipline' of I2S, how do we retain the freshness and spontaneity—how do we accrue the reputational advantages of a discipline without the potential disadvantages of ossification?

Also, we cannot underestimate the politics of disciplines or the power of vested interests. Case studies are clearly crucial to build evidence of success but so is political lobbying—of our peers, of our university leaders and of our funders. How best can we sell the concept in order to change the academic landscape so that we achieve Gabriele's 'virtuous cycle between funding, capacity and demonstrated success' (Chapter 31)? Individuals will inevitably be conflicted between being disciplinary specialists and I2S scholars; how can we best help them to manage these multiple identities within the existing constraints of our academic institutions? Perhaps if I was in a philanthropic mood and had $1 million to spend, I would focus on these issues of recognition, reward and evaluation, and, specifically, I would launch a new international journal of I2S to help establish proof-of-concept and build academic credibility.

Gabriele's very clear, structured approach to setting out her argument may be misinterpreted by critics as an oversimplified, linear, normative approach. Breaking down the steps in order to manage the whole is a key tenet of integrative applied research and Gabriele emphasises that this is an iterative process, not one that is prescriptive but one that recognises and supports multiple approaches. Gabriele is a pioneer, offering us some stepping stones to help us start a worldwide discussion about research that takes place at the boundaries of our current experience.

From my own experience, I see myself as someone endeavouring to sustain an innovative, 'blended' form of scholarship combining world-class research and consultancy with research development, knowledge exchange and capacity building. This embodies the dynamic relationship between theory, practice and impact increasingly demanded of an academic but it does sometimes feel that I don't have a proper intellectual home. Perhaps, in future, I2S can provide one.

Contributed October 2011

References

Abbott, A. (2001). *Chaos of Disciplines*. Chicago and London: University of Chicago Press.

Knight, C. and Lightowler, C. (2010). 'Reflections of "knowledge exchange professionals" in the social sciences: emerging opportunities and challenges for university-based brokers'. *Evidence and Policy*, 6 (4): 543–56.

Lyall, C. and Meagher, L. (2012). 'A masterclass in interdisciplinarity: research into practice in training the next generation of interdisciplinary researchers'. *Futures*, 44 (6): 608–17.

Lyall, C., Bruce, A., Marsden, W. and Meagher, L. (2011a). *Identifying key success factors in the quest for interdisciplinary knowledge*. Report to Natural Environment Research Council.

Lyall, C., Bruce, A., Tait, J. and Meagher, L. (2011b). *Interdisciplinary Research Journeys. Practical strategies for capturing creativity*. London: Bloomsbury Academic.

Meagher, L. and Lyall, C. (2005a). *Evaluation of the ESRC/NERC Interdisciplinary Research Studentship Scheme*. Report to Economic and Social Research Council.

Meagher, L. and Lyall, C. (2005b). *Phase Two Evaluation of Research Development Grant*. Report to Scottish Higher Education Funding Council.

National Academies. (2005). *Facilitating Interdisciplinary Research*. National Academy of Sciences, National Academy of Engineering, and Institute of Medicine. Washington, DC: National Academy Press.

Petts, J., Owens, S. and Bulkeley, H. (2006). 'Crossing boundaries: interdisciplinarity in the context of urban environments'. *Geoforum*, 39 (2): 593–601.

Whitchurch, C. (2009). 'The rise of the blended professional in higher education: a comparison between the United Kingdom, Australia and the United States'. *Higher Education*, 58 (3): 407–18.

Brief Biography

Dr Catherine Lyall was until recently Deputy Director of Innogen, an interdisciplinary research centre studying innovation in the life sciences and the social impact of innovation on global health, agri-food, the environment and the economy. She is now Deputy Director of the Genomics Policy and Research Forum, a sister initiative at the University of Edinburgh which works to widen the reception of social science research beyond existing audiences, and build capacity amongst social scientists for public and policy engagement. She is an experienced science policy researcher and evaluator of knowledge exchange and interdisciplinary research activities who has acted as a consultant to a number of public bodies in Scotland, the United Kingdom and Europe. Her personal research program seeks to advance an understanding of problems of science and technology policy formation and strategic decision making by adopting interdisciplinary and practitioner-based perspectives. She is also Associate Dean Research Careers for the university's College of Humanities and Social Science.

43. The Brazilian Experience with Institutional Arrangements for Interdisciplinary Graduate Programs: I2S may provide a way forward

Marcel Bursztyn and Maria Beatriz Maury[1]

In Brazil, as in other countries, researchers are increasingly working in interdisciplinary teams. In general this cooperation has not effectively leveraged the experiences of team members and the variety of concepts, methods and tools available in their original disciplines. Despite the development of interdisciplinary research and practice, and the exponential growth of interdisciplinary masters and doctoral programs (described below), there are still no initiatives to bring together the knowledge generated. There has been no large-scale attempt to gather the richness of integrative experiences, which are poorly documented and subjected to only very limited analysis. Nor are there standard procedures for establishing what an interdisciplinary program is in concept and practice, or how it can be evaluated and monitored. This creates a vicious cycle of lack of knowledge and communication.

This commentary is based on our studies of the evolution of the debate on interdisciplinarity,[2] and we briefly discuss two issues: institutionalisation within universities and the National System of Accreditation and Evaluation[3] of graduate programs in Brazil.

Interdisciplinary Arrangements in Brazil

In general, new disciplines have been created by fragmentation (for example, the separation of sociology and anthropology within the field of social sciences and the division of natural sciences into geology and biology) or by aggregation of pre-existing disciplines (for example, biology plus physics into biophysics).

---

1   Marcel Bursztyn was invited because of his 'expertise in sustainability science, especially in Brazil'. He invited Maria Beatriz Maury to co-author the commentary.
2   Some authors prefer the use of the term transdisciplinarity; others adopt a multidisciplinary approach. In this commentary, we have adopted the term interdisciplinarity.
3   In Brazil, a strict system centralised by the Coordination for the Improvement of the Higher Education Personnel (CAPES) agency of the Ministry of Education not only coordinates the accreditation of graduate programs (more than 4000 in all), but also regulates the process of evaluation, ranking and grant provision.

Interdisciplinary programs have very different characteristics. They are not a result of either fragmentation or aggregation: they are multiform and nonlinear spaces of integration. Shaped largely in reaction to problem-oriented demands, these programs have, by definition, a complex identity. In particular, the hierarchies of disciplinary components are diverse and ad hoc. Teams organised to address the challenges can (and should) have flexible compositions, responding to the nature of the problem. This represents a challenge in coordination, for which Bammer's work makes an important contribution.

Brazilian experiences follow a global trend where interdisciplinary programs have two kinds of personnel: a few permanent members and a larger group with joint appointments in various disciplines. This is a combination that also provides two-way communication between the disciplinary departments and the interdisciplinary programs. The tenure of those members with joint appointments is likely to vary, depending on the extent of their possible contributions to the topics addressed by the interdisciplinary program. The permanent personnel of the interdisciplinary program are responsible for ensuring continuity, integration and implementation. For that reason, they need special skills, methods and tools, which I2S can provide. After the recent proliferation of interdisciplinary programs in Brazil, faculty and administrators are debating the most effective and productive ways to gather, analyse and evaluate relevant concepts and methods.

The National System of Accreditation and Evaluation

In order to operate and issue degrees, masters and doctoral programs in Brazil need to be accredited by the National System of Accreditation and Evaluation. After meeting initial entry criteria, there are also performance evaluations every three years. Programs are classified into eight 'major areas', 76 'areas' and 340 'sub-areas' of knowledge, using the following definitions.

- Major area: a group of various areas of knowledge aggregated according to the affinity of its objects, cognitive methods and instrumental resources reflecting specific contexts and identities.

- Area: a set of collectively constructed, interrelated knowledge, assembled according to the nature of the object of investigation for purposes of teaching, research and practical applications.

- Sub-area: segmentation of the area of knowledge established on the basis of the object of study and methodological procedures widely employed and recognised.

There is also a fourth category—namely 'specialty', which is the thematic characterisation of research and teaching activities. The same specialty can occur in different major areas, areas and sub-areas.

In 1999, the National System of Accreditation and Evaluation created a 'major area' called 'Multidisciplinary' for programs that did not fit the usual categories. Whereas there has been a 12 per cent increase per year in all new programs over the past two decades, the annual increase in multidisciplinary programs has been 25 per cent. In 2008 the *multidisciplinary* major area listed 293 accredited courses.[4] This was 11 per cent of the total programs and placed this major area on a par with engineering, applied social sciences, exact and earth sciences, and agricultural sciences, and ahead of languages and writing, and biological sciences. Fifty-seven courses focusing on the environment and/or sustainable development were accredited in 2008.

It is worth pointing out that the approval rate for *multidisciplinary* programs, at 15 per cent, is half that of other programs. There are two likely causes, which both seem to operate. On the one hand, there are less adequate program proposals, especially from smaller universities where disciplines lack critical mass. On the other hand, there is a more cautious approach by the accrediting agency to such programs. Particular challenges for programs in the *multidisciplinary* major area also need to be recognised in that they are innovative not only in dealing with complex contemporary issues, but also in terms of their structures within bureaucratic university organisations.[5]

Despite the popularity and expansion of interdisciplinary programs in Brazil, there are still many challenges for implementation, consolidation and evaluation. One is that faculty and students are building new models of research and teaching at the same time as implementing them. This has been likened to building a bicycle while simultaneously riding it. Further, because interdisciplinarity is poorly defined, the analogy is actually more like peddling a moving vehicle without being entirely sure what it is; it might be a bicycle, tricycle or monocycle, or even something completely new. This is also a challenge for evaluators, who are often additionally hampered by strong disciplinary backgrounds and lack of sensitivity to the distinctive characteristics of interdisciplinarity. As a consequence, evaluators are often unable to provide true peer review, especially if they perceive interdisciplinarity as shallow, in contrast with 'deep' established disciplines. This shallow–deep comparison is key to the cautious accreditation approach described earlier.

---

4   <http://www.capes.gov.br> (accessed 20 September 2011).
5   Bursztyn (2004, 2008).

Based on the 2009 evaluation of *multidisciplinary* programs,[6] we suggest that the further development of interdisciplinarity requires

- a search for new theoretical and methodological research, teaching and innovation that will lead us beyond the traditional paradigms of science
- increasingly close dialogue between and among different disciplines to tackle the epistemological challenges that theoretical and methodological innovations pose in interdisciplinary research and teaching
- gradual incorporation of interdisciplinary methodologies in faculty and student research projects
- recognition that interdisciplinary research and teaching are heterogeneous, and valuing this diversity
- definition of the characteristics of pluri-, multi-, inter-, and trans-disciplinarity, especially the underlying theories and methods, recognising that these terms are currently used in loose, overlapping ways.

Final Considerations

The challenges identified in institutionalising interdisciplinary graduate programs in Brazil are similar to those expounded by Bammer's book. Unifying proposals, such as Integration and Implementation Sciences (I2S), may provide a way forward. To this end, we recommend the following.

1. Broadening the debate about the meaning of the new field of research— Integration and Implementation Sciences (I2S)—and its proposal to provide an effective means to document and transfer concepts and methods that support integrative applied research.

2. Recognising and identifying the variety of experiences that can provide relevant material for I2S, especially concepts, methods and study cases. We support the idea of a large-scale project (the I2S Development Drive) to build a more unified and integrated knowledge base for interdisciplinarity.

3. Recognising that we need to make space for creativity and improvisation, as well as a unified, integrated knowledge base.

Nevertheless, we strongly caution against turning interdisciplinarity into a discipline. Interdisciplinarity is a process; it can constitute specific fields, and even lead to the formation of epistemic communities with their own identities. But there will be no integration if the processes of institutionalisation follow

---

6   Relatório de Avaliação 2007–2009—Trienal 2010 (Evaluation Report 2007–09, Triennial 2010), in <http://www.capes.gov.br> (accessed 20 September 2011).

the previous practices of creating university departments. We do not oppose formal interdisciplinary arrangements, but we see these as opening a space where complex problems can be addressed by teams comprising researchers with varied backgrounds. Interdisciplinarity is not anti-disciplinarity, but a bonding environment. The I2S proposal is an important step towards creating such an environment.

Contributed October 2011

Portugese original available at <http://i2s.anu.edu.au/sites/default/files/i2s-book/bursztyn_2012.pdf>

References

Bursztyn, M. (2004). 'The environment and interdisciplinarity: challenges to the academic world'. *Development and Environment (UFPR-Curitiba)*, 10 (1): 67–76.

Bursztyn, M. (2008). *Sustainability science and the university: towards interdisciplinarity*. Working Paper. Cambridge, MA: Center for International Development, Harvard University, [Online], 1–23.

Brief Biographies

Marcel Bursztyn has a BSc in economics and a Masters in urban and regional planning, both from the Federal University of Rio de Janeiro, as well as a Diploma in Planning Studies from the University of Edinburgh and PhDs in social and economic development from the Université de Paris I—Panthéon-Sorbonne (1982) and in economics from the Université de Picardie-France (1988). He was a postdoctoral fellow in public policy at the Université Paris XIII and at the Ecole des Hautes Etudes in Sciences Sociales—Paris (1989–91) and a Senior Research Fellow at the Kennedy School of Government's Sustainability Science Program, Harvard University (2007–08), as well as a former president of Coordination for the Improvement of the Higher Education Personnel (CAPES). He is currently an Associate Professor at the Center for Sustainable Development at the University of Brasilia and Co-Editor of the journal *Sustainability in Debate*. He is the author of 14 books and more than 100 scientific articles and book chapters.

Maria Beatriz Maury is a PhD candidate at the Center for Sustainable Development at the University of Brasilia, a Professor in the Department of Education of the Federal District, Executive Editor of the journal *Sustainability in Debate*, and former Director of Environmental Education at the Institute of Environment and Water Resources of the Federal District.

44. Building Integration and Implementation Sciences: Five areas for development

L. David Brown[1]

I have worked at the intersections of research and practice for most of my career. My dissertation focused on efforts to understand and improve the functioning of a boarding school as a system for developing its students. I have worked on action research projects for organisation development in a variety of organisations and contexts. Over the past 30 years I have been particularly concerned with civil society initiatives to foster social transformations for poor and marginalised groups.[2] In addition to organisation building, those initiatives have often involved cross-organisation and cross-sector initiatives for problem solving at local, national and transnational levels. While I have held academic positions for most of my career, I have been strongly influenced by concerns for impacts on policy and practice as well as by interests in theory and research development.

When Gabriele Bammer and I first met more than a decade ago, we began talking about Integration and Implementation Sciences (I2S) almost immediately. I am convinced that she is correct that many emerging policy and practice challenges demand the insights of multiple disciplines and perspectives. In her visits to the Hauser Center for Nonprofit Organizations, we have had a lot of opportunities to explore the implications of engagements among researchers and practitioners.[3] I am delighted that she has developed such a comprehensive and systematic approach to I2S as a field.

I want to comment briefly from my perspective on what I see as particular strengths of her proposal. Then I will suggest some areas that I think merit further development. Finally I will reflect on more general implications.

---

1   David Brown was invited as a senior scholar 'who has made significant contributions to thinking about practice–research engagement'.
2   Brown (1989).
3   Brown et al. (2003).

Strengths of the I2S Proposal

The book makes an important contribution by articulating the need for a more developed field of knowledge about integration and implementation. The need for systematic approaches to I2S has gradually become more apparent over the past couple of decades, as reflected, for example, in the emergence of academic outlets like the *Action Research Journal* and researcher handbooks of methods for working across theory–practice boundaries.[4] This book makes a strong case for more systematic investment in developing a new field of theory, research and practice.

Gabriele's identification of three domains to be illuminated by the emerging field is also an important contribution. Many of us have been quite aware of the challenges of two of those domains: 'synthesising disciplinary and stakeholder knowledge' and providing 'support for policy and practice change'. But her emphasis on the importance of 'understanding and managing diverse unknowns' is new to me. I am persuaded that more attention to unknowns and their management will be very important to future (I2S) theory and practice.

I am also impressed with Gabriele's proposed I2S Development Drive as a strategy for launching and building the field. In my experience, it is common for people concerned with I2S issues to focus on the immediate processes and issues of work on particular problem areas. They are less likely to think about the long-term, large-scale implications of their experiences for developing a new field. Building storehouses of concepts, methods and cases, creating useful syntheses for managing unknowns and providing integrated support for changing policies and practices are tasks of very substantial scope. Framing these tasks as a Big-Science project makes a lot of sense. Getting support for that approach will require compelling arguments for the critical importance of enhancing I2S capacities for large-scale problem-solving—and we have increasing evidence that those capacities are badly needed.

Areas for Further Development

The book covers a great deal of ground. Gabriele has articulated a very broad range of issues and possibilities in this analysis and readers will differ about which areas deserve more attention. I think at least five areas will need more discussion and debate if I2S is going to realise its potential as a new field.

---

4   Reason and Bradbury (2008).

First, the field will need to further develop *integration and implementation theory*, as some other commentaries have noted. The growing experience with multi- and trans-disciplinary research in areas like ecology preservation, peace building or rights-based development may provide contexts for theory development. Existing research and theory about bringing together diverse groups for joint action, such as public–private partnerships,[5] may provide perspectives and propositions that are relevant for I2S theory. 'There is nothing more practical than a good theory',[6] and that dictum may be especially true for I2S. The accumulation of concepts, methods and cases contemplated by the Development Drive will provide great resources for concept and theory development, and the Drive should also emphasise producing a framework that will guide I2S users.

Second, in my experience of practice–research engagement, the challenges of *recognising and dealing with value differences* have been central. Some value differences are grounded in disciplines: economists, anthropologists, doctors, lawyers and political scientists (to name a few) are trained to frame inquiry and analysis in different ways and may value different ends and means. Other value differences grow from different realms of practice: policy makers, business executives, labour leaders, consumer advocates, environmental activists and journalists often emphasise different value perspectives on the same problem. When practice changes interact with differences in values and ideologies, stakeholders in I2S projects may have dramatically different understandings of issues and radically different interpretations of appropriate actions and outcomes.[7] The term 'values' appears four times in the table of contents in association with the 'which knowledge' questions. Those discussions focus on how values may shape the relevance of knowledge, unknowns or change supports. But the encounter among disciplines and between research and practice often raises fundamental value questions that require negotiating values and ideologies to create shared visions to support joint work. Managing value differences and building consensus across disciplinary and research/ practice boundaries will be central in the future development of I2S.

A third theme that has pervaded my experience with integrating research and practice to solve complex social problems has been *managing issues of power and politics*. Changes in policy and practice often affect the distribution of resources, status, costs and benefits, creating winners and losers who have significant stakes in supporting or resisting those changes. Much of the discussion of I2S is appropriately framed in terms of the technical and intellectual challenges of articulating and developing the field. The terms 'power' and 'politics' do not appear in the table of contents, but I predict that they will be central elements

---

5   Bryson et al. (2006).
6   Lewin (1952).
7   Brown and Tandon (1983).

of the experience of most I2S practitioners and theorists. The challenges of managing power and politics are particularly acute when the parties come from different social positions: research across countries on efforts to build cooperative problem solving across sectors and levels of society suggest that managing power differences is a critical issue.[8] So I believe that as the I2S field grapples with the realities of integrating and implementing across diverse disciplines and stakeholders, it will pay increasing attention to concepts, tools and capacities for constructively managing power differences and political controversies.

Fourth, as a long-term student of organisations, I believe that *building institutional contexts* to support effective work across disciplines or the research–practice divide will be central to I2S as a field. To the extent that universities are dominated by disciplines that emphasise discipline development rather than interdisciplinary work to solve practice problems, universities may become increasingly irrelevant to integration and implementation.[9] The Development Drive may also explore how to build institutional arrangements that support I2S. Some of the most interesting integrative work in international development, for example, is currently emerging from think tanks and consulting firms that are not tied closely to universities, in part because many university reward systems do not recognise contributions to policy and practice changes. Within universities, professional schools that regard practice constituencies as important stakeholders may be less vulnerable to this problem than faculties that respond primarily to research disciplines, but even professional schools are pressing their faculties to publish in 'A journals' that are often uninterested in practice problems. So the institutional location of I2S will be important to how the field develops.

Finally, the evolution of I2S as a field will depend substantially on how and with whom it defines its *bases of legitimacy and standards of accountability*. Legitimacy can be grounded in normative, legal, technical, political, cognitive or associational terms with a wide range of stakeholders; accountability refers to answering expectations established with more specific stakeholders, such as those affected by or affecting particular research or practice programs.[10] Legitimacy and accountability have become important concerns in many arenas, in part because of the widespread failures of accountability in many sectors. By what standards can we assess the legitimacy and accountability of I2S? What will be the measures of its success? My own view is that the intersection of research and practice under some circumstances can catalyse revolutions in both theory and practice—the kind of knowledge epitomised by Pasteur's work

---

8   Brown and Ashman (1996); Weber (2003).
9   Gibbons et al. (1994).
10 Brown (2008).

in developing the germ theory of disease and the practice of pasteurising milk.[11] At its best, I2S practitioners might catalyse better theory and research, as well as better practices and policies at the same time, though we would probably be happy with valuable contributions to one or the other. In any case, it will be important to develop ideas about indicators of I2S performance as a basis for assessing its impacts and enabling its accountability to immediate stakeholders, for building its legitimacy with wider publics, and for catalysing ongoing learning in the field.

Conclusion

I have suggested a lot of areas for further work—in addition to the imposing array of tasks that Gabriele has already articulated for establishing I2S as an independent field. We face an intimidating constellation of complex problems on a planet with increasingly constrained resources. A catastrophic meltdown of our civilisation seems a real possibility given the complexity of the problems, the shortage of resources, the runaway concentrations of wealth and power in small elites, and the dysfunctional nature of many national and global governmental institutions. I2S is not a panacea—but I believe it could make a significant difference to our ability to manage planetary problems if we had the foresight and the political will to invest in it. Gabriele in this volume has greatly expanded our foresight about the possibilities; whether we can amass the political will required to give substance to her visionary analysis is another question.

Contributed October 2011

References

Brown, L. D. (1989). 'Research action in many worlds'. *Journal of Applied Behavioral Science*, 25 (4): 367–82.

Brown, L. D. (2008). *Creating Credibility: Legitimacy and accountability for transnational civil society*. Sterling, VA: Kumarian Press.

Brown, L. D. and Ashman, D. (1996). 'Participation, social capital and intersectoral problem-solving: African and Asian cases'. *World Development*, 24 (9): 1467–79.

---

11   Stokes (1997).

Brown, L. D. and Tandon, R. (1983). 'Ideology and political economy in inquiry: action research and participatory research'. *Journal of Applied Behavioral Science*, 19 (2): 277–94.

Brown, L. D., Bammer, G., Batliwala, S. and Kunreuther, F. (2003). 'Framing practice research engagement for democratizing knowledge'. *Action Research*, 1 (1): 81–102.

Bryson, J. M., Crosby, B. C. and Stone, M. M. (2006). 'The design and implementation of cross-sector collaborations: propositions from the literature'. *Public Administration Review*, 66 (Supplement): 44–55.

Gibbons, M., Limoges, C., Nowotny, H., Schwartzman, S., Scott, P. and Trow, M. (1994). *The New Production of Knowledge. The dynamics of science and research in contemporary societies*. London: Sage.

Lewin, K. (1952). *Field Theory in Social Science: Selected theoretical papers*. London: Tavistock.

Reason, P. and Bradbury, H. (2008). *The Sage Handbook of Action Research: Participative inquiry and practice*. Second Edition. Los Angeles: Sage.

Stokes, D. E. (1997). *Pasteur's Quadrant: Basic science and technological innovation*. Washington, DC: Brookings Institution Press.

Weber, E. (2003). *Bringing Society Back In: Grassroots ecosystem management, accountability and sustainable communities*. Cambridge, MA: MIT Press.

Brief Biography

L. David Brown is semi-retired as a Senior Research Fellow at Harvard University's Hauser Center for Nonprofit Organizations, where earlier he coordinated international programs and lectured at the Kennedy School of Government. Prior to coming to Harvard, he was President of the Institute for Development Research, a think tank for civil society research and consultation, and a Professor of organisational behaviour at Boston University and Case Western Reserve University. He has been particularly interested in action research that strengthens civil society contributions to sustainable development and social transformation. He has worked on issues of civil society capacity building, cooperation across organisational and sectoral boundaries, the legitimacy and accountability of civil society organisations, and the role of civil society actors in transnational advocacy and institution building.

45. From the Classroom to the Field: Reflections from a Pakistani law-enforcement perspective

Fasihuddin[1]

Seeing is believing. Agreed. It never happens unless it happens to you. Accepted. Practice makes perfect. No doubt about it. But what is the relation of all these sayings to this brief commentary? They have considerable relevance to my understanding of Integration and Implementation Sciences (I2S), which stems from being a participant observer in a program for Asia-Pacific research leaders[2] where I not only studied my past work in light of I2S standards, but also visualised causes and effects, and their rational, cost-effective and indigenously devised solutions for the complex and hydra-headed problems faced by Pakistan's law-enforcement agencies and policy makers. I also saw I2S being put into practice by expert colleagues from other countries and now honestly believe that, if given a chance, this approach can do wonders, even in this 'age of theories' in every branch of the social sciences.

Participants in the program on 'Bridging the Research–Policy Divide' analysed case studies based on their own research on a variety of troubling issues in their respective homelands, and, after applying the new (to us) method of 'reflective learning', the main maxim of the I2S paradigm, almost everyone found new dimensions to what happened, who did it, when, why and what more could have been done. Every one of us scrutinised a government policy or practice influenced by our previous research and the in-depth intellectual analysis (a rather serious critique at times) resulted in almost all of us finding potential improvements. A key ingredient was being provided with various tools—for example, some of us benefited from problem-tree analysis and others from situation analysis to narrow the causes, linking them to effects and ultimately to locating meaningful and effective solutions. We also used various models to understand stakeholders. 'Knowing thyself' and 'knowing thine enemy' were not enough, and we all developed insights into stakeholders who could be approached for relevant strengths, resources, legitimacy and interests.

---

1 Fasihuddin was invited as a senior scholar and practitioner 'who thinks about complex security and social problems and bridging the research–policy divide, especially in Asia'.
2 'Bridging the Research Policy Divide' was partially funded through the Australian Agency for International Development (AusAID) Australian Leadership Awards (ALA) Fellowships program; see <http://i2s.anu.edu.au/courses/bridging-the-research-policy-divide>

This intellectual development was surprisingly different from our usual method of learning based on narration and description, whereas the I2S method was profoundly analytical, critical, rational and personal. As well as learning from reflection, we also learnt from each other, developing a sense of belonging and partnership, as well as sharing roles and responsibilities; this was highly integrative and interactive. In our case studies, we found that at times our work had been excellent and at times we were struck by our carelessness, naivety and thoughtlessness about the interplay of various parts of an organic whole.

From the practitioner point of view, anything that gives results—say, for crime in terms of high clearance and arrest rates, high conviction rates, quick response to complaints and calls, early arrival at the crime scene, enhanced community satisfaction and improved media image—is accepted, welcomed and invested in. During 2008–10, as Director General of Human Rights, Conflict Resolution and Peace-Making at the Central Police Office, Peshawar, Khyber Pakhtunkhwa Province, I developed a police-led indigenous juvenile justice system in collaboration with local, national and international stakeholders. We established a Police Child Protection Centre and a new data-collection system on juvenile justice indicators. These achievements have been documented and were praised by senior police officers and judges, civil society and the media. During the difficult period of pushing for these activities and raising the necessary funding, I had not stopped to reflect on and theorise about my work; however, in the cool atmosphere of the classroom at The Australian National University, miles away from the awfully busy and sometimes frustrating life of a policy-implementer practitioner, I realised that we had created research-based policies and triggered more refined innovations and inputs from stakeholders.

I found that I was intuitively well versed with many I2S concepts before embarking on the venture to bring this structural and functional change to the local police office. But I am certain that, had I been aware of I2S, my work would have been more refined, less time-consuming and more systematic, and I would have been able to devote more energy and resources to the stakeholders. I am delighted to have found a theoretical background in the I2S discourse for best practice in a law-enforcement agency, which can strengthen the interaction between researchers and practitioners. A PhD scholar in our University of Peshawar will analyse this approach in more depth in his thesis on juvenile justice.

This is one concrete example for those who want to initiate knowledge-based— or, more accurately, research-based—policy, strategy or reforms in their departments and organisations. What would it mean for terrorism—the largest of today's real-world law-enforcement problems? Pakistan is considered to be a source of, transit hub and destination for many organised crimes, including radicalism and terrorism, and is also the front-line state and major ally in the war on terror. But even after tremendous human and economic sacrifices in the past 10 years, Pakistan has not yet developed any tangible, nationally agreed and democratically approved anti-terrorism or counterinsurgency policy. How can we best analyse this situation of seriously violent extremism and military operations and their colossal socioeconomic implications for the nation? How can we develop a viable and effective policy? The I2S tools potentially provide a different kind of approach, a different kind of systems analysis and a different kind of research-based policy development. The question is: will this new concept, which proved reasonably workable and appealing in the controlled atmosphere of the classroom in analysing past action, also work in the field in developing new approaches?

It is potentially useful not only for terrorism and juvenile justice, but also for many of Pakistan's quixotic problems in the criminal justice system or other social, political or economic sectors. For example, I2S may be able to help analyse and respond to the experiment of new police reforms in Pakistan (Police Order 2002, replacing the colonial *Police Act* of 1861), initiated in 2002, which astonishingly have resulted in the crime rate trajectory continuing to rise and the image of police and community satisfaction staying constant.

There is enough in this new idea of I2S to be tested, challenged, verified and refined further to make local adjustments. What it requires is commitment, passion, hard work, honesty of intention and 'a sense of we' from the stakeholders. As a whole, I am impressed by the creativity, directness, ingenuity and pragmatism of the various steps, skills and tools embedded in I2S. As a police officer and an informal student of criminology and policing studies, I am confident that students, researchers and practitioners in the criminal justice system can learn and improve their practice in light of I2S understandings.

Contributed October 2011, modified May 2012

Brief Biography

Fasihuddin MBBS, MA, LLB is a member of the Police Service of Pakistan, President of the Pakistan Society of Criminology and Editor-in-Chief of the *Pakistan Journal of Criminology*. He has been employed in almost all civil security departments, including the Intelligence Bureau, Frontier Constabulary and Federal Investigation Agency. He is the author of *Expanding Criminology to Pakistan* and has been working to introduce criminology to academic institutions and police training centres in his country. He has designed a new data-collection system for police on juvenile justice indicators to conform with United Nations standards.

46. Moving Competitive Integrated Science Forward: A US land grant research university perspective

M. Duane Nellis[1]

The year 2012 marks the 150th anniversary of the *Morrill Act*, which launched the democratisation of higher education in the United States. The Act, signed into law by President Abraham Lincoln, dedicated federal land and resources to the development and ongoing support of public universities in each State. Through this effort, people from all economic backgrounds were provided with greater access to higher education. Further, resources and faculty expertise in science, engineering and related disciplines at these institutions were committed to applied areas such as agriculture and natural resources to the benefit of each State. Often such research engaged stakeholders at the practical level, including helping stakeholders solve problems such as those related to crop or animal production, or community and family health. Historically, in addition to applied research in areas like agriculture, natural resources and engineering, a significant amount of the basic research and creativity that evolved in these settings tended towards unique disciplinary boundaries, and in many ways followed patterns of creativity and basic science research and reward structures at leading private US universities.

The Context and Challenge at the University of Idaho and Related Universities

At the University of Idaho, which was created as a land grant university in 1889, and at virtually all land grant research and other major public research universities, a more integrative applied research style is becoming recognised as critical to addressing a vast array of the essential questions facing our State, region, nation and the world. To secure and enhance the effective operationalisation of such research processes will require universities like the University of Idaho to overcome a number of barriers and disincentives as well as the development of expertise in integrative applied research consistent with methods in empirical, quantitative and theoretical research. Gabriele Bammer's

1   M. Duane Nellis was invited as a 'university leader who has a longstanding interest in interdisciplinarity and integration to tackle complex real-world problems. Your observations on whether the ideas in the book are workable in an organisation such as the University of Idaho will be very pertinent.'

book, through Integration and Implementation Sciences (I2S), brings into focus methods and concepts needed to effectively operationalise such integrative applied research practices, yet provides enough flexibility to accommodate unique strengths and needs. At the same time, the I2S approach helps preserve the value and importance of different disciplinary and stakeholder approaches, while bringing these perspectives together as a way to deal with unknowns.

Within the context of universities like the University of Idaho, there are a number of barriers and disincentives towards implementing the most effective forms of I2S. As articulated by Klein,[2] these include concerns and challenges in the context of organisational structure and administration, institutional procedures and processes, resources and infrastructure, and recognition, reward and incentives. There is the need for a more robust structural approach that allows the latitude for faculty to participate outside traditional disciplinary and related college or multidisciplinary organisations in ways that facilitate such interactions and provide appropriate reward structures. Too often there are issues of territoriality and turf battles over budget, ownership of the research budget and associated research overheads.

Within procedures and policies, there are often inadequate guidelines that govern faculty rewards for those who participate in cross-university, cross-disciplinary projects. Even when procedures and policies are set at the university level, traditional department and disciplinary boundaries make implementation uneven. And there is often inadequate funding at the university and college levels for those willing to reach out beyond historical boundaries and to find resources, for example, for graduate research assistantship support for such activities. In addition, at many universities, the infrastructure does not support networking channels that extend communication and interactions beyond traditional boundaries. Land grant universities like the University of Idaho have traditional college boundaries in areas like engineering, agriculture, business and the liberal arts and sciences, and college traditions and territorial protection practices may limit full support for university-wide networking and collaborations.

A part of this structural challenge, as articulated by Gabriele Bammer, also relates to the third domain: providing integrated research support for policy and practice change, such as in research translation, knowledge brokering, commercialisation needed to manage unknowns, and related consequences of integrated research. A key dimension of the integrative applied research team is the expectation that many team members have expertise in the complex research problems under consideration and can explicitly interact with stakeholders, policy makers and those in practice. The intentionality of many

---

2   Klein (2010).

current university and college structures in place today, including aspects at the University of Idaho, does not always lead to environments that fully realise the potential of such an integrated approach.

A crucial need in positioning an organisation like the University of Idaho is where we can better address some of the complex issues outside traditional discipline-based inquiry. A key question is 'what type of academic forum or structure creates the greatest sensitivities to facilitate progress towards such possibilities?'. How can a complex, comprehensive, land grant research university, like the University of Idaho, translate the I2S specialisation within the American university structure?

One key in the I2S process is being able to identify more robust ways that promote understanding the unknown in the process of addressing an integrative applied research question. Within the structure of an American university, how does the I2S facilitator operate and understand boundary issues and related unknowns? How have issues that might arise been resolved in case studies related to concepts linked to I2S? As Gabriele Bammer articulates, '[t]he point of integrative applied research is to effectively harness a range of relevant differences to broaden both knowledge about a problem and consideration of diverse unknowns' (Chapter 26). Many US universities have departmental entities, advisory boards or oversight structures that represent a wide range of interests and can add to understanding relative to the complexity of the problem being tackled. At the same time, such organising approaches can be a challenge as well in helping the research agenda work effectively towards addressing the range of complex real-world problems, and, in many cases, they come up incomplete. Departments, for example, can create territorial boundaries for their faculty members that reduce incentives for interdisciplinary work.

Facilitating strategies and mechanisms for interdisciplinarity and environments for I2S will require alternative administrative structures and leadership throughout every level of the university, with appropriate investment, infrastructure support and reward structures. Certainly, central and college-level advocacy and support are crucial, but without interdisciplinarity and facilitation of I2S percolating at the faculty level, such efforts will not work in the environment of a complex public research university like the University of Idaho.

At the University of Idaho, there is strong advocacy at all levels for interdisciplinary research. For me, as President of the university, this has been a key priority and one I speak to within and outside the university on a regular basis. Many of our policies and procedures have been changed in ways that allow for appropriate reward structures for faculty who participate in such activities. Two of the challenges, however, have been lack of central and college-level resources to invest in such initiatives and policy changes that facilitate more robust implementation of these important cultural changes within the university. Significant state disinvestment of public higher education across the United States has created major new challenges for such institutions (and more limited central resources), but at the same time has created opportunities for structural and cultural changes that bring more efficiencies, and which, if implemented appropriately, can facilitate I2S-type efforts. Universities must look creatively at new ways to facilitate such resource investments as we build the 21st century land grant university.

I2S and Interdisciplinary Studies at the University of Idaho

At the University of Idaho, we have a number of key research initiatives that are examples of significant success in interdisciplinary research. Projects like the Institute for Bioinformatics and Evolutionary Studies (IBEST)[3] and Sustainable Agriculture,[4] in addition to efforts and approaches linked to the Toolbox Project[5] and university-wide forums for cross-disciplinary discussion, have each been highly successful relative to their project objectives and for the university, region and nation; however, each has elements that could further benefit from I2S. With the Toolbox Project, for example, they would profit from a better way of addressing unknowns and a more systematic way of identifying ways to impact policy.

The IBEST is a 'grassroots' interdisciplinary faculty group at the University of Idaho focused on understanding the pattern and processes of evolution that occur over comparatively short periods. IBEST places high value on interdisciplinary collaborations that blend the expertise of biologists, biochemists, ecologists, evolutionary biologists, mathematicians, statisticians, computer scientists and other related disciplines to examine the underpinnings of evolutionary biology. The institute facilitates productive interdisciplinary dialogue across the university through seminars, as well as common and open luncheon discussions with those involved in associated projects (including faculty and staff) plus others who may have an interest in dimensions of these projects. In the continuum of this research effort, extensive data sets collected by biologists in contemporary studies of natural and experimentally evolved populations enable mathematicians, statisticians and computer scientists to quantify the problems of various evolutionary events and develop models that can subsequently be empirically evaluated and refined by biologists.

---

3   <www.uidaho.edu/research/ibest> (accessed 14 February 2012).
4   <www.cals.uidaho.edu/sustag/> (accessed 14 February 2012).
5   <www.cals.uidaho.edu/toolbox/> (accessed 14 February 2012).

The National Science Foundation (NSF) funded Toolbox Project, led by the University of Idaho with partners at Boise State University, the University of Alaska–Anchorage and the NSF, has provided a philosophical yet practical enhancement to cross-disciplinary collaborative science. Rooted in philosophical analysis, Toolbox workshops enable cross-disciplinary collaborators to engage in structural dialogue about their research assumptions. This process yields both self-awareness and mutual understanding, creating a strong foundation for effective collaboration research.

Using principles linked to the Toolbox approach, the University of Idaho received its largest grant in university history in spring 2011 of US$20 million. The proposal was led by faculty member Sanford Eigenbrode and involved a team of 22 principal investigators and key collaborators in partnership with two other land grant universities (Oregon State University and Washington State University). This grant focuses on the development of a comprehensive and extensive infrastructure to support research, outreach and education that will support sustainable agriculture in the Pacific North-West region.

The university also has the weekly Renfrew Interdisciplinary Colloquium to facilitate ongoing cross-disciplinary dialogue. This colloquium is well attended by faculty from across the university including faculty from such areas as philosophy, music, chemistry and engineering. And a year ago, as university President, I started a Friday-afternoon faculty gathering once a month to foster informal dialogue with faculty from across the university. Each month these are sponsored by a different college, and have resulted in new connections of faculty from across the university. For example, dialogue with faculty from such diverse departments as English and natural resources has resulted in new opportunities for cross-disciplinary research. At the same time, the Renfrew Colloquium would benefit from I2S through better integration of information across campus.

A Possible Next Step at the University of Idaho or Similar Institutions

Although significant progress has been made in creating an environment that would recognise and appreciate I2S at the University of Idaho, there are additional steps that could evolve that would potentially heighten progress towards such efforts. One such concept that I have discussed with some university faculty, including one of the Toolbox Project investigators, Michael O'Rourke, is creating a School of Interdisciplinary Studies. Such a school might serve as a college-level incubator for interdisciplinary programming. The concept for the school might include joint appointments with traditional colleges. Faculty appointments would need to be recognised and rewarded. The concept should appeal to faculty who want to spend quality time with others who share their belief in the value of interdisciplinary research. Such a school would help facilitate overcoming some of the barriers that were outlined earlier in this commentary. A council of deans could oversee the school to promote the sense of university-wide ownership and input.

Concluding Remarks

Gabriele Bammer's book provides a timely and important approach for conducting integrative applied research. Through I2S, integrative applied research can be more comprehensive, gaining a fuller understanding of the broad range of concepts and methods around key real-world problems. At the University of Idaho, significant progress has been made in facilitating an environment and approach that foster a more complete analysis of cross-disciplinary research. At the same time, there are evolving structural and cultural changes that should facilitate more robust and rewarding environments for such research as we look to creating a different dynamic for the US land grant research university as it moves beyond its 150th anniversary.

Contributed October 2011

Reference

Klein, J. T. (2010). *Creating Interdisciplinary Campus Cultures: A model for strength and sustainability*. San Francisco: Jossey-Bass.

Brief Biography

M. Duane Nellis has been President of the University of Idaho since July 2009. He has been an advocate for key university priorities linked towards being more interdisciplinary, more entrepreneurial, more engaged, more globally connected and more diverse. Prior to appointment at the University of Idaho, he served as Provost and Senior Vice-President at Kansas State University. He is past President of the Association of American Geographers and past President of the National Council for Geographic Education. His research has provided him the opportunity to work in interdisciplinary teams to analyse issues such as desertification along the fringe of the Kalahari Desert in Botswana, and assessment of water-use issues in the Ogallala Aquifer region of western Kansas. He has published more than 100 articles and several books and book chapters.

47. Interdisciplinary Research is about People as well as Concepts and Methods

Ted Lefroy[1]

This commentary starts with responses to four questions posed by the book's author, and finishes with some reflections on a recent interdisciplinary research project in the field of environmental management.

If You Had $1 Million to Spend, Which of the Proposals in this Book Would You Fund to be Further Developed?

First, I applaud the approach proposed in Chapter 34 of investing in systematic case studies of past practice to understand what approaches have been used in interdisciplinary research across a wide range of fields, what has worked and why. The book author has already contributed to this endeavour through publication of a handbook of dialogue methods appropriate to interdisciplinary research,[2] and to capture knowledge from many fields under the five-question framework used in the book would be very valuable; however, I part company with the book author on two aspects of I2S and the I2S Development Drive in particular. One is seemingly trivial but important to the wider application of interdisciplinary research to problem solving, and the other is more fundamental to its practice.

The trivial point is the name, I2S. Acronyms are a barrier to communication, accessible to the initiated and excluding others. I would argue strongly against adopting this or any other inaccessible name, and even against adopting the title Integration and Implementation Sciences. Interdisciplinary research is awkward enough as an umbrella term, but most researchers and many research users can understand what is meant: people from different disciplines working together. Sure, it can and does involve more than that, but the more we get involved in subtleties the more inaccessible we make what is an enabling practice. Given

1   Ted Lefroy was invited as a 'senior researcher who grapples with complex real-world problems requiring research integration and implementation. Your comments on whether the ideas in this book could enhance your ability to undertake such research would be very pertinent.'
2   McDonald et al. (2009).

that engagement with people tackling real-world problems is the common goal of those of us who work in this area, it is important that we describe the field and communicate its achievements in accessible language. Those more deeply involved are naturally interested in the distinctions between multi-, inter- and trans-disciplinary, team science and other variants but devoting time to taxonomy and becoming method focused rather than outcome focused are death to applied research and are only likely to alienate those with whom we wish to work. The further we move from plain English the harder we make our common goal of working with managers and policy makers to solve real-world problems.

That said, it is important to deal with definitions in a book that aims to pull together a new discipline. Early on (Chapter 1) we are told that of several interpretations of interdisciplinary research, this book will concentrate on research that 'involves experts from multiple disciplines working together on a common problem'. Soon after, this becomes research 'involving experts from several disciplines working with stakeholders on a common complex real-world problem'. The difference is significant, and is the distinction used by Tress et al.[3] and Klein[4] to distinguish interdisciplinary from transdisciplinary research or team science. To paraphrase, interdisciplinary research is more than one discipline working together to solve problems, and transdisciplinary research or team science is more than one discipline working with end users to solve problems.

This distinction is significant and brings me to my second point: the relatively passive role of the end users of research implied in this book. We are introduced to the three domains of Integration and Implementation Sciences as knowledge synthesis, managing unknowns and 'providing integrated research support for policy and practice change'. The third domain is further described as 'supplying policy makers and practitioners with a better understanding of the problem (both what is known and what is not known) in a way that supports them in making decisions' (Chapter 1). This sounds like an essentially one-way flow of knowledge, from the experts to the users. Yet a major obstacle to adoption and implementation of innovation is that researchers fail to understand the worlds of policy and practice for which the results of their research are intended, as captured by the quotation from Peter Shergold in Chapter 17. One of the values of close participation with end users in framing questions and engaging in the research process is the opportunity for, if not the obligation of, researchers to understand the policymaking and implementation processes and to adapt to their needs, rather than view them as obstacles to achieving the researchers' goals.

---

3 Tress et al. (2005).
4 Klein (2008).

To dismiss political opportunity, organisational advocacy and financial exigency as capricious is to ignore the realities of the paths to adoption. Evidence, as Frieberg and Carson[5] point out, is not the only seat at the table.

The fields of agricultural and environmental research and development are knee-deep in decision-support tools built with good intention but never used,[6] and researchers have much to learn from practitioners if this is to change. End users often have little role in the development of decision-support tools let alone framing the initial questions. Of course there are exceptions, and the great value of compiling case studies based on the five-question framework used throughout the book (Table 34.1) is the opportunity to identify examples of applied interdisciplinary research that have resulted in implementation and the approaches they employed. To that framework, I would add evaluations of selected case studies from the perspectives of the three major parties involved— that is: the funders with their interest in return on investment, the users from the perspective of the relevance of the research, and researchers who typically place value on the rigour of research outputs and the contribution they make to their professional development.[7] Summative evaluation is a luxury few interdisciplinary research projects experience, partly due to the time delay in the adoption process, and a great deal could be learned by carefully scoped and well-resourced evaluations.[8]

So back to the question of $1 million dollars; I would invest in three things. First, commission systematic reviews of applied interdisciplinary research from each of the major fields in which it is practised (public health, justice, education, environment, security, innovation and business, and so on, as shown in Figure 32.1). Second, convene an international Congress of Interdisciplinary Research at which these would be presented along with other invited papers and an open call. Third, publish, in addition to the proceedings, an analysis of selected case studies to facilitate the exchange of practical experience across these fields.

What is the Book's Greatest Weakness and How could it be Addressed?

I would nominate the two issues discussed in response to question one above. That is, further complicating an already challenging area by attempting to define it as a discipline with an unfriendly name with an inaccessible acronym. Developing a community of practice relevant to many fields would be very timely,

---

5 Frieberg and Carson (2010).
6 Stone and Hochman (2004).
7 Roux et al. (2010).
8 Scriven (1993).

and a welcome opportunity for greater learning, but creating a discipline out of an interdisciplinary activity seems self-defeating. For interdisciplinary research to be effective, effort has to be devoted to breaking down boundaries between disciplines and finding common ground in areas such as the rules of evidence, disciplinary language, reward structures and forms of communication. So, for a relatively immature area of research it seems too early to standardise methods and approaches when there is so little evidence that what has been tried to date actually works. The second weakness is the tendency to view implementation as a process dependent on improving the one-way flow of knowledge from researchers to research users.

Who do You Think Should be Encouraged to be Involved in the Ongoing Discussion about I2S?

Anyone who has published the results of interdisciplinary research or published on the practice of interdisciplinary research, in any field. These could be identified from the literature and invited to submit case studies that would be candidates for commissioned, systematic reviews to be presented at an international congress.

How Do You See Yourself in Relation to I2S?

As a practitioner who, like the book author, is keen to learn from more systematic evaluation of past efforts in this field, but who is quite happy to keep calling it interdisciplinary research.

The Importance of Social Cohesion

Reflecting on a recent experience of interdisciplinary research raises an issue not adequately covered in the book. In this section I briefly outline the project and its context, and then report on a survey conducted at its conclusion that highlighted the issue of social integration or managing the social cohesion of a research partnership.

Landscape Logic was an interdisciplinary research project that ran from 2006 to 2010.[9] It set out to infer causal links between past management interventions

---

9   Lefroy et al. (2012).

and the condition of natural resources in two areas: water quality, and vegetation extent and condition. The two areas were identified by the research users involved in the project (six catchment management organisations in south-eastern Australia), from analysis of their largest areas of investment about which there was greatest uncertainty. The project was prompted by a series of reviews of large public environmental programs by the Australian National Audit Office, which all concluded that, while they could see where the funds had been invested, they could find no evidence that this had resulted in the desired outcomes. The aim was to use retrospective studies to improve the quality of information available to environmental managers about the likely environmental response to management interventions as a guide to future investments. Seven small research teams were set up within three themes: Knowledge Discovery (5), Knowledge Integration (1) and Knowledge Broking (1). The Knowledge Integration (KI) and Knowledge Broking (KB) themes were designed to complement the biophysical and social research of the knowledge discovery projects by performing the following functions.

- Helping to articulate the information needs of natural resource managers (KB).

- Mapping the knowledge base required to elucidate how human interventions, climate change, climate variability and other drivers are likely to have influenced natural resource condition (KI).

- Identifying the appropriate level of information required to relate the essential variables (including the scale and complexity of relationships to be represented), taking into account the data, information and knowledge available, and as far as possible their uncertainty (KI).

- Undertaking these tasks in a participatory and iterative fashion that included the researchers in the knowledge discovery projects, our collaborators in the catchment management organisations and selected industry groups and landholders (KB and KI).

The roles of the integration and knowledge broking projects included incorporating and synthesising many forms of identified knowledge, not just that obtained from the knowledge discovery projects. This existed in many forms including disciplinary socioeconomic and biophysical knowledge, as well as the perspectives and aspirations of environmental managers, industry representatives and landholders.

At the project's conclusion, 89 people associated with the project were invited to respond to an online survey (42 researchers, nine steering committee members and 38 people from partner and stakeholder organisations). From the 41 responses (26 researchers and 15 from partner and stakeholder organisations), several lessons emerged about what worked well and what could have been improved.

1. *Allowing sufficient time for teams to develop.* Acknowledging the sequences involved in group development (storming, forming, norming and performing as described by Tuckman)[10] and allowing sufficient time for their expression proved to be important contributors to a collaborative culture. Our experience was that the length of these phases varied with different teams, which required more flexible time lines for problem definition, scoping research questions and planning research than we had envisaged.

2. *Reaching agreement on the research questions.* This point is closely related to the previous one, and centres on allowing sufficient time for the processes of problem definition and identifying researchable questions. The six months allocated to the 'storming and forming' stages, which included defining research questions, was not sufficient for all areas of research or all teams. Getting the questions right (as in reaching agreement between researchers and research users) has great bearing on the effectiveness of collaborative research, and in hindsight this could have been more flexibly managed to ensure a well-planned start to all projects.

3. *Collaborative model development.* Developing conceptual models or influence diagrams with environmental managers proved to be a very effective tool for involving managers in hypotheses setting and very useful for researchers to gain a better understanding of the systems they were studying. A major factor in their success was their graphical structure and the effort that was put into training by the integration team who introduced the language and associated software of network modelling through 13 workshops with researchers and managers during the first 18 months of the project.[11]

4. *Identifying a 'service' role for research teams.* Three of our seven research teams (spatial analysis, social research and knowledge integration) were originally conceived as providing a service role to what were essentially seen as biophysically driven research questions. This proved to be a mistake, and was acknowledged during the course of the project as under-representing the primary research contribution of these teams to the collaboration. This distinction influenced relationships between teams and presented obstacles to progress that had some negative implications evident throughout the course of the project.

5. *Acknowledging the need for technical and social integration.* Two different aspects of integration were recognised as contributing to a large collaborative project such as this. As well as having the mechanics of integration such as modelling frameworks, software and personnel skilled in integration methods (technical integration), it was just as important to have processes to

---

10   Tuckman (1965).
11   Ticehurst and Pollino (2007).

overcome the geographic, institutional and disciplinary distances between researchers and partners (social integration). While there is a growing array of useful technology at our disposal that can help to break down geographic constraints, such as internet meetings and file-sharing facilities, there proved to be no real substitute to regular meetings of team leaders (monthly), the advisory board (three-monthly), related research teams (six-monthly) and all researchers and partners across the project (annual). Breaking down boundaries and ensuring communication between disparate groups required constant attention from team and project leaders and were important aspects of fostering a collegial culture within and between groups. Social integration essentially meant investing a great deal of time in problem framing, relationship management and stakeholder engagement. The most challenging issues in our experience were achieving the relevant level of commitment from all participants and managing interdependencies between projects (when the outputs of one were inputs to another).

6. *Having dedicated knowledge brokers.* Having skilled communicators with well-established networks across research institutions, government agencies and environmental managers proved to be very valuable in breaking down cultural, institutional and language barriers between researchers and managers at all levels. The knowledge brokers helped to foster a shared understanding between partners from the first stages of scoping questions to exchanging information and new knowledge during the course of the research and negotiating the meanings, implications and implementation of findings in the final stages.

The challenge of social integration was a common feature of many of the issues raised in the survey. Social cohesion, and particularly managing interdependencies between projects, was an important issue and represented the highest area of investment in the project through travel, meetings, teleconferences and other communication events. So in conclusion, an area I would add to the exercise of compiling case studies of concepts and methods is some indication of social cohesion, collaboration and personal and professional satisfaction. Leadership, project management and internal communication methods all contribute to this and are areas in which we could all learn. While the book very thoroughly examines the architecture of interdisciplinary research, this experience suggests to me we would also benefit from a better understanding of the needs and interests of the researchers and the factors influencing the quality of their outputs and experience.

Contributed October 2011

References

Frieberg, A. and Carson, W. G. (2010). 'The limits to evidence-based policy: evidence, emotion and criminal justice'. *The Australian Journal of Public Administration*, 69 (2): 152–64.

Klein, J. T. (2008). 'Evaluation of interdisciplinary and transdisciplinary research: a literature review'. *American Journal of Preventative Medicine*, 35: 116–23.

Lefroy, E. C., Curtis, A. L., Jakeman, A. and McKee, J. (2012). 'Integrating science for landscape management'. In: *Landscape Logic: Integrating science for landscape management*. Collingwood, Vic.: CSIRO Publishing, 283–91.

McDonald, D., Bammer, G. and Deane, P. (2009). *Research Integration Using Dialogue Methods*. Canberra: ANU E Press; <http://epress.anu.edu.au/dialogue_methods_citation>

Roux, D. J., Stirzaker, R. J., Breen, C. M., Lefroy, E. C. and Cresswell, H. P. (2010). 'Framework for participative reflection on the accomplishment of transdisciplinary research programs'. *Environmental Science and Policy*, 13: 733–41.

Scriven, M. (1993). *Hard-Won Lessons in Program Evaluation*. San Francisco: Jossey-Bass.

Stone, P. and Hochman, Z. (2004). 'If interactive decision support systems are the answer, have we been asking the right questions?'. In: *New Directions for a Diverse Planet*. Proceedings of the Fourth International Crop Science Congress, 26 September – 1 October 2004, Brisbane, Australia.

Ticehurst, J. L. and Pollino, C. (2007). 'Build collaborative models or capacity? Comparison of techniques for building Bayesian networks for the natural resource management regions of Australia'. In: *Proceedings of MODSIM Conference*, 10–14 December, Christchurch, New Zealand.

Tress, B., Tress, G. and Fry, G. (2005). 'Researchers' experiences, positive and negative, in integrated landscape projects'. *Environmental Management*, 36 (6): 792–807.

Tuckman, B. (1965). 'Developmental sequence in small groups'. *Psychological Bulletin*, 63 (6): 384–99.

Brief Biography

Ted Lefroy graduated with a degree in agricultural science from the University of Western Australia in 1973, and spent the next 10 years working in rural development and extension in Queensland and Papua New Guinea. In 1987 he returned to Western Australia to work with watershed groups in a United Nations Man and the Biosphere Project on resource management and conservation in the farmlands around the World Heritage Fitzgerald River National Park. He has since held research positions with State departments of agriculture, the University of Western Australia and CSIRO, leading interdisciplinary research teams working with land managers to minimise the environmental impacts of agriculture. In 2005 he was appointed Professor of Environment and Director of the Centre for Environment at the University of Tasmania.

48. Creating the New University

Glenn Withers[1]

The Evolution of the University Enterprise

The original model of the university as it evolved in, say, medieval Oxford and Cambridge emphasised a tradition of scholarship and learning for personal development. This was the model of a teaching university focused on the transmission and interrogation of accrued knowledge so as to mould a person fit to manage a civilised life. The enterprise involved some substantial immersion by the student in the core arts and sciences, but left them to produce their own synthesis. The teachers were scholars who were specialists for the purpose of conveying their particular knowledge to their pupils who synthesised and assimilated the knowledge to customise it for themselves.

The modern research university was a later development, commonly associated with the so-called Humbolt model, where the creation of new knowledge, especially scientific knowledge, became the truly distinguishing characteristic of the university. Scholars became researchers, though the research was felt to also inform the learning and teaching functions that continued to occupy most academics: the 'teaching and research nexus'. This research focus and its link to advanced education cemented the role of systematic and organised disciplines as the vehicles for advancement of knowledge and specialisation and saw disciplinary training increasingly displace the notion of well-rounded personal development.

The American university tradition of the twentieth century, underpinned by the national affluence required to facilitate the investment, tried to combine general undergraduate education with advanced specialised postgraduate training. In Australia, the 'Melbourne Model' now seeks to emulate this for the Antipodes.[2]

The American university also added the distinctive gloss of the professional schools, which were multidisciplinary—for example, graduate business and government schools, the former being the most clearly accepted and adding

---

1   Glenn Withers was invited as a 'senior scholar of public policy and, currently, in leading thinking about how Australian universities can improve their involvement in tackling complex real-world problems'.
2   See <http://theconversation.edu.au/in-defence-of-the-melbourne-model-1083> (accessed 4 December 2012).

pedagogies of holism such as the case method to replace or complement more conventional teaching, especially disciplinary teaching. These professional schools though were devoted more to the training and production of employment-ready practitioners, their staff were as often consultants and advisers as academics, and the research that was conducted was as often still in underlying disciplinary fields that conveyed esteem as in any new emergence of serious interdisciplinary vehicles.

The Present Interdisciplinary Opportunity

Gabriele Bammer's project stands at a critical juncture in this evolution. The challenge ahead of us for the university today is whether the emergence of multidisciplinarity can truly move from teaching, as in liberal arts and sciences undergraduate training and in professional schools such as business and government, to the research that is the source of academic standing. Also required is resolution of the challenge of whether the focus of multidisciplinarity can move from professional training that develops logic and evidentiary capacities for managing change and interrogating problems to instead, or in addition, enable holistic approaches to research into the great problems and challenges of the day.

Why is this critical? Universities have proven to be amongst the most enduring and useful of human institutions. They can and will continue as functional centres for training in management and the professions, and for producing specific research of value, much of it curiosity driven and based in highly productive disciplinary frameworks, approaches and methods.

But there is nothing in the disciplinary research enterprise that ensures comprehensive coverage of the knowledge needs of human kind. Nor is there a clear, efficient mechanism for synergies in learning and knowledge transfer across disciplines. Equally, so much of the problems and concerns of the real world, beyond the more intrinsic imperatives of much disciplinary knowledge pursuit, are complex and holistic, relating to practical problems or concerns the dimensions of which clearly spread across disciplines. The solution of such problems or concerns may depend not just upon the aggregation and synthesis of disciplinary knowledge and the subject matters that such disciplines focus upon, but also upon understanding of their interdependence or synergy in relationships that transcend disciplinary boundaries. This may itself require new or distinctive forms of analysis or, at the very least, will involve wider understanding and sharing of the different and divergent methods used for generating knowledge across present disciplines.

The litmus test for the potential for interdisciplinarity exists in universities and it is to be found in the field of environmental studies. It is here that the holistic nature of the real-world challenges is recognised as immense and it is here that multi/inter/transdisciplinarity has been most pursued in formal university research and teaching. If this effort evolves as a success and multiplies then the modern university will be seen as truly worthy by the society of our age and in new and significant ways. But if the experiment does not advance well then universities may have fallen short of the adaptation that would and could generate a new stage in their contribution to humankind and to what one Australian prime minister termed its 'great moral challenges'.[3]

The Nature of Interdisciplinarity

The greatest weakness of Bammer's project thus far is that it is still grappling with the nature of interdisciplinarity without being clear and precise on what the counterpart, 'disciplinarity', is. 'Discipline' is approached like the blind men and the elephant. Contributors feel their way around the areas they are comfortable and familiar with and illustrate the nature of interdisciplinarity by extension from those areas. This may be essential and of itself very useful and constructive, but the absence of a clear and compelling definition of what a discipline is, as opposed to interdisciplinarity, is still confusing and inhibiting. We have some feeling for the nature of the beast, but not a compelling Platonic type for the base reference point.

The point is important because the fact is that disciplinary boundaries, their subjects and methods are dynamic and blurred, partly from internal evolution as knowledge advances and sometimes because of the tensions emanating from the reasons interdisciplinarity is sought. One possibility is that disciplines are indeed dynamically interdisciplinary—but that interdisciplinarity emerges from a micro-evolution, bottom-up approach and often implicitly rather than explicitly. As weaknesses or opportunities for innovation emerge in present research within disciplines, researchers seek to adjust assumptions, methods and topics to embrace these. Thus economics moves into law once the importance of formal legal rules becomes apparent and the idea becomes clear that these too may be modelled as rational choices therefore taking advantage of the economic method but extending its domain. History moves into 'cliometrics' as better official statistics become available and permit extensive quantification as part of the historical narrative.

---

3   See <http://www.youtube.com/watch?v=CqZvPRjGtGM> (accessed 4 December 2012).

Sometimes intellectual curiosity seeks a more 'big bang' answer. Correspondingly in the Bammer project interdisciplinarity is top down rather than merely incrementalist. It wants overview, taxonomy, method and impact all at once as its overarching ambition. This is no mean ambition. Such a macro-approach can give context and connection in ways that iterative research evolution may not, except by serendipity. The ideal might be in the end for the macro-approach to have micro-foundations, and thus blend the incremental with the bigger picture.

Of course having a science of everything is unmanageable. But with the bulk of research continuing within the train tracks of incremental improvements in knowledge supplemented by the occasional paradigm shift from those who left the tracks to smell the flowers and augmented by those who are consciously seeking to add this up to holistic knowledge, a more balanced portfolio of knowledge generation can emerge and benefit the generation and understanding of the status of that knowledge. The agenda then is to nudge the system into opening its eyes a little wider, while retaining the core disciplinary strengths it has.

Enhancing the Interdisciplinary Agenda

What might be the most productive nudges towards both more 'muddle through' and genuine 'big bang' interdisciplinarity in research? Step one might be projects that codify taxonomies of knowledge, so that the way in which each discipline treats the logical development of theory, the assembly and examination of evidence and the consideration of values in assessment of evidence would be a start. All rational knowledge generation, as opposed to intuition and experience as sources of knowledge for action, must incorporate these elements. But the language and techniques by which these components are expressed are many and various. They can be assembled, explicated and evaluated for what they contribute.

From such an exercise—perhaps commencing separately in the STEM (science, technology, engineering and mathematics) disciplines and the HASS (humanities and social sciences) disciplines and then converging—a knowledge map would emerge. This in turn could form the basis for new courses for graduate students in methodology that would be the foundation for an elite interdisciplinary doctoral coursework program in major universities that would have core transdisciplinary courses as well as special fields.

Those who undertake such studies would need in those universities the establishment of departments of interdisciplinary studies that would reward appointment and promotion based on teaching and publication according to interdisciplinary standards. Similarly the national competitive grants schemes would need to have panels and assessments that drew on this interdisciplinary expertise to encourage and award research support funding in this domain.

Extension of incentives and esteem into impact and engagement alone, as is being done in England currently[4] and is now being belatedly anticipated in Australia, may be insufficient even though helpful. What is also needed is the basic intellectual work on the nature of interdisciplinarity, its theories and methods, from which holistic insight into problems can then emerge. The two together though will be powerful indeed.

Contributed October 2011

Brief Biography

Glenn Withers is currently Professor of Economics at The Australian National University. He was previously Chief Executive Officer of Universities Australia and before that Professor of Public Policy at The Australian National University and also Head of the Economic Planning Advisory Commission and Co-Chair of the National Population Council. His academic work is in public economics, economic history and labour economics. He has written books on conscription, population and immigration, and economics of the performing arts.

---

4   REF2014 website <www.ref.ac.uk> (accessed 4 December 2012).

49. Beyond 'Dialogues of the Deaf': Re-imagining policing and security research for policy and practice

Simon Bronitt[1]

University-based researchers occupy a narrow ledge of legitimacy, striving for acceptance of their published research by academic peers and producing research that has an applied impact on the 'real world'. Too much professional emphasis on one objective, to the detriment of the other, risks ridicule from either the academic or the policy/practice communities. Professor Bammer's framework for the development of the I2S discipline shares these fundamental dilemmas of a scholar seeking to promote the value and legitimacy of their work outside the university research sector—namely attempting to balance the scientific imperative to do good discipline-based work with the desire to make a difference in the 'real world'.

It would be reasonable to presume that this is not a zero-sum game, and that Professor Bammer could achieve both objectives. Surely the key objectives of the Integration and Implementation Sciences (I2S) would be attractive to policy and practice communities? Moreover, the programmatic vision of marking out a new disciplinary territory and enhanced standing for interdisciplinarity is attractive for the academy, bearing in mind the challenges and hostility faced by researchers who embrace methodological pluralism and whose research traverses the boundaries of discipline silos.

The timing for the 'birth' of such a new discipline would seem right. Rarely does a day pass without politicians, policy makers and practitioners peddling the virtues of evidence-based policy and evidence-led practice. But as researchers working in the field of public policy have pointed out, this commitment to science is more often than not hollow rhetoric or, worse still, 'evidence' may be viewed cynically as a malleable tool to be selectively invoked or ignored to suit preconceived political objectives.[2] That the world of ideas and knowledge is inherently 'political' would be no surprise to the father of science, Galileo, who was famously tried for heresy for his scientific theorising that the Earth was not the centre of the universe. Nor would this reality be a surprise to Professor

---

1   Simon Bronitt was invited as a 'senior scholar with a longstanding interest in interdisciplinarity', as well as for his role as Director of the Australian Research Council Centre of Excellence in Policing and Security (CEPS), 'leading a major interdisciplinary research program. Your commentary could be general or targeted at how I2S has assisted, and might assist, CEPS in future.'
2   See, generally, Head (2010).

Bammer, whose pioneering work in the 1990s on the diamorphine trial (better known as the Heroin Trial) was scuppered by the 'Tough on Drugs' policy of the then Prime Minister, John Howard, and scepticism towards harm minimisation.[3] This ultimately manifested in the refusal to give *any* serious weight to the feasibility studies undertaken by Professor Bammer and her colleagues at The Australian National University and the Australian Institute of Criminology. To Australia's enduring shame, the work done by Professor Bammer and her team of colleagues in the mid-1990s was recognised only overseas, informing trials undertaken in Switzerland and the Netherlands, where researchers and policy makers were searching for a rigorous scientific and policy basis to roll out alternatives to criminalisation and decriminalisation strategies. This experience may be viewed as a salutary lesson of international policy transfer or as another depressing illustration of the highly politicised nature of 'knowledge production' in sensitive areas like drug law and policy.

Knowledge Synthesis: Virtuous Cycles or the Dialogue of the Deaf

The I2S idea of synthesising disciplinary and stakeholder knowledge seems like an uncontroversial 'good' in terms of producing research relevant to policy and practice. Such knowledge synthesis would maximise the potential of research to inform policy and practice, in turn stimulating further relevant research questions. But realising this 'virtuous cycle' confronts significant cultural barriers on both sides of the research and policy/practice divide.

Indeed, interactions between research and policy/practice communities can be so fraught that one UK commentator working in the field of police research once described it as the 'dialogue of the deaf'—a description highlighting the different epistemological and normative universes that these communities inhabit.[4] The commentator parodied this dialogue of the deaf as follows.

> Academic: Why do the police ignore research findings? Police: Why don't researchers produce useable knowledge?

> Academic: Why do the police always reject any study that is critical of what they do? Police: Why do researchers always show the police in a bad light?

> Academic: Why don't police officers even read research reports? Police: Why can't researchers write in plain English?

---

3 The background and impact of the Heroin Trial are explored in Bronitt and McSherry (2010).
4 McDonald (1987 paper commissioned by the Police Foundation of England and Wales, cited in Bradley 2005).

Academic: Why are the police so bloody defensive? Police: Why are researchers so bloody virtuous?

Academic: Why are the police unwilling to examine their own organisational performance? Police: Why are researchers unwilling to produce information that a practical person exercising power can use to change a limited aspect of the organisation instead of theoretical and explanatory structures of no use to the problem solver?

Academic: Why do the police insist that they know better, when the researchers are the experts in knowledge construction? Police: Why do researchers write recipes when they can't even cook?

In recounting these observations made 30 years ago, David Bradley, a distinguished police researcher, identified the continuing cultural gulf between university-based and policy-driven research communities in Australia, the United Kingdom and the United States.

In this short commentary on Professor Bammer's book, I wish to reflect further on these 'intercultural differences', which (if not remedied) constitute insurmountable barriers to the development of I2S in 'hot topic' fields like policing and security.[5] In exploring these challenges, I will make specific reference to my own experiences as an academic lawyer and socio-legal researcher working on sensitive policing and security topics over the past two decades. I will particularly draw on my experience in my current role as Director of the Australian Research Council Centre of Excellence in Policing and Security, a centre of research excellence that also has an overt policy and applied focus, with regular engagement with high-level police and government stakeholders.

Intercultural Challenge #1: Understanding the intrinsic difficulty of doing good research

As Professor Bammer identified, researchers confront infinite unknowns though have finite research capability and capacity. Also there are political and administrative barriers to knowledge synthesis, integration and implementation. In my own research of covert policing, terrorism and national security, for example, I have encountered particularly acute sensitivities and reluctance to engage with academic research. When engagement and cooperation do occur, practice and policy communities demand 'focused' research from the academic. The stakeholder clients—the police executives and policy makers— urge academics to do research for a purpose (that is, purposes that they value). But in an era of 'New Public Management', research focuses on establishing to

---

5   Bradley (2005).

Treasury officials and political paymasters the 'effectiveness' of 'X' program or intervention.[6] The stakeholders, however, have limited grasp of what measures, beyond those most easily identified, should be used to determine effectiveness.[7]

Effectiveness is neither self-evident nor universally understood in the same way across policy domains. Indeed, in the field of law-enforcement research, effectiveness is a highly normative question determined by what roles police should legitimately perform in society and what objectives are being pursued. The current tendency in stakeholder groups is to view effectiveness measures in unproblematic terms, focusing on crime rates, drug seizures or conviction rates; however, simply measuring police performance by its success in 'locking up bad guys' or 'taking drugs off the streets' is distorting. In relation to the former, it overlooks the key role that police play in diversionary justice (ensuring that, in appropriate cases, offenders are diverted away from rather than into the system), as well as their critical function in preventing miscarriages of justice (for example, averting situations where an innocent person is wrongfully convicted). In relation to drug law enforcement, a recent research study by the Australian Institute of Criminology has proposed developing a broader set of impact measures for drug law enforcement that extends beyond reducing drug crime and drug-related crime, to include measures such as reducing organised crime, improving public health and improving public amenity.[8]

Research to measure effectiveness in a more empirical and normatively sound way is more complex and costly than simply quantifying rates of enforcement activity—the number of wiretaps issued, arrests made, charges laid and convictions secured cannot serve as an effective performance measure or a proxy for success. Convincing the stakeholders of this fact, however, remains an uphill struggle!

Intercultural Challenge #2: Accepting equivocal research findings

Policy and practice communities demand answers based on the 'best available evidence'. Their need for certainty means that stakeholder communities struggle with equivocation about research findings and conflicting interpretations of data. Research may show what does not work, but cannot establish what actually does work. Yet the idea of accepting the 'least worst' solution, which is often what the research supports, does not fit with the organisational commitment to international 'best practice' standards. From this perspective, equivocation risks serious and irreversible harm (either to the environment or to people)

---

6   The rise of New Public Management and its implications for policing are explored in Bronitt and Legrand (2012).

7   Bronitt and Legrand (2012).

8   Willis et al. (2011).

or chronic policy paralysis. Indeed, policy and practice communities will not wait for certainty, and in some domains it is now established that scientific uncertainty should not preclude action. Indeed, this is exemplified by the rise of the precautionary principle in policy circles in areas as diverse as protection of the environment, human health and national security.[9] While the precautionary principle may be a legitimate interim strategy until states of scientific uncertainty are remedied, significant reforms to policy and practice introduced under the precautionary rubric invariably entrench themselves and will be difficult to reverse notwithstanding the emergence of fresh counterevidence. When applied in this way, the precautionary principle may sideline research in some fields or divert the stakeholder's scarce research resources into sources of knowledge that are less equivocal (such as consultancy research). This must be resisted. Clearly the obligation is on stakeholders and researchers to understand the limitations and equivocal nature of research, and nevertheless remain committed to shared enterprise generating the best *available* evidence.

Intercultural Challenge #3: Government preference for consultancy-driven policy

There is no doubt that, in Australia and elsewhere, much policy is consultancy-driven rather than evidence-led. In Australia, consultancy expertise has flourished following the downsizing of policy and research capacity within government in the early years of the Howard Government. Robert Cornall AO, Secretary of the Attorney-General's Department, in his valedictory speech in 2008, reflected on the rise of consultancy within government, expressing scepticism about the value for money offered by many of these service providers. He acknowledged that consultants bring expertise and experience (some being former government employees) and have the capacity to deliver timely responses; however, in Cornall's view:

> Sometimes, engaging a consultant is a management cop out. It can seem to be an appealing solution to flick pass a difficult and ill-conceived project to a consultant. This can give the temporary impression that some progress is being made and the unsatisfactory result can be blamed on the consultant.[10]

It is clearly harder to disavow academics and censor independent research in this way. But even more problematic is the timeliness issue: academic timelines, spread over years, simply cannot meet the imperatives of the policy cycle and short-term-ism inherent within a typical three-year political horizon for policy development and implementation.

Having identified some intercultural barriers, what are some of the key enablers for I2S?

---

9   See, generally, Fisher et al. (2006).
10   Cornall (2008).

The Way Forward: Embedding policy and practice in research

A key strategy for bridging the intercultural gap, in my experience, is the placement of policy officials and senior practitioners within university research centres. This happens rarely in Australia, or indeed anywhere else. Indeed, the traffic between the policy/practice and research communities is largely one way, with secondments from the university sector into government or industry being more common. There is a long history of renowned scientists, economists, social scientists and legal scholars chairing ad-hoc reviews and inquiries for government. But the reverse is not true. While the modern 'engaged' university hosts numerous specialised policy and practice research centres, and may have even developed partnerships to deliver specialised programs of professional development and training for senior public servants, secondments of senior policy makers and practitioners are a rarity. Indeed, the Australian Research Council Centre of Excellence in Policing and Security is one of a handful of centres that hosts full-time secondments from senior police and government officials to work with researchers on defined projects. The success of these programs is yet to be formally evaluated, though there is scepticism from some academics and stakeholders about the feasibility (and relatively high cost) of these ventures. It is clear that different agencies and researchers value such initiatives differently! In my view, however, the success of I2S depends on embedding policy and practice perspectives into the research enterprise; not only does this lead to more relevant research, it also increases the sophistication of policy and practice engagement with research. Over time, there is a greater appreciation of the value of university-based research, its rigour and validity, compared with other sources of organisational knowledge production, such as consultancies.

This leads to my final observation about risk. I2S involves an academic willingness to accept risk—to commit to a new discipline, to address new perspectives, to engage with policy and practice, and to embrace uncertainty. These factors are critical to the success of I2S. (The flipside of risk acceptance is the risk aversion preoccupying many who work in policy and practice communities, and operating as a significant barrier to I2S!) Professor Bammer recognises the important role played by 'untied research funding', which can be used to foster creative thinking around contemporary research topics. But there are high levels of risk here for the policy and practice communities: high levels of trust are needed for stakeholders to commit to a 'blank research page' in advance and, worse still, to accept that this involves some 'blank-cheque' commitment to funding such research directly or in-kind. The New Public Management and Treasury models of accountability demand proof of an efficient use of public resources and these models do not sit comfortably with uncertainty; project aims must be defined, milestones agreed and key performance indicators quantified and achieved. Demonstrating a 'return on investment' is a pervasive part of the modern stakeholder and, increasingly, researcher lexicons.

While this environment suits short-term, consultancy-driven projects, it operates as a straitjacket for the research as well as the policy and practice communities. Too quickly, stakeholders learn that 'contractualising' research curbs flexibility and prevents research efforts being redirected to address more pressing questions or emerging issues. Due to the timelines of national competitive funding schemes, programs of research have been agreed years in advance. These long timelines have numerous risks for both stakeholders and researchers. The first is the risk of ever-diminishing stakeholder support as the project grows stale, or when government changes or the internal organisational research champions move on. Another challenge flowing from the premature development of research programs is that the data needed to answer the research questions do not exist or cannot be released to researchers.

Who is to blame for such failures? Who is accountable for the substantial costs incurred in projects that subsequently discover that the research question posed is simply unanswerable? From the individual academic perspective, failures such as these can be professionally devastating, especially for early career scholars; with an emphasis from within universities and funding agencies on measurable outputs (such as publications), there is little scope for these failures to be seen as simply one of the 'costs of doing research'. I2S must develop systems to support early involvement of senior policy makers and practitioners in the development of research; feasibility research must be funded separately, and the inherent risk of failure must be understood within both the academic and the stakeholder communities. Secondments of practitioners and policy makers into research centres play a critical role during the development phase (and not merely during the operational phase) of the research project.

This brings me to my final observation about I2S and the Development Drive. The challenge for Professor Bammer and colleagues who support this initiative (including myself) is to not only promote the value of I2S to the research community, but also to educate the stakeholder communities about its potential pay-offs, as well as pitfalls. This is no mean feat, but clearly a challenge worth undertaking.

Contributed October 2011

References

Bradley, D. (2005). Tackling the knowledge deficit in policing: strategic change versus adhockery and paint jobs. Paper presented at the Australian Institute of Criminology Conference on Safety, Crime and Justice: From Data to Policy; <www.aic.gov.au/criminal_justice_system/policing> (accessed 28 October 2011).

Bronitt, S. and Legrand, T. (2012). '(Re)constructing best practice in policing'. In: Prenzler, T. (ed.). *Policing and Security in Practice: Challenges and achievements*. Houndmills Hampshire: Palgrave Macmillan.

Bronitt, S. and McSherry, B. (2010). *Principles of Criminal Law*. Third Edition. New York: Thomson Reuters, Chapter 14.

Cornall, R. (2008). Valedictory address: Reflections on eight and half years in the nation's capital; <www.apsc.gov.au/media/cornall180808.htm> (accessed 28 October 2011).

Fisher, E., Jones, J. and von Schomberg, R. (eds). (2006). *Implementing the Precautionary Principle—Perspectives and prospects*. Cheltenham, UK: Edward Elgar.

Head, B. (2010). 'Reconsidering evidence-based policy: key issues and challenges'. *Policy and Society: An Interdisciplinary Journal of Policy Research*, 29 (2): 77–94.

Willis, K., Anderson, J. and Homel, P. (2011). *Measuring the effectiveness of drug law enforcement*. Australian Institute of Criminology Trends and Issues in Crime and Criminal Justice No. 406. Canberra: Australian Institute of Criminology.

Brief Biography

Simon Bronitt is Director of the Australian Research Council (ARC) Centre of Excellence in Policing and Security (CEPS) and Professor in the School of Criminology and Criminal Justice, Griffith University. He was previously Professor of Law at The Australian National University (ANU) in the ANU College of Law, and Associate Director of the Australian Centre for Military Law and Justice, ANU. Between 2006 and 2009 he served as the Director of the ANU Centre of European Studies in the Research School of Humanities. Drawing on comparative and interdisciplinary perspectives, he has published widely on criminal justice issues, including counter-terrorism law and human rights, covert policing, telecommunications interception and international criminal law. His publications include *Principles of Criminal Law* (Third edn, 2010) and *Law in Context* (Fourth edn, 2012). He was the lead Chief Investigator of an ARC-funded Discovery Project on counter-terrorism law (2005–08), which culminated in the publication of Miriam Gani and Penelope Mathew (eds), *Fresh Perspectives on the 'War on Terror'* (2008).

50. Applying the I2S Framework to Air Pollution and Health in Indonesia

Budi Haryanto[1]

In reading this book I was surprised to find that it reflected a wide variety of my work experiences, which were based on intuition, innovation and creativity rather than any scientifically structured arrangement. I never imagined that my environmental health research and its use in informing government policy were based on a theory. Let me provide some illustrations from my research on air pollution health impacts in Indonesia.

I have been interested in studying the health effects resulting from the use of lead additives in gasoline in Indonesia since 1992. These had been banned in other countries since the 1980s and, although senior colleagues had examined lead exposure among high-risk groups such as bus, taxi and three-wheeler drivers, as well as policemen, there were no government regulations to prevent and control airborne lead pollution in Indonesia. Their research, along with my study of lead exposure among people working in the streets of Bandung for more than eight hours per day, did not result in new government regulations until 2001.

Based on this experience, I changed my research strategy and interactions with policy makers. In 2001 I started by moving my focus from adults exclusively to also include children, as they are more vulnerable to air pollution. I studied traffic policemen, as well as commuters in private cars and on public transport, and elementary schoolchildren, comparing vehicles and schools with and without airconditioning. I expanded from lead to considering ultrafine particles, particulate matter less than 2.5 micrometres and carbon monoxide, which are routinely used in US environmental studies.

I also moved from passive dissemination of my research results (waiting for an invitation to present at a seminar or workshop) to more actively generating occasions, in collaboration with relevant non-government organisations (NGOs). This happened because I was on the Board of Directors of the Indonesian Clean Air Partnership, a national NGO. They taught me how such organisations convey messages to government. My research findings started being transmitted in various ways, involving key people locally or nationally at strategically chosen events. For example, an event was held at the US Embassy to commemorate Earth

---

1   Budi Haryanto was invited as a 'senior scholar who thinks about complex environmental health problems and bridging the research–policy divide, especially in Asia'.

Day in 2004 and there I measured the blood-lead level of the US Ambassador, Ralph Boys. At the 2005 World Environment Day, I measured the blood-lead levels of the Minister of Environment, Rahmat Witoelar, as well as some senators. In 2005, in publicising my research on individual exposure measurement, I measured the air quality in the office of the Governor of Jakarta, Sutiyoso, at his request, as he was concerned about a long-term cough. When launching my investigation into blood-lead levels among elementary schoolchildren in the city of Bandung, I measured the blood-lead level of the Mayor of Bandung, Dada Suhada, and some of Bandung's senators. These events were all attractive to the mass media, who continued to contact me for interviews about the research results days, sometimes even weeks, afterwards.

These events also resulted in invitations from local authorities and the Central Government. Initially they asked me to be a resource person and speaker at their in-house and roadshow seminars and workshops. Then I became a consultant for a project based on the results of my research. I was also asked to become one of the key team developing an academic draft for local and national regulations on the prevention and control of air pollution. One outcome is Jakarta Regional Regulation No. 2/2005. And, a year and half later, on 1 July 2006, the Central Government officially announced that it would no longer allow lead additives in gasoline. Since the regulations were passed, I have also helped promulgate them in workshops and seminars. In this long struggle, I was part of an advocacy coalition of researchers and NGOs who had been working for change since 1984.

Analysis Using the I2S Framework

In summary, my experience had the following steps

1. starting from research of real problems

2. disseminating results openly through seminars, symposia, workshops and roundtable discussions

3. involving key decision makers, politicians and other people at events of international, national and/or local importance, in the dissemination of the research results or measurement of the health effects of air pollution

4. involving mass media in publicising the events and disseminating the research results

5. the initial government invitation to be a resource person and then to become a member of the team preparing the draft government regulations

6. becoming a government messenger to implement the regulations.

Let us examine these steps using the five-question framework.

1. Starting from Research of Real Problems

The purpose of the research was to demonstrate that the problems were real and to provide information to the Government for developing policy to prevent and control the problems. The response to the question 'For what' is: a) to develop policy to protect humans from the risk of diseases related to air pollution; b) to improve air quality; c) to provide a safer environment; d) to prevent humans from being exposed to air pollution; e) to protect humans against illness; f) to avoid absenteeism; and g) to enhance people's productivity. Examining 'For whom' identified the following beneficiaries: a) the general population; b) workers (who avoid loss of income and high healthcare costs); c) commuters and drivers; d) the Central Government (improvements in the national economy); e) academics (advancement of science); and f) the Provincial Government (improved work efficiency, and so on).

If we examine 'Which knowledge', we see involvement of a wide range of experts from various scientific disciplines, including environmental health, epidemiology, environmental assessment, transportation, nutrition, toxicology, medicine and psychology. 'Taking a systems view' involves examining the policy system for both the local government of DKI Jakarta[2] and the Central Government Ministry of Energy and Natural Resources. Both governments operate in a top-down manner, appointing a division to develop new policy, which in turn generates a team to develop an academic draft by involving other divisions, sectors, stakeholders, academics and NGOs.

'Scoping' was used in selecting the research team in order to get maximum contributions from all relevant experts including specialists in children's blood-lead levels and children's acute respiratory infection, and personal exposure measurement for commuters, policemen and children. 'Boundary setting' involved considering the various limitations of time, human resources, data collection and budget. For example, it involved organising an effective communication system between data collectors and schoolteachers, who assigned children for daily monitoring of acute respiratory illness.

'Framing' was used to get a clear picture of the complexity of the problems, effects, causes and solutions to provide recommendations on priority actions for government. 'Harnessing and managing differences' was used to maximise the benefits of the multidisciplinary research team. Ensuring the same vision of the research aim was the most important key to getting agreement among the experts.

'How' included combining: 1) approaches from epidemiology and psychology with biomarker measurements in blood-lead research, 2) epidemiology models

---

2   Daerah Khusus Ibukota Jakarta, translated as the Special Capital City District of Jakarta.

with environmental and personal exposure measurements for ultrafine particles, particulate matter less than 2.5 micrometres and carbon monoxide, and 3) approaches from epidemiology with a medical model of children's acute respiratory illness.

'Overall contextual factors' included the issuing of national Law No. 23/1993 on Live Environmental Control and the Minister of Health's Decree No. 1405/2002 on Environmental and Occupational Health Offices and Industries, which were judged to be ineffective in their implementation because cases of diseases related to air pollution continued to increase from year to year. This raised the demand for new regulations.

'Authorisation' (or legitimacy) was given to me as research team leader, based on the reputation of my research and my leadership skills. I gained the trust of donor agencies and other researchers. Regarding 'organisational facilitators and barriers', the University of Indonesia's culture was very supportive and there were no substantial barriers.

Finally, in terms of 'outcome', the results of the research were able to address all research questions and research hypotheses. Furthermore, the important findings could be translated into a language that is more easily digested by policy and decision makers.

2. Disseminating Results Openly through Seminars, Symposia, Workshops and Roundtable Discussions;

3. Involving Key Decision Makers, Politicians and other People at Events of International, National and/or Local Importance, in the Dissemination of the Research Results or Measurement of the Health Effects of Air Pollution; and

4. Involving Mass Media in Publicising the Events and Disseminating the Research Results

These three innovative activities were successful in Indonesia, where the general public and government officers are influenced by the mass media. The officials were spurred to make a fast response and quickly improve their performance. The collaboration of researchers with interested NGOs and the mass media can be viewed as an 'advocacy coalition'.[3]

---

3   Sabatier and Weible (2007).

5. The Initial Government Invitation to be a Resource Person and then to become a Member of the Team Preparing the Draft Government Regulations

I found various theoretical policy models useful in helping to explain the preparation of the draft government regulations

1. when the Jakarta Governor or minister appointed one of its divisions to develop an academic draft, this can be seen as a step in the 'stages' policy model[4]

2. when the appointed division invited me and others to form an expert team, this can be seen as an 'incremental' advance[5]

3. during the development of the academic draft, there was intense discussion among multidisciplinary experts, which can be explained by the 'advocacy coalition'[6] and 'bounded rationality'[7] policy models

4. when the academic draft was finished and the appointed division reported back to the Governor or minister, the approach taken can be explained by the 'stages' policy model, including when the Governor or minister appointed the division of law to translate the academic draft into the draft regulation

5. when the Governor or minister finally announced the Government's regulation on the prevention and control of air pollution in Jakarta and the phasing out of leaded gasoline in Indonesia, respectively, the approach used can be explained by the 'incremental' policy model.

6. Becoming a Government Messenger to Implement the Regulations

Governments need credible and knowledgeable messengers, familiar with the regulations, to inform the general public and get them to support implementation.

***

In conclusion, I increasingly see my role as a knowledge broker. Other government regulations that have used my research in processes similar to the ones described above are the following.

1. Governor of Jakarta Provincial Regulations about Indoor Air Quality Monitoring at Public Places, Offices, and Basement Parking Area 2010. This

4   See Figure 19.1; the stages model is also referred to as the technical-rational cycle. Althaus et al. (2007).
5   Following Lindblom (1959, 1979).
6   Sabatier and Weible (2007).
7   Smith and Larimer (2009).

regulation was based on my research on sick building syndrome among employees in offices in high buildings in Jakarta, 2008–09, as well as the studies of others.

2. Government Regulation Draft on the Strategic Plan for Health Adaptation to Climate Change and Ministerial Health Regulation Draft on the Guidelines for Training of Trainers Training Modules for Health Adaptation to Climate Change 2011. This regulation was based on my research on the health impacts of climate change and adaptation.

3. National Environmental Health Action Plan 2010, a product of the Ministry of Health and the Ministry of Environment, is based on my work on the review of Indonesia's environmental health profile in 2009.

By following the steps of the systematic I2S approach developed in this book, I am sure that more research results can be translated into public policy, which in turn will improve the welfare of the community.

Contributed October 2011

References

Althaus, C., Bridgman, P. and Davis, G. (2007). *The Australian Policy Handbook*. Fourth Edition. Crows Nest, NSW: Allen & Unwin.

Lindblom, C. E. (1959). 'The science of "muddling through"'. *Public Administration Review*, 19 (2): 79–88.

Lindblom, C. E. (1979). 'Still muddling, not yet through'. *Public Administration Review*, 39 (6): 517–26.

Sabatier, P. A. and Weible, C. M. (2007). 'The advocacy coalition framework: innovations and clarifications'. In: Sabatier, P. A. (ed.). *Theories of the Policy Process*. Boulder, CO: Westview, 189–220.

Smith, K. B. and Larimer, C. W. (2009). *The Public Policy Theory Primer*. Boulder, CO: Westview.

Brief Biography

Dr Budi Haryanto MSPH MSc is an Associate Professor at the University of Indonesia and Head of Research Division of the Research Center for Climate Change. He is also the former Chair of the Department of Environmental

Health, Faculty of Public Health (2004–11). He has participated in numerous environmental epidemiology studies, including the health effects on children of air pollution, the effects of magnetic fields on human health, a community trial of calcium supplement intervention to reduce children's blood-lead levels, and antioxidant intervention to reduce sick building syndrome among professionals working in highrise buildings in Jakarta. Most recently he has actively contributed to studies of health adaptation to climate change as well as development of policy and action plans. He is a Board Director of the Pacific Basin Consortium on Environment and Health, and a member of numerous international and national professional societies and organisations, including the International Society of Environmental Epidemiology and Clean Air Initiative in Asian Cities.

51. Integration and Implementation in Action at Mistra-Urban Futures: A transdisciplinary centre for sustainable urban development

Merritt Polk[1]

The framework presented in this book, with three domains (knowledge synthesis, managing unknowns and integrated policy support) and five focus areas (aims and beneficiaries, knowledge needs, methods, context and outcomes), lays the foundation for an overall approach to a new discipline for Integration and Implementation Sciences (I2S). As noted repeatedly, there are many examples of research projects, educational programs and research centres around the world that are working with developing similar types of collaborative knowledge production and educational skills that can contribute to solving complex social and environmental problems. This commentary will present one such example that grapples with similar issues regarding the identification and integration of different types of knowledge, from both research and practice, and how they can be tailored and translated to optimise policy support and implementation. The example presented is the work being done at a transdisciplinary[2] centre for sustainable urban development in Göteborg, Sweden: Mistra-Urban Futures. This centre is co-owned and managed by seven organisations: three research and educational institutions and four public bodies.[3] It was started in 2010, and has just completed its second year of establishment. This commentary will present the methodological work that has been accomplished thus far on integrating and implementing different sources of knowledge and expertise for sustainable urban futures.

---

1   Merritt Polk was invited as a 'senior researcher who grapples with complex real-world problems requiring research integration and implementation. Your comments on whether the ideas in this book could enhance your ability to undertake such research would be very pertinent.'

2   While transdisciplinarity is used in different ways, at Mistra-Urban Futures it refers to a strategic approach to knowledge production that combines scientific perspectives with other types of knowledge sources such as knowledge and experiences from practice, decision making, and business and community life—in other words, joint knowledge production between different types of practitioners and researchers. This approach draws upon a wealth of different disciplines and research areas from within the science and policy discussion, including: action research, post-normal science, triple-helix, Mode 2, sustainability science, research by design, Integration and Implementation Sciences, and interdisciplinary studies.

3   City of Gothenburg, Göteborg Region Association of Local Authorities, Region Västra Götaland, County Administration Board, the University of Gothenburg, IVL Swedish Environmental Research Institute and Chalmers University of Technology.

The Transdisciplinary Context: Achieving sustainable urban futures

Urbanisation is a manifest and growing trend worldwide. The importance of cities for economic development and social cohesion is widely acknowledged; however, problems such as global risks and resource constraints, poverty, poor health and diseases, and social tensions and inequalities all pose significant challenges to the efforts of cities and urban areas to achieve long-term sustainable development. Furthermore, contemporary urban transitions and their implications for sustainable development are poorly understood. There is a great need for sound advice and recommendations for urban policy and visions. There is also a great need for improved institutional and human capacities for urban governance, and for support in harnessing and guiding the economic, material and human resources required for positive urban transformation. Currently responses are not designed to match such needs in an integrated and holistic manner. Most issues and problems in sustainable urban development are addressed within traditional disciplinary and sector boundaries as well as through existing organisational structures that rarely facilitate the necessary collaboration between practice and research. It is therefore urgent to create new cross-sector and interdisciplinary capacities for change among organisations and individuals. The complexity of urban challenges calls for the use of novel approaches in the production of new knowledge, in the building of required capacities, in the coordination of diverse actors and in the implementation and management of innovative urban solutions. The vision of Mistra-Urban Futures is to increase capacities to transform current, unsustainable urban development pathways to more sustainable urban futures in the global South and North, through integrative and collaborative processes for joint knowledge production.

The Challenges: Multiple framings, knowledge diversity, broader legitimacy

Three characteristics of urban problems have been targeted as especially challenging for addressing the complexity of urban areas: the multiple framings of sustainable development promoted by different urban actors, the diversity of knowledge and know-how that exists in urban areas, and the need for broad, legitimate platforms for sustainable urban change. These challenges point to the need for a revised and developed approach to transdisciplinary knowledge production and problem solving.

Multiple Framings

Sustainable development and sustainability are vague and ambiguous terms. They can be used to refer to many different approaches along a continuum from short-term, local economic growth to long-term, global environmental conservation and social justice. While sustainable development is often defined following the classic Brundtland definition,[4] it is a highly contested and debated term the world over. The way that sustainable development is applied is continually adapted and revised to fit the needs and underlying world views of the involved stakeholders, be they politicians, researchers, representatives from community-based organisations or business owners. To be viable over a longer period, any attempt to realise urban development must be tailored to meet this diversity of values and needs from a variety of interest groups and be able to negotiate often contradictory and incommensurable definitions and positions. The first methodological challenge for our project is to capture the diversity of world views, priorities and values that exists within different contexts and actors. With regard to *multiple framings* of sustainable urban futures, the first methodological focus is to create arenas where this diversity of different understandings and approaches to sustainable urban futures can meet and interact agonistically,[5] constructively and creatively with each other.

Knowledge Diversity

Sustainable urban futures cannot be achieved without tapping into the broad base of experience and expertise that exists within different actor and interest groups in the urban field. This need for *knowledge diversity* is a direct consequence of the number and variety of actors combined with the multifaceted social challenges and environmental constraints that exist in urban areas. The specific complexity of current urban areas creates novel needs for knowledge exchange, synthesis, integration and co-production. To meet such needs, new types of knowledge production and problem solving need to combine the theoretical and cumulative foundations of scientific knowledge with other types of knowledge, such as know-how and practical expertise from residents, businesses, community organisations, planners, administrators and politicians. Not only do different values and world views result in different framings of sustainable development, different framings also determine what are seen as valid sources of knowledge and expertise. The second methodological challenge for Mistra-Urban Futures is to harness a broad base of knowledge and expertise. The second methodological focus therefore concerns how different types of scientific and practice-based

---

4   See <http://www.un-documents.net/ocf-02.htm> (accessed 15 December 2011).
5   Since consensus is not always possible or desirable, agonism is used to capture the need for constructive conflicts where opposing positions exist side by side in non-antagonistic disagreement (Mouffe 2005).

knowledge and expertise can be identified and encouraged to interact creatively and innovatively. The focus on multiple framings and knowledge diversity sets the stage for the more effective achievement of the context sensitivity that is necessary for creating robust city systems.

Broad Legitimacy

Dealing with extreme power differentials is one of the main challenges for urban development. The fact that sustainable urban development itself is a highly contested term is foundational to the political discussions and visioning processes taking place in urban areas today. One of the main problems in creating robust and liveable city spaces the world over is the ability to set the agenda for sustainable urban development in the context of scarce resources and extreme power asymmetries. Who controls the agenda for sustainable urban development? What framings of urban futures are seen as the most legitimate? What types of knowledge are seen as most relevant for creating solutions? Issues of legitimacy are central when decisions are made regarding what framings of sustainable urban futures are chosen and what types of knowledge are seen as most feasible for creating viable solutions. One way of addressing the extreme power differentials in urban areas is to create meaningful, long-term inclusive processes where not only disenfranchised groups, but also a broader plurality of actors can gain influence and visibility, thereby increasing the legitimacy of alternative framings, knowledge and impact.

Our third methodological focus is therefore to create conditions or spaces where a broader combination of framings and knowledge for sustainable urban futures can gain real *legitimacy*, and, through this, visibility and influence. There are two main issues regarding legitimacy that need to be addressed. The first is *internal legitimacy*, which refers to how the partners who make up Mistra-Urban Futures are included in and entitled to the activities at the centre, both organisationally and in practice. The methodological challenge of internal legitimacy is to create arenas where representatives from different groups are mobilised and entitled to interactive and integrative processes of joint problem framing and problem solving around sustainable urban futures. The methodological focus is on designing processes and activities for joint knowledge production and problem solving, and ensuring that they are jointly developed and carried out. The second issue is *external legitimacy*. Mistra-Urban Futures' reputation for inclusive and effective knowledge production and problem solving within different urban issues must be linked to effective impacts in the specific local contexts of the participating international partners. The work being done at Mistra-Urban Futures needs to be tightly anchored in and linked to the decision-making processes and interest groups both within and outside the consortium partners in the different local contexts.

These challenges are summarised in Table 51.1.

Table 51.1 Addressing the Methodological Challenges of Urban Change

The challenges	What is the challenge?	What are the methodological issues?	Guidelines for addressing these issues
Multiple framings	A diverse group of urban actors and framings of sustainable urban futures	Identifying actors and capturing the needed world views, values and perspectives for each substantive issue	Joint problem formulation and project design
Knowledge diversity	Broad and diverse base of applicable experience, knowledge and expertise within urban areas	Identifying knowledge needs, integrating different sectors, disciplines and approaches in knowledge production and problem solving	Co-generation of information, joint analysis and implementation of solutions
Broader legitimacy	The need for a broad agenda for sustainable urban futures that legitimises a variety of actors and approaches	Identifying and reconciling the different demands and conditions for excellence and effectiveness for both research and practice	Ongoing evaluation of both internal and external processes and impacts

Guidelines and Qualities for Supporting Joint Knowledge Production and Problem Solving in Urban Areas

The goal of joint knowledge production and problem solving at Mistra-Urban Futures is to establish a neutral arena for new knowledge production and problem solving. This arena subsumes a combination of both different disciplines (interdisciplinary) and non-academic knowledge sources such as practical and professional knowledge, know-how and expertise from different types of urban actors, and breaks up the linear relationship that often exists between research and practice in more applied research and consultancy contexts. The goal at Mistra-Urban Futures is to develop an open knowledge-production process, where traditional types of linear knowledge production are replaced with co-owned, co-led and co-produced processes based on continual and in-depth collaboration between different urban actors. This open approach allows a continual re-contextualisation of both practical and scientific/technical contexts throughout the entire knowledge-production and problem-solving process.

The three methodological challenges noted above form the basis of guidelines that have been developed to support joint knowledge production and problem solving. These guidelines are not formal requirements. They should instead be seen as *guiding principles*, which can be used to improve the quality and effectiveness of collaboration. They have been designed to ensure that multiple framings, knowledge diversity and broad legitimacy are promoted in all of the projects at Mistra-Urban Futures. The goal of the methodology development is to continually refine these guidelines so that they give a maximum amount of freedom to the participants to create and carry out their projects in ways that are most effective for their specific context and problem area. Overall, the structure of knowledge-producing processes should be envisioned as a scaffold, as setting up certain guidelines while leaving the spaces within the scaffold empty and undefined. It is this project space that is autonomous, open, unpredictable, dynamic and jointly filled with meaning and activities by the participating actors in interactive and dialogical processes. The guidelines are summarised in Table 51.2.

'*Formulate*' focuses on capturing the multiple framings of sustainable urban development by ensuring that the joint problem formulation and project design are actually inclusive and collaborative, with the involved actor groups feeling engaged and being entitled to and/or owning the process. *Formulate* consists of two parts. The first, '*Initiation*', focuses on generating and collecting project ideas from a variety of actors, both within and outside the consortium. The goal of *Initiation* is to form a project idea that fulfils the ambition of optimal ambiguity. What this means is that the embryo of a project idea must be formulated with an optimal amount of ambiguity that attracts different stakeholders from practice and research so that they feel entitled and motivated to engage in the project. This embryo is then developed in the second part, '*Revise and revisit*'. Here the aim is that the project co-evolves through collaboration between interested stakeholder framings and knowledge needs. The result is a joint problem description including the project formulation, staff, planning, design and budget, as well as communication, implementation and evaluation plans for the entire project process.

'*Generate*' encompasses all of the work done with knowledge production, problem solving, analysis, output dissemination and implementation. In order to fulfil the mission of the centre, all projects are required to produce results that can have an actual impact in practice and research. Here, a variety of methods and processes is used to harness the knowledge that is needed to fulfil the centre's and project's goals. The form and content of the results must be tailored to the specific substantive issues and constellations of involved actors— for example, in different types of policy input such as for visioning and policy processes, and results such as scientific articles and books. The goal of *Generate* is to support and promote integrative, innovative and creative processes that can capture a diversity of different sources of knowledge and expertise and effectively integrate and transform them into concrete policy input and the skills and expertise needed for capacity building.

Evaluate occurs continually throughout the process. Formative process evaluations focus on ensuring the internal legitimacy of the processes as they are carried out. This includes ongoing evaluation tools that focus on the centre's goals for inclusive, collaborative and integrative processes. This also includes periodic review of the communication and implementation plans so that they are updated for the specific problem context and actors. Summative process evaluations will also be carried out at the end of each project. Impact evaluations focus on the form and effectiveness of the project outputs and on identifying medium and long-term project outcomes.

Table 51.2 Guidelines for Joint Knowledge Production and Problem Solving

The challenges	Central parts of joint knowledge production and problem solving
Multiple framings a⟳b	**Formulate:** joint problem formulation and project design a) **Initiation:** generating and collecting project ideas b) **Revise and revisit:** co-evolution of understanding, in-depth mapping of stakeholders and knowledge needs, alignment of goals, problem formulation, project planning and design
Knowledge diversity a⟳b⟳c	**Generate:** co-generation of knowledge and solutions a) **Information collection:** joint design and collection of information and data, integration with specialised expertise when needed b) **Innovation and analysis:** creating joint solutions, products and conclusions c) **Implementation and communication:** application in policy and practice, test cases, scientific publications
Limited legitimacy a⟳b	**Evaluate:** ongoing evaluation of process and impacts a) **Process:** formative and summative evaluations, internal legitimacy b) **Impact:** formative and summative evaluations, assessment of the external legitimacy of output, outcomes, results

Along with these guidelines, five qualities or attributes of joint problem-solving processes have also been identified based on experiences of collaboration and the challenges of urban complexity. These have been the initial focus of research regarding the development of a transdisciplinary methodology. These qualities are: inclusion, collaboration, integration, usability and co-reflection. Inclusion, collaboration and integration refer to activities that are closely entwined in practice, and in some instances inseparable. There is, however, an analytical distinction between *inclusion* (the identification, engagement and entitlement of different groups), *collaboration* (the processes and methods for participating as well as the quality and degree of the participation) and *integration* (the degree of assimilation, combination, synthesis or merging of different perspectives and approaches to problem solving). *Usability* refers to the applicability of the results in actual ongoing policy and implementation processes. *Co-reflection* embodies the explicit attention to learning and self- and mutual reflection that are central for achieving success within such processes.

At present, transdisciplinary research is under way to investigate these different qualities and their applicability and effectiveness for promoting the types of joint processes that are the goal of the centre. This research includes experiences with the processes, their impact on practical and scientific outputs, and the organisational needs of these types of activities. These qualities are summarised in Table 51.3.

Table 51.3 Qualities for Transdisciplinary Knowledge Production and Problem Solving

The challenges	Guidelines	Key topics	Qualities
Multiple framings	Formulate • Initiate • Revise and revisit	Representation Entitlement In-depth collaboration Negotiation	Inclusion Collaboration Usability
Knowledge diversity	Generate • Information collection • Innovation and analysis • Implementation • Communication	Mapping knowledge needs Knowledge integration Joint analysis In-depth collaboration	Collaboration Integration
Limited legitimacy	Evaluate • Process • Impact	Transparency Accountability Co-reflection Assessing impact	Usability Co-reflection

Concluding Comments

This commentary is one example of how integrative and implementation research can be applied within a concrete context such as sustainable urban development. As we can see from this example, the work presented in this book reflects crucial concerns of researchers and practitioners who are grappling with complex social and environmental problems. While the guidelines and qualities outlined above are in a different form from those presented in this book, the overall issues and goals are the same—namely the need for effective processes that can identify, harness and motivate collaboration and integration for knowledge production and problem solving that can support policy and implementation for more sustainable futures. Educational curricula that provide researchers with the skills to participate in such processes are fundamental to their success. At Mistra-Urban Futures, a great deal of time and energy is currently being put into supporting the joint knowledge-production processes themselves. This occurs in the form of different types of support activities for participants so that they can effectively deal with the difficulties that such processes entail. The creation of an Integration and Implementation Sciences discipline, as outlined in this book, could greatly contribute to producing researchers and practitioners with the skills needed to undertake the challenges involved in addressing current social and environmental problems.

Contributed October 2011

Reference

Mouffe, C. (2005). *On the Political*. London: Routledge.

Brief Biography

Merritt Polk is an Associate Professor in Human Ecology at the University of Gothenburg School of Global Studies in Sweden. She is currently working at Mistra-Urban Futures, where she is responsible for developing a transdisciplinary methodology for joint knowledge production and capacity building between university, private, semi-private and public organisations. Since the 1990s she has worked extensively with practitioners in the field of gender mainstreaming and transport with a focus on travel patterns, attitudes and policy, and applied this work to the interactions between gender equality, sustainable transportation and climate change. She has taught diverse courses such as sustainable cities, sustainable development and conflicts, as well as interdisciplinary and transdisciplinary methods in Human Ecology. More recently she has done research on urban planning with a focus on multilevel stakeholder processes and the framing and implementation of sustainable development. For the past six years, she has worked on developing transdisciplinary methods for sustainable urban development, with a focus on combining interdisciplinary and cross-sector approaches in urban and transport planning.

52. Philosophy as a Theoretical Foundation for I2S

Michael O'Rourke[1]

Integrative applied research is a process of addressing consequential problems by: a) synthesising what is known about them by disciplinary experts and stakeholders, b) integrating that synthesis with a thoughtful response to what is unknown about them, and c) bringing the results to bear on both policy and practice aimed at ameliorating them. In the words of the US National Academies' Committee on Facilitating Interdisciplinary Research, work of this sort 'has delivered much already and promises more—a sustainable environment, healthier and more prosperous lives, new discoveries and technologies to inspire young minds, and a deeper understanding of our place in space and time'.[2] But integrative applied research is an exceedingly complex activity, involving a combination of players, contexts and challenges that is often *sui generis*. Those of us who engage in integrative applied research do our best to rely on experience as our guide when we launch a new project, but there is always a nagging concern that we could do better. How? One obvious method would be to check our plans against the best practices in the field. But there is simply no good, centralised 'storehouse' for expert opinion, relevant literature and 'best practices' related to the conduct of integrative applied research.

In her sweeping call to action in this book, Gabriele Bammer argues that we should address this problem by creating a new discipline: Integration and Implementation Sciences (I2S). In this book, she outlines what such a discipline might look like, beginning with broad, constituent domains (for example, knowledge synthesis and the integration and management of diverse unknowns) and moving through successively more focused framing questions, issues and examples. The vision put forward in this book reflects a mature, experienced appreciation for the shape and practice of integrative applied research, highlighting among many other things the importance of systems perspectives on this complex research mode, the centrality of communication issues to integrative applied research in all of its stages, and the existence and value of various nuanced responses to what is unknown about a research problem. In this commentary, I focus on theoretical aspects of this vision, arguing that philosophy could play a significant role in supplying a discipline like I2S with a secure conceptual foundation.

---

1   Michael O'Rourke was invited as a senior scholar 'who has been influential in stimulating interdisciplinary communication, including through the Toolbox Project'.
2   National Academies (2005, p. 1).

Disciplining Interdisciplinarity and the Role of Theory

I find the discussion highly stimulating, even while I remain uncertain about the prospects of a discipline emerging from the activities that surround and support integrative applied research. I take disciplines to be intrinsically constituted sets of methods, principles and practices sufficiently widespread and stable to receive institutional support. There will be those who resist *disciplining* interdisciplinarity because of a perceived threat to the flexibility and reach of interdisciplinary activity, but that is not my concern. That institutionalised communities of practice will form around interdisciplinary support activities is clear—it is already happening, as evinced by the Association for Integrative Studies and the work of the Science of Team Science network, among others— and these will quite likely lead to the development of the normed methods and confirmation regimens that mark *disciplinary* activity.

My concern is that I2S is too broad in scope to be anything more than a family of research activities. I suspect that I2S will be to disciplined interdisciplinarity what biological science is to microbiology and evolutionary biology—that is, an umbrella area covering a number of more or less loosely connected disciplines. The domains of knowledge synthesis, understanding and managing diverse unknowns, and policy and practice implementation are home to various integrative pursuits, but as Bammer herself points out, they are wide areas of intellectual endeavour that differ significantly in character. Will one community of practice emerge to bind them all or will there arise a number of more focused research communities?

Whether we see one discipline (such as I2S) or many emerge out of work that supports integrative applied research will depend in part on whether Bammer is correct in her assessment of the elements that constitute the Integration and Implementation Sciences. Little is said to motivate the selection of the three principle domains or the questions that subdivide them. What is missing—and here I second the commentary from Alison Ritter—is a theoretical foundation that can supply a disciplinary structure and justify these choices. A good disciplinary theory should satisfy two desiderata: a) supply a systematic conceptual foundation for the discipline that unifies its questions, methods and confirmation standards, and b) frame the disciplinary problem space in ways that are productive of new questions and insights. In the remainder of this commentary, I outline the prospects for philosophy as a source for such a theory, considering each of the desiderata in turn.

Philosophy and Theoretical Foundations

We can begin by distinguishing between two questions that one might ask prior to initiating the development of a new theory for a prospective discipline such as I2S: 1) what concepts figure principally into the work of I2S that require analysis, and 2) how might those concepts be synthesised into a foundation for the whole of the discipline? This way of putting it suggests that analysis precedes synthesis, but the development process is typically more complex than that. Top-down, *a priori* intuitions about the conditions that make I2S possible will guide theorists in identifying which concepts are relevant, while bottom-up, *a posteriori* reflection on critical, paradigmatic concepts (for example, *integration, communication, complexity, uncertainty*) will influence intuitions about what the overall conceptual framework should be. In practice, these orientations would relate to one another in a feedback loop, mutually informing the theorist as she characterises the conceptual commitments of those who practise I2S. There is no single entry point into this loop, but adequate theoretical development will require sensitivity to both kinds of considerations and a considered effort to achieve reflective equilibrium.[3]

I will consider the second question first in relation to I2S. In Bammer's view, I2S is 'the discipline that underpins integrative applied research' (Chapter 2), and so it acquires its character in relation to integrative applied research. Thus, in theorising the philosophical foundations of I2S, it is critical that one takes seriously the fact that integrative applied research is first and foremost a form of *research*. Research is an activity that aims to augment our knowledge, and so it is fundamentally *epistemological*. First philosophy for I2S will therefore be epistemology. This is not to say that metaphysical or axiological concerns will not figure importantly into the foundations of I2S, but they will be framed by a concern with knowledge production. The theoretical prominence of epistemology in this context is reflected in Bammer's three domains: the synthesis of knowledge, the management of unknowns, and efforts to influence policy and practice are all essentially connected with the development of a more comprehensive understanding of the problems at issue.

She also gives privilege of place to two concepts that will figure importantly into the epistemology of I2S: *synthesis* and *integration*. She distinguishes these, taking the former to be 'the bringing together of disciplinary and stakeholder knowledge'—a task made complex by the incommensurability of the different ways of knowing involved[4]—and the latter to involve 'the combination of the synthesised knowledge with a considered response to the remaining unknowns

---

3   Daniels (2011).
4   Miller et al. (2008).

about the problem' (Chapter 2). While I agree that this distinction captures an important difference in epistemic orientation while emphasising the central role to be played by what we *don't* know, it isn't clear to me that this is the best way to draw this distinction relative to integrative applied research.

The problem is in taking synthesis to require involvement of stakeholder knowledge. Surely synthesis—understood as an epistemic process that involves working with what you have in integrative applied research—is manifest in a translational research process involving cross-disciplinary collaborators who may not yet have access to stakeholder perspectives. (Consider, for example, work in the translational health sciences at the interface of bench and clinical research.) Instead, it may be more theoretically fecund to associate synthesis with the systematic, negotiated development of collective knowledge in general, and integration with the negotiated, reflective combination of what is known with what has been identified as unknown. So drawn, this distinction could be crossed with another distinction that introduces stakeholder perspectives.

This second distinction focuses on three types of combination familiar to those working in integrative applied research, specifically, *disciplinary*, *translational* and *professional* combinations (Table 52.1). Disciplinary combination comprises either synthesis or integration involving multiple disciplines; translational combination includes the disciplines as well as non-research partners in other sectors, including managers, policy makers and stakeholders; professional combination focuses on the individual researcher, who is often asked to combine multiple scopes of work into one unified professional identity. As an example of the last sort of combination, consider the academic who may aim to combine research, teaching and outreach activities into a coherent identity as an integrative applied research professional.

Turning now to the first question, we find a number of concepts that figure importantly into integration and implementation that raise interesting philosophical issues. We can use the standard, three-part distinction of philosophy into epistemology, metaphysics and axiology to help classify these. Within epistemology, some concepts will concern more local aspects of integrative applied research practice, such as the relationship among the six identified ways of dealing with unknowns, while others will concern topics of exogenous interest to philosophers, such as the prospects for *reasonable* disagreement in integrative applied research.[5] Many issues of theoretical interest will fall under the banner of metaphysics, including those related to the disparate scales that figure into integration and implementation, the character of emergent phenomena in complex systems and the ontological status of various boundary objects used to effect synthesis and integration. With respect to axiology,

---

5   O'Rourke and Crowley (forthcoming).

Bammer has emphasised the importance of 'dealing with values', and that will be an important topic for philosophical theory. Ethical considerations will come into play across the trajectory of integration and implementation, as will issues of advocacy, bias and cultural variation. Philosophical attention to these topics and many others will be an important part of theoretical development of an enterprise such as I2S.

Table 52.1 A Framework for Epistemological Combination in Integrative Applied Research

	Disciplinary	**Translational**	**Professional**
Synthesis	Combination of knowledge contributed by multiple disciplines to a cross-disciplinary research effort	Combination of knowledge about an applied research problem involving contributions from non-research sectors (for example, stakeholders)	Combination of what one knows about one's own professional commitments into a coherent identity
Integration	Combination of the product of disciplinary synthesis with a considered assessment of relevant disciplinary unknowns	Combination of translational synthesis with a considered assessment of unknowns from the constituent sectors	Combination of professional synthesis with a reasonable and balanced assessment of what one does not know about one's professional situation

Philosophy and Theoretical Productivity

One important test of the developing theory will be how it engages with the practice of I2S. Does the theory support the practice, generating insights as it grounds the development of the discipline, or does it swing free of the day-to-day business of I2S, remaining the province of just those who happen to be theoretically inclined? The goal should be theory of the first sort— robust, engaged and embodied in the life of I2S and the professional lives of its practitioners. While notoriously abstract, philosophy has been applied to integrative applied research with positive effect. Philosophical reflection on the theoretical commitments of interdisciplinary activity has generated just this sort of engaged theorising, contributing, for example, to the emergence of 'field' philosophy,[6] interactional expertise[7] and, in the case of my research group, the Toolbox Project.[8]

The Toolbox Project, developed out of the frustration produced by the challenges associated with integrative applied research, is a good case in point.

---

6   Frodeman (2008).
7   Gorman (2010).
8   Eigenbrode et al. (2007).

In 2001, the University of Idaho and CATIE (Turrialba, Costa Rica) received a US National Science Foundation Integrative Graduate Education and Traineeship (IGERT) grant to underwrite an interdisciplinary PhD program that focused on biodiversity conservation and sustainable agriculture in fragmented landscapes. Among the innovations in this project were the requirements that students work in teams of three to four from the start, identify a common, overarching research question, and write dissertations on aspects of this question. Students in each team were expected to produce publishable collaborative research and co-author a collective dissertation chapter. The work put the teams in contact with place-based stakeholder groups, adding implementation to integration as an additional dimension of their graduate education. Some of the teams struggled to find the key to integrative success and, as a result, students approached the principal investigator team and requested that the project seminar in the autumn of 2005 be devoted to philosophical issues in interdisciplinary research. Philosophy, they thought, might supply just the sort of abstract perspective that might facilitate the integration of the constituent disciplines in their teams.

Work in the seminar led to development of the Toolbox approach to cross-disciplinary communication. Philosophical thinking about the challenge of communicating across disciplinary boundaries led us to recognise the potential of philosophy to supply common ground for disciplinary synthesis. Participants in the seminar recognised that conceptual incommensurability was one important obstacle to effective cross-disciplinary work. It manifested itself in the form of terminological, methodological and ontological difference. Fundamentally different disciplinary epistemologies went unrecognised, generating the illusions of both disagreement and agreement, and leading to 'discourse' that was more an exercise in talking past one another. The group determined that collaborators could work out some of these differences in a dialogue structured to reveal conceptual differences systematically and efficiently. Cue philosophical theory. Drawing from both epistemology and the philosophy of science, the group developed a 'Toolbox' of prompts that limns the fundamental epistemological and metaphysical commitments of scientific researchers, exposing the elements that frame their research world views. By discussing these prompts in a workshop setting, collaborators acquire mutual appreciation of their conceptual assumptions, coming to see their research project through each other's eyes. The result is a type of dialogue method[9] that combines philosophy's ability to abstract away from disciplinary difference towards common ground with its

---

9   McDonald et al. (2009).

theoretically systematic appreciation for the fundamental character of scientific research practice. The Toolbox approach was introduced by Eigenbrode and others[10] and subsequently funded by the US National Science Foundation.[11]

Philosophy in Relation to I2S

Should I2S emerge as a discipline, there is no doubt that philosophers will turn their attention to it and examine its conceptual character; this is what philosophers do. The philosophy of I2S would certainly join the philosophy of music, the philosophy of sport and the philosophy of geography as a 'philosophy of' sub-discipline. But the relationship between philosophy and I2S could be much more vigorous and essential, yielding great value on both sides. In one direction, philosophy could take the lead in supplying a robust and coherent theoretical foundation that could support disciplinary development of I2S. While I agree with Michael Smithson's commentary that philosophy is not a good 'template' for I2S as a discipline, it is worth emphasising that I2S is in its nascent stage and at present lacks a 'philosophical consensus' about its 'ontology and epistemology'; in fact, it is precisely this consensus that *constitutes* a theoretical foundation, and what better discipline to supply this foundation than philosophy? In the other direction, I2S could serve as a type of 'full-service' platform for philosophical work, similar to science and the environment, supporting interesting work in the three main philosophical branches identified above: epistemology, metaphysics and axiology. Sadly, though, at this time few philosophers recognise the potential that integrative applied research holds for their discipline. While there are exceptions,[12] this is a reflection of philosophy's staid, traditional nature, especially in its more hallowed halls.[13] Whether work that falls under Bammer's term 'Integration and Implementation Sciences' will constitute a single discipline is unclear to me, but I am hopeful that as it continues to gain momentum and stature, it will take philosophy along with it (even if it goes kicking and screaming).

Contributed November 2011

---

10 Eigenbrode et al. (2007).
11 SES-0823058. For additional details, please visit <http://www.cals.uidaho.edu/toolbox/> (accessed 15 February 2012).
12 For example, Frodeman (2008).
13 For an expression of this nature, see Stanley (2010).   **413**

References

Daniels, N. (2011). 'Reflective equilibrium'. In: Zalta, E. N. (ed.). *The Stanford Encyclopedia of Philosophy*. Stanford, CA: Stanford University Press; <http://plato.stanford.edu/archives/spr2011/entries/reflective-equilibrium/> (accessed 8 August 2012).

Eigenbrode, S. D., O'Rourke, M., Althoff, D., Goldberg, C., Merrill, K., Morse, W., Nielsen-Pincus, M., Stephens, J., Winowiecki, L., Wulfhorst, J. D. and Bosque-Pérez, N. (2007). 'Employing philosophical dialogue in collaborative science'. *BioScience*, 57: 55–64.

Frodeman, R. (2008). 'Philosophy unbound: environmental thinking at the end of the earth'. *Environmental Ethics*, 30: 313–24.

Gorman, M. (ed.). (2010). *Trading Zones and Interactional Expertise*. Cambridge, MA: MIT Press.

McDonald, D., Bammer, G. and Deane, P. (2009). *Research Integration Using Dialogue Methods*. Canberra: ANU E Press; <http://epress.anu.edu.au/dialogue_methods_citation.html>

Miller, T. R., Baird, T. D., Littlefield, C. M., Kofinas, G., Chapin III, F. S. and Redman, C. L. (2008). 'Epistemological pluralism: reorganizing interdisciplinary research'. *Ecology and Society*, 13 (2): article 46; <http://www.ecologyandsociety.org/vol13/iss2/art46/> (accessed 8 August 2012).

National Academies. (2005). *Facilitating Interdisciplinary Research*. Washington, DC: The National Academies Press.

O'Rourke, M. and Crowley, S. (forthcoming). 'Philosophical intervention and cross-disciplinary science: the story of the Toolbox Project'. *Synthese*.

Stanley, J. (2010). 'The crisis of philosophy'. *Inside Higher Education*, 5 April; <http://www.insidehighered.com/views/2010/04/05/stanley> (accessed 8 August 2012).

Brief Biography

Michael O'Rourke is Professor of Philosophy at Michigan State University. His research interests include the nature of epistemic integration and communication in collaborative, cross-disciplinary research and the nature of linguistic communication between intelligent agents. He is Director of the Toolbox Project, which conducts research into philosophical approaches to facilitating interdisciplinary research. He has published extensively on the topic of communication, both within philosophy and within the field of robotic agent design. He has been a co-principal investigator and collaborator on several funded projects involving autonomous underwater vehicles. He co-founded and served as co-director of the Inland Northwest Philosophy Conference, an interdisciplinary conference on philosophical themes, and as co-editor of the Topics in Contemporary Philosophy series published by the Massachusetts Institute of Technology (MIT) Press.

53. Interdisciplinarity without Borders

Howard Gadlin and L. Michelle Bennett[1]

O wonder! How many goodly creatures are there here! How beauteous mankind is! O brave new world! That has such people in it.

— Shakespeare, *The Tempest*, Act v, Scene 1

After reading Gabriele Bammer's majestic and inspiring manuscript along with commentaries by an array of distinguished colleagues, it seems almost churlish to express any qualms about I2S, a project that in principle represents the apotheosis of collaborative work conducted from multi- inter- and trans-disciplinary perspectives. While we share an interest and commitment to collaborative interdisciplinary research, we have concerns about both the desirability and the feasibility of establishing I2S as a distinct discipline. At the risk of being labelled latter-day Luddites, we will explore those concerns here. Mind you, although we raise questions about the notion of I2S as a discipline, we are also enormously excited by and committed to the challenge that stimulates this book: 'How can academic research enhance its contributions to addressing…major problems facing human societies?' In addition, we share Bammer's belief that there is enormous promise to interdisciplinary research: it opens a path to understanding and solving complex scientific problems that were previously beyond the reach of researchers working within the confines of single disciplines and limited in their ability to collaborate with others. The integrative approach that is proving so fruitful in addressing scientific problems is not, however, necessarily transferable to tackling complex social problems, even those for which scientific findings are relevant.

Our hesitations increase when we note that I2S is intended to be much more than an approach to interdisciplinary research; it also entails an almost utopian vision of evidence-based, fundamentally rational decision making applied to significant social problems. The proposed discipline is intended to synthesise the work of policy makers and stakeholders as well as researchers. Please note, we are not objecting in principle to all approaches that incorporate the consideration of scientific findings into policy considerations and related efforts to delineate and resolve social problems. It is the proposal to merge the distinct domains of inquiry, advocacy and policy analysis/formation into an integrated discipline that gives us pause. With the combination of scientists, policy makers

---

1 Howard Gadlin and Michelle Bennett were each invited as senior scholars who have 'made significant contributions to thinking about collaborative research'. They chose to co-author a joint commentary.

and stakeholders in mind, we tried to envision an I2S approach to addressing one of the more volatile issues of our time: climate change. It is hard not to test the thoughtful, rational and dialogical processes of I2S against the realities of current acrimonious, politicised policy debate. In the climate change matter, for example, even scientific expertise is attacked and de-legitimised as the effort of technocratic elites to impose their liberal perspective on everyone else. In this controversy, overwhelming evidence of the seriousness of the problem is ignored in part because of the very source of the knowledge (scientists) and in part because it leads to conclusions regarding necessary regulations and limitations on pollution, which are opposed because of a generalised resistance to regulations qua regulations. And climate change is hardly unique in terms of the dynamic of the conflict. Look at health care, drug policy, screening mammography, nuclear power or comparative effectiveness research and you see the same dynamic. The challenge is much more complicated than making research findings relevant to decisions regarding policies designed to address social, economic and environmental problems. Fundamentally the task is a political and socio/cultural endeavour not a disciplinary one.

When Alice Roughley states '[t]he absolute brilliance of the book is that with the foundational research into dialogue methods it tackles the most critical integration methodology issue, that of analysing data generated through different disciplines and stakeholder perspectives/values', we share her admiration for Bammer's vision but not her belief that the issue has been resolved. While it is true that 'dialogue-based methods use conversation to…"*jointly create meaning and shared understanding*"' (Chapter 6), these methods (which we practise and promote heartily) cannot be effective with stakeholders who do not desire jointly created meaning or shared understanding. Furthermore, while dialogue-based methods are essential to create understanding, other factors must be addressed before such methods can move from shared meaning to decision making.

This is no mean feat and entails coming to terms with more than differences in meaning and understanding of key concepts and perspectives. Any attempt to integrate facts, values and interests into a decision-making matrix must first address questions of scope: what topics are under consideration; what are the appropriate methods of defining and selecting the topics; which stakeholders and which perspectives are to be included; who decides all this and according to what criteria? While considering these questions it should also be noted that one of the most effective and best-known programs for bringing together opposing sides on highly controversial issues for the purpose of finding areas of shared understanding, the Public Conversations Project,[2] has been somewhat successful only because its programs eschew decision making. Sometimes, the

---

2   <http://www.publicconversations.org/> (accessed 15 February 2012).

only way to move opposing stakeholders to listen to one another is to reassure them that understanding each other's position does not require that they come to an agreement about a decision.

Of course there are many examples of successful decision-making processes that involve the participation of scientific experts, policy makers and stakeholders, but almost all of these begin with participants committed to generating possible solutions to a policy matter or a social or environmental problem. We do not doubt that one can develop processes for setting policy or making crucial decisions that involve people from the three domains (science, advocacy and policy), but we believe that the challenge in doing this is very different from the challenge of integrating multiple scientific disciplines and methodologies into an inter- or trans-disciplinary field. I2S is an attempt to bring together components that are incommensurable and we believe that any approach for dealing with incommensurability must be based on acknowledging and maintaining the distinctiveness.

In her commentary, Alison Ritter asserts that I2S transforms the 'impasse between passive delivery of scientific evidence and convincing persuasion'. She then identifies functions that define work within Bammer's I2S framework

- inclusive participatory processes
- dealing with values, value congruence, boundaries and scoping
- dealing with unknowns within the research process
- being a member of a scholarly discipline

and asserts that each of these serves to resolve the research–advocacy dilemma. Not only do we believe Ritter is mistaken—the dilemma is not resolved— we also suggest that the research–advocacy dilemma ought not be resolved. It is precisely this dilemma that provides the creative tensions necessary for democratic policy decision-making processes.

Interestingly there is already a considerable amount of theorising, thinking and activity directed towards creating decision-making processes for controversial, multi-party issues and conflicts that require cooperation and collaboration among groups of people quite disparate in values, perspective, culture, power and just about every dimension of identity you can list. A brief overview of this work reveals an intense focus on process and attention to the dynamics of communication, dialogue, empowerment and participation. It should be noted that each of the four factors listed above is regularly attended to, directly or indirectly, in the work of those who facilitate/mediate controversial, multi-party issues. One of the most influential areas of activity is in the area of participatory democracy, much of which is inspired by and flows from the work of the German philosopher Jürgen Habermas.[3] His analysis of conditions that foster communicative rationality and his thinking about the public sphere have stimulated widespread discussions, theorising and research about democratic processes, voting and decision making. Closely related is a vast amount of work in the area of collaborative governance, which has led to revisions in ideas about the nature of leadership, processes for decision making and effective organisational structure.[4]

Among the other related developments has been the growth, in the United States, of negotiated rule-making (reg-neg), a process whereby federal agencies work with stakeholders and interest groups to negotiate the substance of proposed rules, which are then submitted for public review and comment. Naturally such processes involve attending to the dynamics of negotiation and require the leadership of skilled facilitators able to enhance the quality of communication across the various interest groups. Such processes also raise important questions about the composition of such groups—a matter to which we will return later because it has some bearing on the I2S vision as well.

Federal agencies are not the only organisations experimenting with processes for bringing together diverse groups of people to address matters of policy or to consider approaches to the solution of social problems. Non-government organisations such as the Keystone Center[5] and CDR Associates[6] have been working in the very same areas I2S aspires to for dozens of years now. The Keystone Center describes its mission as bringing 'together today's public, private and civic sector leaders to advance solutions to society's most challenging environmental, energy, and public health problems'. The Keystone Center has just completed facilitation of a 'Research Integrity Dialogue' addressing issues involving the use of scientific results in the chemical, agricultural and pharmaceutical industries.[7] CDR describes itself as helping 'people—leaders and managers in the private sector, government, diverse organizations and public interest groups—talk, find common ground and reach agreements on difficult issues'.

In all of the efforts described above there is considerable attention paid to, and experience in, work with dialogue-based methods and much that we in the interdisciplinary sciences can learn from. One of the most important lessons is that there is much, much more to establishing collaborative interdisciplinary teams than 'knowledge synthesis'. In addition, when we go beyond integrating

---

3   Habermas (1991).
4   See O'Leary and Bingham (2007, 2009).
5   <http://www.keystone.org/> (accessed 15 February 2012).
6   <http://www.mediate.org/> (accessed 15 February 2012).
7   <http://www.keystone.org/images/keystone-center/spp-documents/Health/Research%20Integrity%20 Rountable%20Report.pdf> (accessed 26 September 2012).

knowledge from different disciplines and methodologies into decision making and policy formation we have to be very careful about thinking of this as an integrative process.

Missing from consideration in the I2S book are two issues that we consider central to any effort to better incorporate scientific knowledge and stakeholders into public policy decision making: conflict of interest and bias. The US Institute of Medicine defines conflict of interest as 'circumstances that create a risk that professional judgments or actions regarding a primary interest will be unduly influenced by a secondary interest'. Attending to conflict of interest and bias is not a mere formality. It is essential to establish the credibility of the scientific information that is incorporated into policy formation and decision making. Two recent papers[8] attest to the necessity to attend to these matters.

It is in considering issues of conflict of interest and bias that we have our strongest hesitations when we envision I2S. At the National Institutes of Health (NIH), where we work, conflict of interest and bias generally are handled by maintaining sharp distinctions between stakeholders and decision makers. Consider, for example, the description in Box 53.1 of the NIH Consensus Development Program for reviewing evidence about a particular medical topic. We have also added some of the considerations and recommendations of the US Bipartisan Policy Committee.

Box 53.1 Description of the NIH Consensus Development Program[9] and Some Considerations and Recommendations of the US Bipartisan Policy Committee

A consensus development process is initiated when the scientific leadership in one of the 27 NIH Institutes determines that there is likely to be sufficient convergence among the research findings in a particular area to reach consensus, sometimes on highly controversial topics. This initiates a systematic evidence review on the chosen topic performed by one of the Agency for Healthcare Research and Quality's Evidence-Based Practice Centers. The resulting report is circulated to the consensus panel members and also posted to the Consensus Development website approximately six weeks prior to the conference. Once the conference begins, the report serves as a foundation of high-quality evidence upon which the conference will build.

---

8   Conrad and Becker (2011); The International Life Sciences Institute North America Working Group on Guiding Principles (2009).

9   Taken (often verbatim) from <http://prevention.nih.gov/cdp/about.aspx> (accessed 4 September 2012).

The conferences are held over two and a half days. The first one and a half days are dedicated to plenary sessions, during which invited expert speakers present information. These speakers are followed by 'town hall forums', in which open discussion occurs among the speakers, panellists and the general public in attendance. The panel then develops a draft statement on the afternoon and evening of the second day, and presents it on the morning of the third day for audience commentary. The panel considers these comments in executive session and revises its draft accordingly. The conference ends with a press briefing, during which reporters are invited to question the panellists about their findings.

Each conference panel comprises 12 to 16 members, who can give balanced, objective and informed attention to the topic. Panel members

1. must not be employees of the US Department of Health and Human Services

2. must not hold financial or career (research) interests in the conference topic

3. may be knowledgeable about the general topic under consideration, but must not have published on or have a publicly stated opinion on the topic

4. represent a variety of perspectives, to include
    *   practicing and academic health professionals
    *   biostatisticians and epidemiologists
    *   clinical trialists and researchers
    *   non-health professionals with expertise in fields relevant to the specific topic (e.g. ethicists, economists, attorneys)
    *   individuals representing public-centred values and concerns.

In addition, the panel as a whole should appropriately reflect racial and ethnic diversity. Panel members are not paid a fee or honorarium for their efforts. They are, however, reimbursed for travel expenses related to their participation in the conference.

The conferences typically feature approximately 21 speakers: three present the information found in the Evidence-Based Practice Center's systematic review of the literature; the other 18 are experts in the topic at hand, have likely published on the topic and may have strong opinions or beliefs on the topic. Where multiple viewpoints on a topic exist, every effort is made to include speakers who address all sides of the issue.

The panel's draft report is released online late in the conference's third and final day. The final report is released approximately six weeks later. During the intervening period, the panel may edit its statement for clarity and correct any factual errors that might be discovered. No substantive changes to the panel's findings are made during this period.

Each Consensus Development or State-of-the-Science Conference Statement reflects an independent panel's assessment of the medical knowledge available at the time the statement is written; as such, it provides a 'snapshot in time' of the state of knowledge on the conference topic. It is not a policy statement of the NIH or the Federal Government.

Notice how carefully the distinction is made between scientific consensus and policy.

Look also at the recommendations of the Bipartisan Policy Committee,[a] a committee formed by four former US Senate Majority Leaders to address the following dilemma described in the introduction to the report:

> The use of science in the formulation of regulatory policy—by both the Executive Branch and the Congress—has been a political flashpoint in recent decades. Policymakers often claim that particular regulatory decisions have been driven by, or even required by science; their critics, in turn, have attacked the quality or the interpretation of that science. Such has left the U.S. with a system that is plagued by charges that science is being 'politicized' and that regulation lacks a solid scientific basis. As a result, needed regulation may be stymied, dubious regulations may be adopted, issues can drag on without conclusion and policy debate is degraded. Moreover, the morale of scientists is weakened, and public faith in both government and science is undermined.

> The question is not whether scientific results should be used in developing regulatory policy, but how they should be used. This report is structured around three sets of questions that are at the heart of the debate over the use of science in regulatory policy. Those questions are:

> • What kinds of activities or decision making amount to 'politicizing' science? How and to what extent can one differentiate between the aspects of regulatory policy that involve scientific judgments and those that involve making policy recommendations (which are inherently political)?

- When and how should Federal agencies empanel advisory committees? How should members be selected? How should conflicts of interest and biases of potential members be handled? What is scientific balance and how can it be achieved? How can the independence and integrity of committees' deliberations be assured?

- What studies should agencies and advisory committees review in formulating regulatory policy? How should they be weighed? What role should peer review play and how might peer review be modified and strengthened?

Among the recommendations are the following.

Recommendation One: The Administration needs to promulgate guidelines (through executive orders or other instruments) to ensure that when federal agencies are developing regulatory policies, they explicitly differentiate, to the extent possible, between questions that involve scientific judgments and questions that involve judgments about economics, ethics and other matters of policy.

Recommendation Two: The Administration should promulgate guidelines (through executive orders or other instruments) directing agencies to follow the policies described below on: when to consult advisory panels on scientific questions, how to appoint them (including how to deal with conflicts of interest and biases) and how they should operate. Congress should pass, and the President should sign into law, any statutory changes needed to implement these policies.

a. <http://bipartisanpolicy.org/library/report/science-policy-project-final-report> (accessed 4 September 2012).

Including these references is not meant to endorse them. Important to notice in these various efforts are the incredible challenges associated with our efforts to have scientific knowledge contribute more directly to the solution of social problems and the formulation of policies intended to improve the quality of life. While we share Gabriele's desire to find ways to have knowledge matter more than it does nowadays and we agree with the unarguable observation that current decision making is under-informed by rigorous research and that methodologically sound interdisciplinary research could help enormously in understanding and addressing major social and environmental problems, we are wary of the idea of I2S as a discipline. We must remind ourselves that scientific and technological professionals tend to believe that their expertise is under-appreciated and under-utilised. But even if this is true, we have to be careful to educate about and advocate for the potential value of the knowledge we create and we have to be equally careful not to slip into the elitist assumption that those who know the most know the best.

When we look at some of the new disciplines that have resulted from interdisciplinary mergers—bioengineering, neuroscience, biochemistry, systems biology—we see fields that were created by taking one way of thinking and applying that to problems in other fields (bioengineering) or we see the results of interdisciplinary efforts to address complex scientific problems that could not be addressed within any single discipline. But in all cases the new discipline was driven by scientists attempting to solve problems, to find ways to conduct research on complex phenomena. The new disciplines were emergent phenomena. No-one set about to create a new discipline and then try to apply it. It was all about the science. But in the case of I2S we face a problem of a different sort from those faced by scientific disciplines. The aim of I2S is not to bring together fundamentally similar components but rather to bring together incommensurable components. Interdisciplinarity is a common thread in the newly emergent disciplines; it is an approach, but the components of the approach are called forth by the problems. Our quarrel is with the push to carve out a discipline of interdisciplinarity.

In this regard, we share the conclusion reached by Dawn Youngblood in a recent study of interdisciplinary studies and bridging disciplines: 'What interdisciplinary studies can therefore learn from the bridging disciplines is the importance of not becoming a domain, as domain creates territory and territory creates niche dominance. Instead focus on the process of finding solutions to problems and answers to important questions.'

Contributed November 2011

References

Conrad, J. W. and Becker, R. A. (2011). 'Enhancing credibility of chemical safety studies: emerging consensus on key assessment criteria'. *Environmental Health Perspectives*, 119 (6), 757-64.

Habermas, J. (1991). *The Structural Transformation of the Public Sphere: An inquiry into a category of bourgeois society*. Cambridge, MA: MIT Press.

O'Leary, R. and Bingham, L. B. (2007). *A Manager's Guide to Resolving Conflicts in Collaborative Networks*. Arlington, VA: IBM Center for the Business of Government.

O'Leary, R. and Bingham, L. B. (eds). (2009). *The Collaborative Public Manager*. Washington, DC: Georgetown University Press.

The International Life Sciences Institute North America Working Group on Guiding Principles. (2009). 'Funding food science and nutrition research: financial conflicts and scientific integrity'. *American Journal of Clinical Nutrition*, 8 April; <http://www.ajcn.org/content/early/2009/04/08/ajcn.2009.27604> (accessed 30 November 2011).

Brief Biographies

Howard Gadlin has been Ombudsman and Director of the Center for Cooperative Resolution at the National Institutes of Health since 1999. Previously he was University Ombudsperson at the University of California Los Angeles (UCLA) where he was also Director of the UCLA Conflict Mediation Program and Co-Director of the Center for the Study and Resolution of Interethnic/Interracial Conflict. He is a former Professor of Psychology and is currently studying the dynamics of scientific teams and collaborations, and developing new approaches to addressing conflicts among scientists.

Dr L. Michelle Bennett is the Deputy Scientific Director for the National Heart Lung and Blood Institute (NHLBI), National Institutes of Health (NIH), in Bethesda, Maryland. She is responsible for programmatic integration and strategic planning across the basic, translational and clinical areas of the organisation. Applying her knowledge of the critical elements that enable team science and collaboration, she facilitates interdisciplinary efforts by bringing together scientists with diverse expertise to solve complex scientific problems.

Bennett, Gadlin and Samantha Levine-Finley co-led an initiative to understand the fundamental characteristics that contribute to successful scientific team functioning, which resulted in the development of a workbook, *Collaboration and Team Science: A field guide*, which serves as a primer for investigators who are building or participating on a research team.

54. When the Network Becomes the Platform

Julie Thompson Klein[1]

Gabriele Bammer's call for an I2S Development Drive in support of 'integrative applied research' comes at a crucial time in the history of interdisciplinarity. Publications and conference presentations proliferate across the academic sphere, amplified by calls for new approaches to research and education from professional associations, science policy bodies and other organisations. Yet, efforts are scattered, resulting in shortfalls of wisdom and practice. Some groups interact, but too many efforts have been isolated. Their collective existence affirms the importance and prominence of integrative applied research. Yet, groups are often small, marginal or, even when achieving a threshold point of size and strength, unaware of new developments in other organisations and networks. As a result, resources are under-utilised, cross-fertilisations foreshortened and progress in establishing an identifiable field stalled by fragmentation and marginalisation. The fragility and vulnerability of local projects and programs mirror this problem at the level of individuals and teams. Ill-informed definitions, shallow practices and inappropriate criteria for evaluation also prevail.

The 'floor plan' Bammer calls for would provide a systematic approach that is greater than any single method or theory. Systematic does not mean universalist. The Drive begins by recognising the limits of its own endeavour. Gaps and errors are inevitable; however, the price of waiting is high, impeding progress at a critical moment in the host of problems in need of integrative applied research. The Drive also begins by accepting, not minimising or erasing, the diversity of forms of research on real-world problems. Examples abound, documented by the exponential growth of related literatures. Yet, they must be identified and synthesised—'harnessed', in a core metaphor of the Drive— before it is possible to engage in comparative weighing of advantages and limits of particular methods and approaches. Only then can appropriate options for particular contexts be determined. The task is complicated by a long-recognised challenge in the literature of library and information sciences: the problem of scatter.

---

1   Julie Thompson Klein was invited as a 'senior scholar who has pioneered, and continues to advance thinking about, interdisciplinary research, in addition to being an assiduous networker'.

Interdisciplinary fields and other boundary-crossing initiatives are all too familiar with the problem of 'information scatter,' resulting from the distribution of knowledge and information. Scatter occurs in all areas, including disciplines. Yet, the dispersal of information and knowledge is greater in interdisciplinary fields. Advances in database-searching tools are a boon to serving information needs in these areas, including federated search engines that seek relevant materials across disciplines and fields as well as alert services that allow users to customise searches. Yet, many searches do not go beyond the blunt instrument of a simple Google quest or Wikipedia entry.

In the case of an I2S Development Drive, the problem of scatter is compounded by the ambitious scale of the project, posited at the level of a Big-Science project such as the Human Genome Project and the Manhattan Project. Prior efforts to collect pertinent materials have yielded helpful but partial results on a small scale. They brought to light many primary works but not the full extent of grey literature consisting of work published in small and peripheral venues, internal reports and informal records, let alone the wisdom of practice that is never written down.

Large as the challenge is, the Drive is at a readiness point, able to leverage and synergise a vast array of human and material resources already identified within the Integration and Implementation Sciences network. It also has links to the leadership of organisations poised to partner in this initiative, major among them the Science of Team Science network and the US National Institutes of Health Toolkit Project, as well as the European-based transdisciplinarity.net. Partnership is all the more crucial given the dynamic nature of the literature and the broader family of discourses that have important though under-realised congruencies. Beyond communities dedicated to interdisciplinary and transdisciplinary work, they include the discourses of post-normal science, systemic intervention, integrated assessment, sustainability science, team science, Mode 2 and action research. Current increased interest in research translation, knowledge brokering and impacts on policy and practice widens this spectrum. It expands even further with the enormous number of problem domains, not the least of which are sustainability, participatory democracy, and health and wellbeing.

Allied interests are not uniformly aligned with integrative applied research. Rather, they are loosely and tightly coupled, with differing boundaries and arrangements with common objectives across domains. Bammer's proposal to posit I2S as a 'discipline' underscores the need for a robust structure that is more than an add-on to existing ones. 'Discipline', though, is a limited concept for the complexity and scale of the strong 'knowledge base' that is needed. 'Interdiscipline' would be more appropriate, although even it does not acknowledge the 'inter-professional' dimensions of practice. Yet 'interdiscipline', at least, takes into account the relevance of not only disciplines but also interdisciplinary fields and networks as well as the interfaces of disciplinary, interdisciplinary and professional spheres.

The analogy of statistics highlights the methodological character of a Drive focused on the 'best available' information and methodology. At the same time, there is a theoretical dimension. A fully developed science of integrative applied research is not simply a toolkit—large and influential though such a 'storehouse' could become. It also entails new conceptual approaches that are capable of transforming current paradigms of both knowing and doing. Action research and other endeavours that merge 'know-how' with 'know-what' interrogate the strict dichotomy of practical and theoretical knowledge, academic and stakeholder knowledge, and individual and epistemological knowledge. Ultimately, too, the formation of a 'new research style' (Chapter 1) anchored by an identifiable body of knowledge and practices has implications for current taxonomies and typologies.

The 'agility' that accompanies a new research style also has implications for degrees of expertise. A core community of I2S specialists would possess the most consolidated and fully developed expertise. In assuming responsibility for its development, they would perform the dual functions of repository and vision. Repository ensures collection and codification. Vision scaffolds from that foundation to develop new approaches, to foster innovations that are not yet imagined, to encourage reflection and to strengthen the vital infrastructure of meeting and funding. Beyond this I2S 'home', a much larger and dispersed body of individuals needs expertise for doing integrative work both within and across disciplinary, interdisciplinary, professional and stakeholder contexts. Their newly honed capacity for integration and collaboration will not lie strictly outside their original homes. They will be the most dependent on a robust storehouse complete with customised guides genuinely capable of fast-tracking integrative applied work. At a time when new demands are being made on traditional research styles, they will also recognise the need to internalise new competencies of integration and collaboration in all of their locations.

Finally, building the foundation that is needed will not only require broadcasting results in familiar forums, including journals and conferences that have long been sites of mutual learning. It will also require a prominent virtual presence. A closing analogy comes from the world of digital cyber-infrastructure—that of 'platform'. John Unsworth's description of the shift from Web 1.0 to Web 2.0 suggests a useful way of thinking. The introduction of Web 2.0 shifted emphasis from the computer as platform to the network as platform, especially the network of interactions and synergies. An I2S 'college of peers' beckons a networked platform that is not possible with current groups operating in separate or even in tandem fashion. It requires the traction that cannot only derive from a concerted effort.

Contributed November 2011

Further Reading

On the topic of scatter, see: Palmer, C. L. (2010). 'Information research on interdisciplinarity'. In: Frodeman, R. (ed.), Klein, J. T. and Mitcham, C. (assoc. eds). *The Oxford Handbook of Interdisciplinarity*. Oxford: Oxford University Press, 176–7.

On the metaphor of platform, see: Unsworth, J. (2008). 'University 2.0'. In: Katz, R. N. (ed.). *The Tower and the Cloud: Higher education in the age of cloud computing*. Washington, DC: EDUCAUSE, 227.

On the relationship of individual and epistemic knowledge, see: Krohn, W. (2010). 'Interdisciplinary cases and disciplinary knowledge'. In: Frodeman, R. (ed.), Klein, J. T. and Mitcham, C. (assoc. eds). *The Oxford Handbook of Interdisciplinarity*. Oxford: Oxford University Press, 42–3.

Brief Biography

Julie Thompson Klein is Professor of Humanities in the English Department and Faculty Fellow for Interdisciplinary Development in the Division of Research at Wayne State University (Detroit, USA). She is an internationally known expert on the history, theory and practice of interdisciplinarity. Her authored and co-edited books include *Interdisciplinarity: History, theory, and practice* (1990), *Interdisciplinary Studies Today* (1994), *Crossing Boundaries: Knowledge, disciplinarities, and interdisciplinarities* (1996), *Transdisciplinarity: Joint problem solving among science, technology, and society* (2001), *Interdisciplinary Education in K–12 and College* (2002), the monograph *Mapping Interdisciplinary Studies* (1999), *Humanities, Culture, and Interdisciplinarity: The changing American academy* (2005), and *The Oxford Handbook of Interdisciplinarity* (2010). Klein is a recipient of the Kenneth Boulding Award for outstanding scholarship on interdisciplinarity, the Ramamoorthy & Yeh Distinguished Transdisciplinary Achievement Award and the Joseph Katz Award for Distinguished Contributions to the Practice and Discourse of General and Liberal Education. She is currently co-editor of the University of Michigan Press series Digital Humanities@ digitalculturebooks, and her book *Mapping Digital Humanities* is forthcoming.

55. Tackling Integrative Applied Research: Lessons from the management of innovation

Ian Elsum[1]

Far better an approximate answer to the right question, which is often vague, than an exact answer to the wrong question, which can always be made precise.

— John Tukey

Even the dogs may eat the crumbs which fall from the rich man's table; and in these days, when the rich in knowledge eat such specialised food at such separate tables, only the dogs have a chance of a balanced diet.

— Sir Geoffrey Vickers, Introduction to *The Art of Judgment*

I have spent nearly 25 years grappling with the complexities of the strategic management of applied research. Most of my experience is with CSIRO—a large, diverse applied research and technology-transfer organisation[2]—where I have worked on increasing the effectiveness of the research effort at both whole-of-CSIRO and research division levels. This has been through strategic planning, investment and assessment, as well as work on the factors necessary for excellence in applied research.

I agree wholeheartedly with the importance, and urgency, of the problem domain of Gabriele's book: the use of integrative applied research to tackle complex real-world problems. Integrative applied research has many of the same characteristics as innovation,[3] and the practice of integrative applied research can learn from the practice of innovation. This is the perspective I bring to this commentary.

---

1   Ian Elsum was invited as a 'member of the research leadership team at CSIRO and as someone who has a longstanding interest in integration to tackle complex real-world problems. Your observations on whether the ideas in the book are workable in an organisation such as yours will be very pertinent.'

2   The Commonwealth Scientific and Industrial Research Organisation (CSIRO) was founded in 1926 as a scientific research institute for Australia. It has 6500 staff and an annual budget of $1.5 billion. The organisation emphasises integration of its broad range of scientific and technological areas to address problems across a very broad range of application areas; see <www.csiro.au> (accessed 15 February 2012).

3   Innovation has two components: creation of new knowledge (invention) and exploitation of the new knowledge—that is, putting it to use to create value. Both components are essential.

An overarching challenge of integrative applied research is that it is an inextricable combination of a quest for fundamental understanding and practical use of this understanding. This is Pasteur's quadrant.[4] Managing the tension between the traditional approach to the quest for fundamental understanding (reductionism and increasingly specialised disciplines) and the needs of complex real-world problems (integration of knowledge from multiple areas at a system level) is critical to success.

My starting point is to examine some of the characteristics of integrative applied research and complex real-world problems as these characteristics determine the approach needed for success.

Applied Research

Applied research is fascinating, complex and hard because it is a system problem in which technical factors and factors to do with adoption and use are inextricably linked. As adoption of a technical solution and its use are an integral part of the problem, human, organisational and societal factors impinging upon adoption and use must be an integral part of the research from the beginning of an applied research project.

It is important in applied research to differentiate between adoption and use. Adoption—the willingness and ability to take research results and convert them into something that is useable more broadly—and use by others apart from the adopter must be considered separately as they are distinct processes: the factors causing a person or organisation to adopt research results and incorporate them into an artefact, service or advice will differ in many important ways from those factors pertinent to a person or organisation deciding to use the artefact, service or advice.

Consider, for example, research resulting in a new measuring instrument. The adopter of the research will be an instrument manufacturer; the users will be those organisations that might benefit from utilising the instrument in their operations. Very different sets of factors influence the decisions to manufacture the instrument and to buy it. Another example is public policy and programs where the adopting organisation might be a government agency that will develop policy and programs based on the research results, while the users will be the sections of society that are targeted through the programs.

The need to understand this 'external' (to the research organisation) context for adoption and use can be difficult for many researchers—it is rarely covered

---

4   Stokes (1997).

in research training in universities—and the incorporation of this perspective into research programs has been a major part of CSIRO's journey as an applied research organisation since the late 1980s.

Applied research involves searching for a workable solution to a fixed real-world problem. The fixed nature of the problem is important: the real world cannot be changed to make the problem more tractable, although the problem can be reframed. 'Workable' because a solution involves a blend of technical factors and factors to do with adoption and use, none of which may be optimum within its particular domain.

What is important for effectiveness in applied research is what works in the particular circumstances (time, place, stakeholders, and so on). Time constraints are also often very important—the first workable solution found is often the one that is used rather than continuing to search for the (probably non-existent) 'perfect' solution. This acceptance of 'less than perfect' can be difficult for many researchers. It has definitely been a difficult cultural challenge in parts of CSIRO as they shifted from pure to applied research.

Acceptance of less than a technically perfect solution is part of the cultural difference between pure and applied research: excellence in applied research is measured by the contribution research makes to enabling a solution to be adopted and used. This can involve significant advances in scientific understanding, but not always; it may, for example, rely more upon insightful integration of existing knowledge. Consequently, the stress that Gabriele places upon accepting the inevitability of imperfection is important for the development of integrative applied research.

The system aspects of applied research become much more complicated, exhibiting many elements of 'wickedness'[5] for the complex real-world problems that are the focus of Gabriele's book. The development of the CSIRO National Research Flagship Program,[6] which is targeted at complex real-world problems, illustrates the challenges inherent in such research.[7]

The challenges of applied research underlie much of what Gabriele covers in this book.

---

5   Wicked problem: Wikipedia <http://en.wikipedia.org/wiki/Wicked_problem> (accessed 15 February 2012).

6   <http://www.csiro.au/partnerships/NRF.html> (accessed 15 February 2012).

7   See the commentary by O'Connell et al. (Chapter 37).

Uncertainty—Unknowns

Gabriele rightly places strong emphasis on the importance of explicitly dealing with unknowns. Accepted management practices, in business, government and society generally, assume that the ratio of unknowns to knowns is low. There are a number of domains, which include radical or breakthrough innovation[8] and complex social and environmental problems, where this assumption is not true. Development of widely accepted management practices for these domains is a major research challenge, which must be a high priority for integrative applied research.

A corollary of a high ratio of unknowns to knowns is a high level of uncertainty. Most people are not comfortable with a high level of uncertainty and avoid situations in which it is present. The Ellsberg paradox—people so strongly prefer definite information over ambiguity that they make choices consistent neither with the laws of probability nor with themselves—is one manifestation of this aversion to uncertain or ambiguous choices.[9]

High levels of uncertainty or ambiguity are very often equated with high levels of risk. Uncertainty is *not* the same as risk. Risk is best understood as describing a known probability of an event. Uncertainty refers to the absence of sufficient information to predict probabilities of occurrence or results. The ability to describe risk implies some prior experience. If a research team is attempting to overcome a challenge that is truly novel, it may more properly be said to be facing uncertainty rather than risk. The distinction between risk and uncertainty is critical because managing risk is very different from managing uncertainty and the inappropriate use of a risk-management framework can doom a project to failure.

Frameworks for managing when there is a high ratio of unknowns to knowns must

- be loose, as adaptability and flexibility are needed because of high uncertainty
- be learning based
- utilise a decision-making style appropriate for high levels of uncertainty.

In applied research, a learning-based approach will typically include iteration between the technical and adoption/use domains—'probe and learn', for example.[10]

---

8   Leifer et al. (2000).

9   Ellsberg (1961).

10   Lynn et al. (1996).

Intuition in decision making is not generally regarded favourably; however, it is often the only way to handle high complexity and uncertainty—many unknowables and variables—as it enables integration of multiple factors for which there are few hard data.

> There are too many unknowables, variables...Ultimately, one must use intuition, a complex feeling, calibrated by experience...It's a judgement about people, commitment and probabilities...You dare not use milestones too rigidly.[11]

Improving the effectiveness of decision making when there are many unknowns and uncertainty is high is a critical area for integrative applied research and is a high research priority.

Complexity and Integration

Just as the whole is more than the sum of its parts, solving a complex problem is more difficult than solving its sub-problems. One common strategy to address a complex problem is to divide it into manageable parts (that is, sub-problems). This can introduce a major danger as making a sub-problem tractable can introduce change and making all sub-problems tractable can introduce a lot of change. Solving the sub-problems can result in them diverging in the pursuit of research that can be done successfully, and reintegration can grow increasingly difficult. The larger a scientific collaboration and the greater the number of sub-problems, the more difficult integration becomes. Penders and colleagues[12] provide an example of this in a large-scale research program.

Development of strategies for modularising a complex problem so that work on sub-problems can be reintegrated into the whole without distortion will need to be a high priority for integrative applied research.

Diversity

Diversity is important in solving hard problems because of the different perspectives and heuristics brought to bear on the problem.[13] Jeppesen and Lakhani's work illustrates this through an analysis of the results of 166 science

---

11   Quinn (1985).
12   Penders et al. (2009).
13   See, for example, Fleming (2007); Jeppesen and Lakhani (2010).

challenges involving more than 12 000 scientists. They found that providing a winning solution was positively related to increasing distance between the solver's field of technical expertise and the focal field of the problem.

Diversity is one aspect of 'difference' that must be highlighted because of its importance for integrative applied research. Research teams which encompass significant diversity must be led and managed differently from less diverse teams.[14] This is one important area for advancing the practice of integrative applied research.

Integrative Applied Research: How? Why a discipline?

How you innovate determines what you innovate; for example, management frameworks for incremental and radical innovation are very different and if an inappropriate framework is used then failure will follow—the desired innovation will not eventuate.[15] Integrative applied research is the same: 'how' will determine 'what'. In this situation the lack of widely agreed management frameworks, which also applies to radical innovation, is a significant issue for the field.

Two aspects of 'how' need emphasis. The first is that research on complex real-world problems is a complex social process, yet the great majority of descriptions of 'how' neglect the people and social dimension. Values are part of this; however, the issue is much broader than values.

The second aspect requiring emphasis is the inherent 'messiness' of the process. This is similar to radical innovation, which has been described as unpredictable, sporadic, nonlinear, stochastic (key players change, priorities change, exogenous events are critical) and context dependent (history, experience, culture, personalities and informal relations all matter).[16] This can be a difficult environment in which to work, particularly in the public sphere of many social and environmental problems. One particular difficulty is people's desire to impose order on an inherently chaotic process[17]—to construct and try to adhere to a structured plan with predetermined milestones, for example.

---

14   Post et al. (2009).
15   O'Connor et al. (2008).
16   Leifer et al. (2000).
17   Cheng and Van de Ven (1996).

Success in integrative applied research will require solutions to these issues (among others). As Gabriele points out in this book, effort to address the 'how' of integrative applied research is fragmented. So, a vital early step is to foster communities of practice where learning can be shared.

So, how should communities of practice be fostered? In this book Gabriele is advocating the creation of a new discipline (Integration and Implementation Sciences or I2S). The history of the development of disciplines, especially their increasing specialisation and self-referential character, makes me very wary of this path because an external orientation—the 'know–do' link, especially connectivity and iteration between technical disciplines and adoption and use—is fundamental to success in this field. Gabriele acknowledges this danger in the closing section of the book (Chapter 34):

> [T]he danger that I2S becomes self-referential rather than engaged. What I refer to here is the risk that I2S specialists will research and write for each other on ever more arcane aspects of the I2S discipline rather than being part of integrative applied research teams addressing complex real-world problems.

If a new discipline is not the best path forward then what action should be taken?

Sharing knowledge and learning is key to advancing the practice of integrative applied research. There are many ways in which this can be done without creating a discipline. For example, bodies of knowledge can be assembled by practitioners[18] and knowledge shared and extended through conferences, workshops and 'seed' research projects.[19] These forums and mechanisms run across existing disciplines.

Mechanisms running across disciplines can be multiple disciplines coalescing either around a real-world problem or around shared interest in methods, tools, techniques, and so on. Both need to be actively fostered—for example, Flagships and Transformational Capability Platforms respectively in CSIRO. This is a challenge because they cut across organisational structures that are usually discipline based (universities) or application-area based, such as the food-processing industry (applied research institutes).

Despite—maybe because of—these organisational barriers, institutions devoted to research and learning, such as universities, research institutes and research funders, have a responsibility to establish and maintain such mechanisms. They

---

18   For an example in new product development, see <http://www.pdma.org/knowledge_get.cfm> (accessed 15 February 2012).

19   CSIRO's Transformational Capability Platforms is one example; <http://www.csiro.au/files/files/pmva.pdf> (accessed 15 February 2012).

must recognise and reward integrative applied research and foster communities of practice and other networks of practitioners. Universities have a particular responsibility because students, both graduate and undergraduate, must experience learning across disciplines as well as within the specialisations of traditional disciplines.

Conclusion

There can be no doubt about the importance, and research challenges, of complex real-world problems. Strategies that have been effective for building our knowledge base over the past couple of centuries—reductionism and increasing the specialisation of disciplines—are not sufficient for tackling these kinds of problems. There is an urgent need to devise new approaches. Integrative applied research, as described in Gabriele's book, encompasses most of the elements needed for an effective new approach. The challenge for researchers, research institutions and research funders is to foster a community of reflective practitioners of this new approach. The initial step should be support for organisational centres and networks and recognition and reward for researchers who contribute to the advancement of integrative applied research.

Contributed November 2011

References

Cheng, Y. and Van de Ven, A. H. (1996). 'Learning the innovation journey: order out of chaos?'. *Organization Science*, 7 (6): 593–614.

Ellsberg, D. (1961). 'Risk, ambiguity, and the savage axioms'. *Quarterly Journal of Economics*, 75 (4): 643–69.

Fleming, L. (2007). 'Breakthroughs and the "long tail" of innovation'. *MIT Sloan Management Review*, 49 (1): 69–74.

Jeppesen, L. B. and Lakhani, K. R. (2010). 'Marginality and problem-solving effectiveness in broadcast search'. *Organization Science*, 21 (5): 1016–33.

Leifer, R., McDermott, C. M., O'Connor, G. C., Peters, L. S., Rice, M. P. and Veryzer, R. W. (2000). *Radical Innovation: How mature companies can outsmart upstarts*. Boston, MA: Harvard Business School Press.

Lynn, G. S., Morone, J. G. and Paulson, A. S. (1996). 'Marketing and discontinuous innovation: the probe and learn process'. *California Management Review*, 38 (3): 8–37.

O'Connor, G. C., Leifer, R., Paulson, A. S. and Peters, L. S. (2008). *Grabbing Lightning: Building a capability for breakthrough innovation*. San Francisco, CA: Jossey-Bass/Wiley.

Penders, B., Vos, R. and Horstman, K. (2009). 'Side effects of problem-solving strategies in large-scale nutrition science: towards a diversification of health'. *British Journal of Nutrition*, 102: 1400–3.

Post, C., De Lia, E., DiTomaso, N., Tirpak, T. M. and Borwankar, R. (2009). 'Capitalizing on thought diversity for innovation research'. *Technology Management*, 52 (6): 14–25.

Quinn, J. B. (1985). 'Managing innovation: controlled chaos'. *Harvard Business Review*, 63 (3): 73–84.

Stokes, D. E. (1997). *Pasteur's Quadrant: Basic science and technological innovation*. Washington, DC: Brookings Institution Press.

Brief Biography

Ian Elsum is a Visiting Fellow in the Research School of Management at The Australian National University where he undertakes research on the management of innovation. He was, until recently, Principal Adviser in the Science Strategy and Investment Group of Australia's CSIRO. He is active within the Industrial Research Institute where he has co-chaired Research-on-Research investigations of radical innovation, management of high-uncertainty research and development and the challenges of business model innovation. He has 24 years of experience in the strategic management of applied research, with an emphasis on increasing research effectiveness through strategic planning, investment and assessment as well as work on the factors necessary for excellence in applied research. Ian has been a member of a number of boards and management and advisory committees and is currently chairing the Science Advisory Panel of the Institute of Environmental Science and Research. He has also been a regular participant in forums for the development of industry and innovation policy.

56. The Fourth Frontier

Michael Wesley[1]

This book is the product of a long search by its author to systematise the mutually strengthening linkages among different fields of research and focusing their attentions on addressing real social problems. I must declare at the outset that I am a card-carrying partisan of this cause, having grown progressively disillusioned with discipline-bound research for its own sake, pursued solely for the purposes of reputation, seniority and bragging rights. Indeed I fear that the worldwide movement towards government-led 'assessment' of research performance, measured by appearances in the world's 'top' journals, will further distort academic research towards discipline-bound research for its own sake.

Those who occupy the privileged position of scholars should always be mindful of their obligations towards improving the society that ultimately makes their positions possible. Arguably, my own discipline, International Relations (IR), has the largest divide between academics and practitioners of any of the social sciences. Here is how Allan Gyngell and I described that divide nearly ten years ago:

> On the academic side, as IR cements its position within Australian universities, it has succumbed to the common tendency for academic disciplines to privilege theoretical over applied inquiry as they seek to consolidate their positions and build respect within the academic world. In the process, the attention of the academic IR community has become increasingly focused inwards. Debates among IR academics have singularly failed to arouse the attention or interest of any but the IR community; and measures of professional esteem largely seem to be internally set. For its part, the practitioner community seems to have grown increasingly uninterested in the results of academic research, thinking it lacks much relevance to the real world...The practitioner's view of foreign policy is of a world of complex detail and incessant demands on time, attention and resources. The policy field of the practitioner resists simple solutions and evades summary or generalization...Practitioners look for exceptions to general statements about foreign policy issues. Their experience of trying to implement

---

1   Michael Wesley was invited as a 'senior scholar and practitioner who has been innovative in dealing with complex problems and bridging the research–policy divide'.

policy in the difficult, wilful, resistant world of IR makes them sceptical of high-sounding schemes and principles, as well as the moral simplicity and unqualified solutions offered by academics and public alike.[2]

The framework of Integration and Implementation Sciences (I2S) is Gabriele Bammer's impressive attempt to mediate a double divide at the heart of the pragmatic research enterprise. One is a disciplinary divide between scholars who look at the social world from the viewpoint of different approaches, preoccupations and methodologies rooted in the centuries-old division of the social sciences into different disciplines. The other is the vocational divide between scholars and practitioners.

Both divides are extremely difficult to bridge in a meaningful and sustained way. The systematic richness of Gabriele Bammer's frameworks for doing so is testament to years of patient research and discussion, trial and error. I2S has the feel about it of a framework that will inspire further work by other scholars, that will see it develop into a rich meta-discipline over time.

Having said that, I think there is a major element missing in the I2S framework. As it exists it is a framework that lives in the rarefied world of rational discussion, away from the messy world of politics, rivalries, rent-seeking and egos. In many ways this is a good thing, but for a framework that intends to grapple with policy problems, it could be a major disadvantage.

What I am arguing is that there is a third major divide that the I2S framework needs to bridge: the divide between policy and politics. Or, more accurately, it needs to address the problems thrown up by a crumbling divide between politics and policy. While we need to be careful of the golden-age fallacy, there has been a progressive diminution of the distinctions between these realms. Politics is the purview of contested values, world views, conceptions of change and agency, whereas policy is the realm of objective expertise and management, the rational workings of the benign influence of the state on society.

The divide between politics and policy was never clear and wide, but in recent years we have watched with dismay as the domain of objective policy analysis and actions has been dragged into that of values-based contestation and the contending of absolute knowledge claims. A classic example was the weapons of mass destruction–based case for the 2003 invasion of Iraq. In several countries, the politics of the Iraq war came to depend heavily on the policy questions of whether Iraq did or did not possess weapons of mass destruction. The search for supporting evidence became all consuming, while corrupting all processes of

---

2   Gyngell and Wesley (2003).

rational data gathering and evaluation. On the other side, sceptics of the case for Iraq's possession of weapons of mass destruction had their motives impugned and their reputations held up to question.

The greatest casualties outside Iraq were the integrity and reputation of the intelligence and policy agencies that are required to analyse, act and advise objectively. Expertise has become something that can be challenged and questioned from any quarter, irrespective of the expertise or position of the sceptic. What we have seen is the slow diminution of the authority and legitimacy of the realm of objective analysis and knowledge.

There is perhaps no greater example than the case of climate change. The scientific case for the science of climate change has been under sustained attack for several years, and most intensely since late 2009. Both sides of this argument (it is surely not a debate) now marshal impressive statistics and data to back their case. The ordinary person in the street now confronts a range of vociferously disagreeing partisans (even the sceptics disagree over whether the Earth is actually cooling or whether it is warming but humans have nothing to do with it). Ultimately the only person who could make an informed assessment of the cases would be someone with the requisite training in a range of disciplines, from atmospheric physics to geology. But because there are so few of the general public with these skills, the mass of society is thrown back on pre-existing prejudices and commitments to make the choice about which side to believe. Politics, not objective knowledge, determines the level of popular support for one side of the argument or the other.

Politics intrudes on both sides of the I2S equation. Before I2S kicks into action, integrating and applying interdisciplinary expertise to a real-world problem, there will inevitably be a political contest over the problem itself. Partly this is a question of sequencing. When the problem is identified first, the politics will start to divide opinion about how to attack it. Should it be a government-led or private-sector-led solution? Is the cause of the problem too much 'nanny state' intervention or the perverse outcomes of the market? Where does this problem sit as a priority among all the other issues that demand attention and resources? On the other hand, when the political contest discovers the problem, the politics can be even more intense. One side of politics can choose to identify a policy problem as a way of highlighting a weakness on the other side. The other side's response will be fairly predictable.

After I2S has proposed a solution, politics comes back. The solution—any solution—will immediately be interpreted in a partisan way. It will be either overkill or a squib. It will either worsen the problem or be ineffective. And its implementation will draw close scrutiny, with a marked preference for finding failures over reporting successes. In politics, Ken Henry argued, 'penalties and rewards are not scored symmetrically; losses are valued much more heavily than gains'.[3]

Solutions, once they are promulgated and even more after they are adopted, inevitably become part of the political contest. Either supporting or questioning a policy is immediately interpreted in terms of the presumed allegiances of the supporter or questioner. In May 2011, the Lowy Institute published a careful analysis that argued that the five-year Australian Government policy on selective isolation of Fiji's military regime had not worked and had little prospect of assisting Fiji to return to democracy. The analysis proposed a comprehensive new approach.[4] The Australian Government responded by disparaging the research and accusing its author of supporting the Fijian dictator, Commodore Bainimarama.[5] Rather than disagreeing with and attempting to refute the analysis and its proposals, the response was to impugn the author's motives.

It is worth asking whether there are any policy problems that exist free of actual or potential political contestation. I can't think of any. In the meantime the genuine policy problems faced by our society are poorly addressed because of the rising tide of partisan politics.

So while I admire and endorse Gabriele Bammer's I2S framework, I urge her to take one further step: to address this fourth frontier, without which even the best academic analysis and policy design won't translate into effective solutions. This may be the most difficult of all the divides to mediate. It will involve holding contested cases to account and adjudicating between their alternative research and knowledge bases. Potentially, the politicisation of policy can be reversed—but it will require an enterprise every bit as ambitious and detailed as I2S to do so.

Contributed November 2011

References

Gyngell, A. and Wesley, M. (2003). *Making Australian Foreign Policy*. Melbourne: Cambridge University Press.

Hayward-Jones, J. (2011). *Policy overboard: Australia's increasingly costly Fiji drift*. Lowy Institute Policy Brief. Sydney: Lowy Institute.

---

3   Henry (2007).
4   Hayward-Jones (2011).
5   Marles (2011).

Henry, K. (2007). Political awareness. Address to the International Project Managers Symposium, Canberra, 9 February.

Marles, R. (2011). Why the Pacific matters. Speech to the Lowy Institute, 28 September.

Brief Biography

Michael Wesley is the Executive Director of the Lowy Institute for International Policy. He is a Non-Resident Senior Fellow at the Brookings Institution and an Adjunct Professor at Griffith University and the University of Sydney. Previously he was Professor of International Relations and Director of the Griffith Asia Institute at Griffith University. Prior to this, he was the Assistant Director-General for Transnational Issues at the Office of National Assessments, and a Senior Lecturer in International Relations at the University of New South Wales. Between 2007 and 2009, he was the Editor of the *Australian Journal of International Affairs*. He has served on the Australian Research Council's College of Experts and the Queensland Art Gallery's Board of Trustees. His most recent book, *There Goes the Neighbourhood: Australia and the rise of Asia* (NewSouth Books, 2011), won the 2011 John Button Prize for best writing on Australian public policy.

57. How Theory Can Help Set Priorities for the I2S Development Drive

Christian Pohl[1]

When Gabriele Bammer made a presentation about her book *Research Integration Using Dialogue Methods*[2] at the 2009 international transdisciplinarity conference in Berne, Switzerland, the audience reaction was highly charged. The heated discussion was not, however, about the book, but that Gabriele had introduced it as a first book of methods for a new discipline. Some people were strongly challenged and somewhat upset by the idea. They insisted that a transdisciplinary or I2S discipline was a contradiction in terms and therefore impossible. In their view, transdisciplinary or I2S research is always a collaborative effort bringing together different disciplines and experts from various societal sectors who engage in a process of co-producing knowledge. So how (for heaven's sake) could such collaborative processes be delegated to a specific discipline?

I did not expect that reaction and was puzzled by it, as I believe Gabriele was also. What deep convictions had been disturbed by the idea of a specialisation in collaborative research processes for policy-relevant research? Was it that the researchers feared that some specialists would take over transdisciplinary research as a whole? Or, that the specialists would always intervene and further complicate the already challenging co-production of knowledge? The discussion was not conclusive, but it was clear that Gabriele had presented an impertinent idea.

It is a pleasure to see how this idea is further elaborated in the present book. Since I have heard a number of Gabriele's presentations, read some of her papers and had discussions with her, I already knew some pieces. Now I can see how they combine to form the universe of I2S.

I2S is positioned as a specific way of doing relevant science. It cuts across issues or sectors like innovation and business, risk and security, health and the environment (see Chapter 32, especially Figure 32.1). Hence, if research in such sectors is to be policy relevant, it must draw on the competencies, methods and practices of I2S. I2S as a discipline is about producing, organising, assessing and transferring knowledge in a system of world views. As the metaphor of statistics

---

1   Christian Pohl was invited as a 'senior scholar who has pioneered thinking about transdisciplinarity'.
2   McDonald et al. (2009).

suggests, I2S does not interfere with the subject matter, but provides methods to organise knowledge on that specific subject matter in a more relevant way. I found Chapter 31, 'A view of the future', particularly elucidating, starting with the vision of 2025, with the following chapter presenting the discipline and the sub-groups one might belong to: the inner circle, 'Theory and methods'; the second circle, 'Methodological development with respect to a sector'; and the outer circle, 'Application in a specific sector'. Also very helpful is the differentiation between I2S team leader, I2S disciplinary specialist and the other researchers and societal actors involved, along with the respective allocations of I2S competencies and tasks, which are presented as the last chapter in each of the previous sections. This allocation helps understanding that not everybody has to know everything or be able to answer all the questions asked; I did not count, but they must number in the hundreds. Instead we are talking about a specialisation in terms of competencies and a division of labour in terms of tasks and responsibilities. Another precondition for being able to address the numerous open questions is what Gabriele calls the I2S Development Drive. It captures the magnitude of the scientific endeavour we are talking about—one that requires big money, a lot of brain power and the engagement of a wide range of scholars.

The background for this commentary is my specific understanding of transdisciplinary research, based on sustainability research in German-speaking European and Scandinavian countries.[3] Like I2S, such transdisciplinary research stands for a particular way of producing knowledge that primarily helps address socially relevant issues, as opposed to knowledge that primarily advances scientific understanding. In transdisciplinary research, academics from different disciplines and civil society actors, along with the private and the public sectors, co-produce knowledge with specific purposes.

[I]n order to be relevant and useful for societal problem handling, transdisciplinary researchers have to frame, analyse and process an issue in such a manner that

1. they grasp the complexity of the issue;

2. they take the diverse perspectives on the issue into account;

3. they link abstract and case-specific knowledge;

4. they develop descriptive, normative, and practical knowledge that promotes what is perceived to be the common good.[4]

---

3   Bunders et al. (2010).
4   Pohl (2011, p. 620); Hirsch Hadorn et al. (2010, p. 432).

The collaboration of disciplines with societal actors is a means to meet these four purposes. In the same way that Gabriele has done for I2S, we have described the specific challenges transdisciplinary research is exposed to, as well as the methods it might use, in *Principles for Designing Transdisciplinary Research*,[5] the *Handbook of Transdisciplinary Research*[6] and in *Methods of Transdisciplinary Research*.[7] We are all part of the same Development Drive and believe in the big project—namely that transdisciplinary or I2S research can be done better compared with the present state of knowledge production, in the sense of better integrating different forms of knowledge and providing knowledge that is more relevant to and useful for specific societal actors; and that the knowledge of how to better co-produce knowledge can be formulated in methods and tools, which can be stored and taught.

Gabriele discusses some of the differences between I2S and transdisciplinary research in Chapter 33. One is the emphasis given to understanding and managing diverse unknowns—something that clearly distinguishes I2S and transdisciplinary research. Our approach to unknowns is less direct and more procedural. We consider the results and recommendations produced in a transdisciplinary research process as preliminary. Any attempt to bring results to fruition has to be understood and designed as an 'experimental implementation'[8] or a 'real-world experiment'.[9] Hence, the process of knowledge co-production does not end by making recommendations or producing policy briefs. Rather the effects that such recommendations and policy briefs have on society or policy have to be further studied and analysed for surprises. Surprises indicate uncertainties and unknowns in the underlying understanding of how the recommendations will change things. Therefore the transdisciplinary research process as a whole has two additional research phases not found in disciplinary research: a phase of joint problem framing and a phase of bringing results to fruition, each requiring money, time and brain power.[10]

A second difference, which Gabriele does not discuss, is the pragmatic approach of I2S and the more theoretical approach of transdisciplinary research. I2S is a radically pragmatic approach in the sense that every method or concept described is assessed under the question of what is its use for

1. synthesising disciplinary and stakeholder knowledge

2. understanding and managing diverse unknowns

---

5   Pohl and Hirsch Hadorn (2007).
6   Hirsch Hadorn et al. (2008).
7   (*Methoden transdisziplinärer Forschung*) Bergmann et al. (2010).
8   van den Daele and Krohn (1998).
9   Gross and Hoffmann-Riem (2005).
10   Pohl and Hirsch Hadorn (2007).

3. providing integrated research support for policy and practice change?

I2S is a storehouse for concepts, methods, case examples and guides (as described in Chapter 2, especially Figures 2.1 and 2.2). As far as I understand, there is no further theoretical background, for instance, of what co-production of knowledge between science and society means or how disciplinary and societal actors are distinguished and included in the research process. This apparent difference attracts my attention because there is lively discussion about the theoretical understanding of the transdisciplinary research process.[11]

What is such a theoretical understanding good for? The main effect is that a theory simplifies the world by reducing its complexity. It increases our awareness of some aspects while making others less important. This is different from a storehouse's shelves embodying a matrix of three domains and five questions. Shelves call for completion, for filling all empty spaces with concepts, methods, case examples and guides. Theory, on the other hand, places emphasis on those aspects deemed relevant by the theory. (There is, however, the danger that the theory is wrong and attention is given to irrelevant aspects.)

To give an example: in our work on transdisciplinary research for sustainable development, we conceive different disciplines or stakeholders as thought collectives that look at an issue 'through the eyes' of a specific thought style.[12] The academic thought collectives are disciplines like biology, medicine or sociology. Within society we distinguish three further thought collectives: civil society, the private and the public sectors.[13] Further, we understand the thought collectives' significance for co-producing policy-relevant knowledge as a question of the thought collectives' expertise, power and interests in relation to any particular issue.[14] This simple theorising results in the following question to be addressed at the beginning of any project: what thought collectives from academia, civil society, the private and the public sectors are relevant for our project's contribution to sustainable development in terms of their expertise, power and interests? This question makes the research manageable.

There are further orientations given by the simplifying theory. One is what Gabriele calls 'achieving congruence between the methods used across the three domains' (Chapter 27). A theory of what is happening in the processes of co-producing knowledge will make the selection of concepts and methods more congruent (even though there is no guarantee they are on the right track).

---

11   Carew and Wickson (2010); Jahn (2008); Pohl (2011); Stauffacher et al. (2008).
12   Fleck (1986a, 1986b).
13   Pohl and Hirsch Hadorn (2007).
14   Wuelser et al. (2012).

Another orientation is that theories of co-producing knowledge might link some of the numerous questions that have to be dealt with separately in Gabriele's storehouse of concepts, methods, case examples and guides. For example, in our theoretical understanding we do not handle values separately from viewpoints or perspectives. Values are part of any thought collective's particular thought style and are expressed in how they frame an issue. In our approach, taking values into account, along with harnessing and managing differences, becomes an integral part of integrating thought styles. For instance, how a problem is framed and what is seen as an adequate solution always depend on the particular thought style and its underlying values. According to requirement (4) of the definition of transdisciplinary research presented earlier, the question of how a specific solution promotes the common good is an explicit task to be addressed and deliberated on by the research team. Again this is different from I2S, where 'the creation of public value' is something additional to have in mind to minimise 'the temptations to compromise research integrity' (Chapter 26).

A theory, furthermore, helps to identify the next steps. For instance, the question of how to assess and justify knowledge claims of thought collectives becomes an issue in co-production of knowledge. In academic collectives this is done by peer review. And how do non-academic thought collectives assess and justify their knowledge?

Another crucial next step is how, in practice, to integrate or synthesise the knowledge of thought collectives. Here we are back to the pragmatic question of how to do better transdisciplinary and I2S research, which is where the interests and expertise of transdisciplinary research and I2S strongly overlap. The challenge of integration will also answer the question of whether or not a specialisation in transdisciplinary research and I2S is needed. The specialisation makes sense if it makes co-production of knowledge in addressing societal concerns more effective and efficient. What specialists have to come up with are methods and tools, and successful applications in real processes of co-producing knowledge. To achieve this specialists have to be familiar with the methods and tools and have to understand the challenges of any specific situation of knowledge co-production. If I had $1 million to spend it would be on the methodology that assigns methods to problem types, funding the (daring) scholars who explore the methods and tools in co-production processes; however, in selecting the most relevant problems of integration, I would use a theory of co-producing knowledge to get an idea of what empty spaces in the storehouse's shelves are the most relevant to fill with concepts, methods, case examples and guides.

Contributed November 2011

References

Bergmann, M., Jahn, T., Knobloch, T., Krohn, W., Pohl, C. and Schramm, E. (2010). *Methoden transdisziplinärer Forschung: Ein Überblick mit Anwendungsbeispielen*. Frankfurt am Main: Campus Verlag.

Bunders, J. F. G., Broerse, J. E. W., Keil, F., Pohl, C., Scholz, R. W. and Zweekhorst, M. B. M. (2010). 'How can transdisciplinary research contribute to knowledge democracy?'. In: 't Veld, R. J. (ed.). *Knowledge Democracy: Consequences for science, politics, and media*. New York: Springer, 125–52.

Carew, A. L. and Wickson, F. (2010). 'The TD wheel: a heuristic to shape, support and evaluate transdisciplinary research'. *Futures*, 42 (10): 1146–55.

Fleck, L. [1947] (1986a). 'The problem of epistemology'. In: Cohen, R. S. and Schnelle, T. (eds). *Cognition and Facts: Materials on Ludwik Fleck*. Dordrecht: Reidel, 79–112.

Fleck, L. [1947] (1986b). 'To look, to see, to know'. In: Cohen, R. S. and Schnelle, T. (eds). *Cognition and Fact: Materials on Ludwik Fleck*. Dordrecht: Reidel, 129–51.

Gross, M. and Hoffmann-Riem, H. (2005). 'Ecological restoration as a real-world experiment: designing robust implementation strategies in an urban environment'. *Public Understanding of Science*, 14: 269–84.

Hirsch Hadorn, G., Hoffmann-Riem, H., Biber-Klemm, S., Grossenbacher-Mansuy, W., Joye, D., Pohl, C., Wiesmann, U. and Zemp, E. (eds). (2008). *Handbook of Transdisciplinary Research*. Dordrecht: Springer.

Hirsch Hadorn, G., Pohl, C. and Bammer, G. (2010). 'Solving problems through transdisciplinary research'. In: Frodeman, R., Thompson Klein, J. and Mitcham, C. (eds). *The Oxford Handbook of Interdisciplinarity*. Oxford: Oxford University Press, 431–52.

Jahn, T. (2008). 'Transdisziplinarität in der Forschungspraxis'. In: Bergmann, M. and Schramm, E. (eds). *Transdisziplinäre Forschung. Integrative Forschungsprozesse verstehen und bewerten*. Frankfurt Campus: Verlag, 21–37.

McDonald, D., Bammer, G. and Deane, P. (2009). *Research Integration Using Dialogue Methods*. Canberra: ANU E Press; <http://epress.anu.edu.au/dialogue_methods_citation.html>

Pohl, C. (2011). 'What is progress in transdisciplinary research?'. *Futures*, 43: 618–26.

Pohl, C. and Hirsch Hadorn, G. (2007). *Principles for Designing Transdisciplinary Research—Proposed by the Swiss Academies of Arts and Sciences*. München: oekom Verlag.

Stauffacher, M., Flueler, T., Krutli, P. and Scholz, R. W. (2008). 'Analytic and dynamic approach to collaboration: a transdisciplinary case study on sustainable landscape development in a Swiss prealpine region'. *Systemic Practice and Action Research*, 21 (6): 409–22.

van den Daele, W. and Krohn, W. (1998). 'Experimental implementation as linking mechanism in the process of innovation'. *Research Policy*, 27: 853–68.

Wuelser, G., Pohl, C. and Hirsch Hadorn, G. (2012). 'Structuring complexity for tailoring research contributions to sustainable development: a framework'. *Sustainability Science*, 7 (1): 81–93.

Brief Biography

Christian Pohl is Co-Director of the transdisciplinarity-net of the Swiss Academies of Arts and Sciences and Senior Research Fellow at the Department of Environmental Sciences at ETH Zurich (Swiss Federal Institute of Technology Zurich). He has a PhD in environmental sciences and has investigated uncertainty in environmental assessments, as well as undertaking a comparative analysis of the collaboration of natural and social sciences in Swiss and Swedish environmental research. His current research interest is the analysis and design of transdisciplinary research as a means to connect science and society, specifically in the field of sustainable development.

58. I2S and Research Development Professionals: Time to develop a mutually advantageous relationship

Holly J. Falk-Krzesinski[1]

This commentary presents a perspective of integrative applied research and Integration and Implementation Sciences (I2S) as they pertain to advancing research development activities[2] and team science.[3]

Research Development, Team Science and Integrative Applied Research

The National Organization of Research Development Professionals (NORDP) facilitates research excellence and enables interdisciplinary research and collaborative partnerships affecting scientific and scholarly research projects at non-profit research institutions, predominantly academic institutions, across the globe. NORDP was established in 2010 as part of a grassroots movement to build a community of research development professionals driven to enhance the research enterprise at their institutions. Research development encompasses a set of strategic, proactive, catalytic and capacity-building activities designed to facilitate teams of researchers, initiating and nurturing critical partnerships and alliances throughout the institutional research enterprise, between institutions and, importantly, with external stakeholders.

Team science is characterised by large multi, inter and transdisciplinary collaborative research projects comprising large teams of scientists, which most often integrate research with broader goals including education, technology or practice transfer, and policy change. A recent description of 'big tent team science'[4] shares considerable similarities with integrative applied research as defined in this book.

---

1   Holly Falk-Krzesinski was invited as a 'research development practitioner and scholar of the science of team science'.
2   See <http://www.nordp.org/about-us> (accessed 14 February 2012).
3   See <http://en.wikipedia.org/wiki/Science_of_team_science> (accessed 14 February 2012).
4   See <http://www.ipscell.com/2011/09/big-tent-team-science-new-ideas-about-clinical-trials/> (accessed 14 February 2012).

More and more, research development professionals find that they are catalysing and facilitating team science to address complex real-world problems, in part leveraging the research and scholarship expertise found at academic institutions. But the academic resources are insufficient to fully address such problems. Consequently research development professionals are increasingly charged with reaching out beyond the ivory tower into other sectors. As action-oriented rainmakers, research development professionals serve to benefit from, and can foster the advancement of, integrative applied research and I2S.

Research Development Professionals as I2S Specialists

Integrative applied research requires the knowledge-brokerage skills and vision advantage that research development professionals practise; research development professionals can, in turn, benefit from I2S to foster efficacious real-world problem-solving teams. Integrative applied research is involved with bringing experts together and synthesising what is known from both the academic and the practical perspectives. This is becoming a critical set of activities for research development professionals fostering team science initiatives; however, research development professionals often have no formal training in these activities or formally developed skills. I2S affords the development of evidence-based approaches and methodologies—which can be used across projects—in which research development professionals can be trained.

Moreover, research development professionals are prime candidates to become a class of I2S specialists. They are already engaged in cross-disciplinary, boundary-spanning activities across units, institutions and sectors. For example, research development professionals are taking prominent roles in research centres and institutes at universities, which have historically served as the nexus of problem-based teams. These units often lack the necessary skills to effectively reach out to external stakeholders and form sustainable, strategic alliances that last beyond a cycle of grant funding. And while traditionally providing consultative services to newly developed teams, research development professionals are more often becoming embedded as integral members of the team as the driving problem gets more complex and relevant to society. Rather than ceasing engagement with the team after its initial formation and start-up phase, a recent trend is developing in which research development professionals remain engaged throughout the duration of the team-based initiative, intimately involved in the management and growth of the team and often as lynchpins in outreach activities. And importantly, research development professionals concurrently serve in that capacity on more than one team science initiative.

As trained I2S specialists, research development professionals would be a very willing group that can assist with the cross-fertilisation of ideas across projects for team science initiatives aiming to address real-world, complex problems. They can provide feedback into the development of I2S concepts and methodologies about issues related to academia and government funding agencies, which are central areas of expertise for them. The culture, structure and bureaucracies of these two sectors often baffle external stakeholders and can prove to be substantial barriers to collaboration and alliances and the success of integrative applied research.

Forming Teams

One area of significant importance for research development professionals is the formation development of teams and alliances at the beginning of new initiatives, and managing the teams and alliances over time—often considerable periods. While the science of team science field is beginning to address issues related to team composition and leadership types, thus far research focuses only on academic-based teams and has not extended to include the formation and development of teams that include external stakeholders and involve intersectoral alliances. I2S is positioned to be an important driver in this area, supporting research about the formation of real-world teams in which 'team' is considered both at the macro and at the meso levels and simultaneously embedded in the context of multiple organisations. The approaches developed by I2S would be immediately consumed by research development professionals who are actively seeking evidence-based guidance for effective practices around team formation.

Knowledge Synthesis

Research development professionals generally hold advanced degrees (masters and doctoral or equivalent) in areas of research and scholarship but do not lead research programs or initiatives of their own. They are motivated to advance science and solve problems through the use of science and scholarship as servant leaders, always partnered with investigators, scholars, practitioners and policy makers. Consequently they are afforded the opportunity to become pan-scientists, learning something about the language, concepts, models and cultures from numerous disciplines. Since research development professionals themselves are not leading the research within academia, they also have more flexibility to engage externally and become better acquainted with various stakeholder and partner groups and communities; however, they frequently lack the knowledge about how best to synthesise information across disciplinary and sectoral domains and integrate it with stakeholder knowledge necessary to translate findings from the academic environment into the real world. With its very focus on integrative applied research, I2S offers a very exciting opportunity to develop a robust toolbox that research development professionals could access for enhanced knowledge synthesis.

Managing Unknowns

Research development professionals often encounter the problems of expertise and reputation when working with academic-based investigators considering partnerships with external stakeholders. The academic investigators and scholars are experts in their fields, with expertise defined by what they *know*. Since recognition and reputation that rely on such expertise are so critical for advancement within academia, investigators and scholars in this realm often exhibit an unwillingness to express that which they don't know or understand. Consequently the unknowns that have to be considered from the stakeholder perspective are often neglected and may, worse, even be considered irrelevant by academic partners.

Trained as a class of I2S specialists, research development professionals could help funders and stakeholders navigate the limitations academicians bring to partnerships. Moreover, they could provide professional development and training for faculty and university leadership in basic I2S concepts and methods to enable them to gain a better understanding of considering unknowns in their research and the most effective mechanisms for extending their findings.

Support for Policy and Practice Change

I2S-trained research development professionals would be important catalysts in perpetuating and extending successful integrative applied research initiatives. With one foot firmly in academia and the flexibility to move the other to a variety of stakeholder domains, these I2S specialists serve as valuable activists in creating highly effective integrative applied research teams. Through principles developed by way of I2S research findings, which include an understanding of how to manage disparate and often conflicting reward and recognition systems, research development professionals could serve to unify team members around a shared goal of translating discoveries and new knowledge from multiple domains into effective policy and practice.

I2S Impact on Research Development, Team Science and the Science of Team Science

While both research development and team science are concerned with cross-disciplinary collaborations that often involve external partners, these areas have been inwardly focused on the academic domains from which both arose. I2S offers an opportunity to change their perspective for the better. Combined with guidance from the science of team science, I2S defines the structures and processes for effective team science to address highly complex real-world societal problems. Research development, in turn, is then better able to focus on the practical issues to enable integrative applied research teams that combine academic and other sector participants by virtue of the lessons from I2S.

The synergies between research development, team science and integrative applied research are exciting. Research development professionals have served as drivers in the team science arena and could be considered as sources of knowledge about advancing I2S as much as they can benefit from I2S training and skill building.

This book is a comprehensive text that will enlighten the research development community and have a strong transformational effect on the practice of team science. The book also carefully lays out a roadmap for integrative applied research and circumspect direction for the development of I2S as a discipline. The science of team science—another emerging discipline—can build on strategies for developing I2S as the roadmap for team science research continues to evolve as well.

Contributed November 2011

Brief Biography

Holly Falk-Krzesinski PhD recently joined Elsevier as the Vice President of Global Academic Relations and Strategic Alliances, having previously served as the Director of Research Team Support and Development at Northwestern University. Her interests focus on translating empirical research findings about team science (the *science* of team science) into evidence-based effective practices for scientific teams, institutional leaders, and funders of collaborative team science (the *praxis* of team science). She is also interested in approaches to evaluating and assessing collaboration and interdisciplinary research effectiveness. As inaugural chair of the Annual International Science of Team Science (SciTS) Conference, she has been instrumental in developing a strong, interdisciplinary community of practice for team science and interdisciplinary training.

59. Integration and Implementation Sciences: How it relates to scientific thinking and public health strategies

Linda Neuhauser[1]

Gabriele Bammer's book is a major contribution to address the critical area of applying scientific knowledge to successful action. In my view, the so-called 'know–do gap'[2] is the single most important barrier to addressing the world's seemingly intractable problems—from poverty to climate change. Integrative applied research has become an area of intense interest and debate. In my view, this is partly because so many efforts to solve difficult problems have failed, and partly because of major shifts in scientific thinking and processes over the past 50 years. I2S aligns well with the new scientific paradigm and offers a welcome approach to reduce the gap between knowledge and action.

In my own work, I have similarly focused on working across disciplines and sectors, especially on health-related problems. In addition, I have been involved in transforming university training so that students will have an appreciation of these issues and the skills to do better. In this commentary, I use a public health perspective. Public health is one of the most interdisciplinary disciplines, both in the university and in real-world settings, and provides an excellent platform on which to build and test the I2S concepts. In this chapter, I comment on the scientific basis for Integration and Implementation Sciences, relevant I2S thinking and action in public health, my experiences heading a UC Berkeley centre that incorporates I2S strategies, and on training students, researchers, practitioners and policy makers in this area.

The Case for Advancing Integration and Implementation Sciences

Bammer argues convincingly for the value of I2S, both theoretically and from her own research experiences. Narrow disciplinary and abstract thinking have had little impact on solving complex global problems. Maintaining rigid disciplinary perspectives not only limits our knowledge about the determinants

---

1   Linda Neuhauser was invited as a 'senior scholar who has made significant contributions to thinking about research translation'.
2   WHO (2004).

of issues, but also constrains our ability to apply research findings towards the development of solutions. While there is little evidence about the uptake of research for effective action, Jensen[3] estimated that, in the health area, even the most successful interventions rarely reach more than 1 per cent of the target population. Our challenge is to develop a research approach that actively integrates knowledge from many disciplines and uses it to promote effective action within the cultural norms and organisational processes of specific settings.[4]

Although Bammer notes that the book is 'based on practice rather than philosophy' (Chapter 2), her thinking reflects the major shifts in the philosophy of science. Before the mid-twentieth century, the dominant 'positivist' view was that 'truth' is knowable and generalisable, and the focus was on discovering the unchanging laws that govern the physical world. In the newer paradigm, 'critical realists' posit that it is impossible to fully perceive the real world and its ever changing causal forces, and that claims about reality should be subjected to the widest possible examination.[5] These now dominant thinkers recommend using multiple theoretical frameworks and methods in diverse settings, and many interpretations of evidence—a process known as 'critical multiplism'.[6]

In this scientific era, 'human sciences' that seek to better understand the seeming unpredictability of people's perceptions and behaviours and 'design, or artificial, sciences' that are concerned 'not with how things are, but with how they might be'[7] have become increasingly important. These sciences draw on theoretical models from many disciplines, and employ a mix of quantitative, qualitative and iterative strategies to investigate phenomena. They are frequently primarily issue or problem based, rather than theoretically driven at the outset. For this reason, they are particularly useful to understand complex problems and invent ways to address them. For example, when developers create novel electronic health communications that include artificial intelligence applications (such as virtual coaches for patients), they usually lack robust models to guide their work. Instead, they typically rely on the heuristics (experience-based approaches to problem solving and discovery) inherent in design sciences to iteratively find a solution by working closely with the intended users.

Bammer's three-domain framework that advocates obtaining knowledge from multiple disciplines and stakeholders, understanding and managing uncertainty, and providing research support for policy and practice action mirrors the major shifts in scientific thinking and processes. The kinds of research questions and

---

3   Jensen (2003).
4   Bammer (2005); Green and Glasgow (2006); Sussman et al. (2006).
5   Cook (1985); Cook and Campbell (1979).
6   Cook (1985).
7   Simon (1996); see also commentary by Cram (Chapter 41).

diverse methods she proposes acknowledge that reality is complex, fraught with unknowns and changeable. Her comprehensive, step-wise model of engaging researchers, policy makers, practitioners and other stakeholders emphasises that knowledge needed for action is affected by different stakeholder viewpoints and contexts, and is only revealed through an intensive process of engagement. I appreciate her recommendation to build I2S using an inductive, problem-based approach—rather than defining an initial theory to test that is not necessarily a good fit with the complexity of this work.

Understanding and adopting the newer scientific paradigm are challenging and, in my view, Bammer's approach aligns well with that goal. It is not surprising that she uses the term 'Big Science' for the ambitious effort to define and implement the I2S work plan.

I2S as a Discipline

As a scientific practice, I2S has indisputable value, but as a number of contributors have commented, it is not yet a 'discipline'. To rise to this level, I2S would need a stronger theoretical foundation, better-defined methods and rigorous testing in multiple contexts. Because I2S is currently a primarily practice-oriented endeavour, there is still a long way to go before it can be considered a discipline. Bammer's proposed I2S Development Drive to build I2S would certainly help catalyse that process.

There is an obvious 'cognitive dissonance' in attempting to create a single discipline that integrates thinking and methods from many disciplines. Bammer suggests that statistics is analogous to how I2S functions as a discipline. The idea is enticing, given that statistics supports research in many individual disciplines, as well as across disciplines, for interdisciplinary work; however, statistics is a field with well-defined theoretical frameworks, methods and a long history of testing. It is more supportable to say that, from a practice point of view, statisticians and the proposed I2S specialists would share some similarities in their interdisciplinary approaches.

I2S in Public Health

A key step in the proposed I2S Development Drive is to gather existing concepts, methods and case examples. I suggest that a focus on I2S elements in public health would be a fruitful way to begin this process. Public health is one of the most interdisciplinary disciplines both within and outside the university. Schools of public health include faculty trained in medicine, sociology, public policy, business, psychology, anthropology, biology, communication, education, economics, law, environmental science, architecture, city planning, government and many other fields, and joint appointments with other disciplinary schools are common. In addition, many public health academics have expertise not only in research, but also in practice with government, communities, policy institutes and/or the private sector. Public health can provide a rich 'laboratory' in which to investigate I2S issues, models and strategies.

Because public health problems intersect biological, behavioural, environmental and other domains, they are inherently complex to understand and to address. Efforts over the past 30 years to examine disciplinary integration and implementation efforts in public health research and interventions[8] could greatly inform I2S development.

The most commonly accepted 'overarching' models in public health are currently social-ecological models that encompass a broad range of disciplinary domains and span all sectoral levels—including individual, family, community, organisations and society.[9] These are also systems models that encompass interactions among components of the model (for example, how smoking policy decisions affect individuals and healthcare institutions, or how community actions impact on the environment).

Definitions and Models of Integration and Implementation in Public Health

The cross-disciplinary definitions 'multidisciplinary', 'interdisciplinary' and 'transdisciplinary' used in public health are similar to those in Bammer's book. Frequently 'interdisciplinary' and 'transdisciplinary' have been used interchangeably; however, there is a general view that transdisciplinarity requires that people from different disciplines work together from the outset and create a new joint concept, theory and/or method. Since 2000, public health efforts in the United States to integrate disciplines have tended to advocate the goal of transdisciplinarity.

In public health, 'implementation' has generally been referred to as 'research translation', which can be defined as '[a]n extended process of how research knowledge that is directly or indirectly relevant to health or well-being eventually

---

8   Neuhauser et al. (2007b).
9   Stokols (2000).

serves the public'.[10] 'Translation' is sometimes referred to as 'dissemination': 'an active and strategically planned process whereby new or existing knowledge, interventions, or practices are spread'.[11]

In the initial public health efforts related to disciplinary integration and implementation/translation, most models focused on either one or the other. For example, Best and colleagues[12] traced the evolution of thinking about translational health. The earliest models portrayed knowledge as a 'product' to be passively transferred from researchers to practitioners to users. The latest translational models emphasise knowledge 'integration' in which knowledge is tightly woven within priorities, culture and contexts. This whole-system perspective means that relationships at all levels are important to assure that scientific findings are effectively adopted.

More recently, public health models that include both disciplinary integration and implementation/translation have started to emerge. Stokols' 'transdisciplinary action research'[13] matrix describes how transdisciplinary research needs to be integrated into a collaborative action (implementation) cycle with three dimensions: analytic scope (biological to policy), organisational scope (intra-organisational to intersectoral) and geographic scope (local to global). Sussman and colleagues' model[14] proposes how cross-disciplinary researchers and practitioners might collaborate at multiple translational phases to transform science into action. These models could provide rich guidance for I2S development. For example, Stokols' use of analytical, organisational and geographic dimensions could be considered to enhance the I2S model. Similarly Sussman and colleagues' emphasis on cyclical phases of interdisciplinary and implementation activity could help refine I2S. Synergistically the proposed I2S approach could help build current public health models and strategies.

In the United States, the National Institutes of Health (NIH) has contributed hundreds of millions of dollars to transdisciplinary and translational research. This funding has helped develop science centres that bring together researchers from multiple disciplines to move science to action.[15] Evaluations of this work could help inform I2S efforts.[16]

---

10   Adapted from Sussman et al. (2006).
11   Kiefer et al. (2005, p. 14).
12   Best et al. (2008).
13   Stokols (2006).
14   Sussman et al. (2006).
15   National Institutes of Health (2005).
16   Stokols et al. (2005).

Linking Research and Practice: The Health Research for Action model

Both Bammer and the commentators cite fundamental challenges to forging strong relationships between researchers from various disciplines and the policymakers and practitioners they are to support with integrative applied research. These include the perceived importance of separating research activities from direct implementation, as well as the differing perceptions, work styles, time, budget constraints and motivations of these groups. The book identifies excellent ways to strengthen researcher–stakeholder relationships; however, my views—shaped by shifts in scientific thinking and by my own experiences—differ from those presented in a number of important areas. I will start with what I have learned from doing integrative applied research.

Twenty years ago, I was involved in creating what is now known as the Health Research for Action Center at the University of California, Berkeley School of Public Health.[17] The impetus to develop the centre came from recognising that many public health efforts have been unsuccessful and that doing better will involve a broader understanding of cross-disciplinary factors that influence health and more powerful strategies to translate research into effective interventions. We designed the centre to include researchers, practitioners and policy makers who would work together on health issues and interventions. The idea was to concurrently bring together academics from multiple disciplines and have them engage with stakeholders from many sectors (including policy makers, representatives of community organisations, individuals and families affected by the issues, media experts and other groups). We chose to use highly participatory processes to ensure that we were tightly connected to the affected audiences as well as to the many relevant stakeholders—to understand issues and act on them.

Having researchers, practitioners and policymakers working together in one physical space and reaching out to many stakeholders in local communities, States, nationally or internationally has helped us reduce the common I2S barriers among these groups. We have learned that closely linking researchers across disciplines and stakeholders in many sectors is critical to produce rigorous, meaningful research and successful interventions. Interestingly although we did not have the benefit of the detailed I2S guidance in this book, we have experimented with and adopted many of the I2S engagement practices recommended in the book, such as scoping, involving stakeholders in advisory

---

17 <http:www.healthresearchforaction.org> (accessed 14 February 2012).

committees, holding 'executive sessions' for policy makers, and focusing on communication. Our integrative applied research approach is central to our success in large-scale interventions.[18]

In light of these experiences, I suggest that I2S advocates more boldly for closer connections between researchers and stakeholders. For example, consider this statement in Chapter 17:

> For researchers, this involves performing at least four important functions—namely
>
> 1. making available what is known, including what has worked and has not worked, so that policy makers and practitioners can develop effective actions
>
> 2. providing a digest of remaining unknowns to help policy makers and practitioners take these into account in their decision making, as well as to reduce, or at least be better prepared for, unintended consequences of their initiatives
>
> 3. providing critique of current and proposed policy and practice
>
> 4. providing new ideas for policy and practice.

I argue that knowledge is not a product delivered by researchers to stakeholders to implement, but is created by both groups working together synergistically from the outset. Likewise, that partnership should ideally extend to jointly developing and implementing interventions. For example, our centre staff was involved with both research and implementation of a parenting education kit for 500 000 parents in the United States.[19] A major reason for the success of this program was the highly participatory process among researchers, policy makers, practitioners and parents. Research findings iteratively influenced the design and refinement of the project, and stakeholders helped define research issues and interpret the results.

Current scientific thinking also supports the view that researchers and stakeholders should work closely from the outset—so that the phenomena studied are truly understood, and so that interventions and policies are successful. Human and design sciences provide good guidance about such collaborative processes. Obviously, it is difficult for researchers to transition from the traditional approach of providing study findings *to* stakeholders who are expected to implement them, to one in which researchers and stakeholders are intimately bound up in both investigation and change. The book provides

---

18   See Neuhauser (2010); Neuhauser et al. (2009).
19   Neuhauser (2010); Neuhauser et al. (2007a).

strong guidance about integrating researchers across disciplines, but not enough about engaging stakeholders in the research process. In my view, the processes to integrate stakeholders must be as explicit as those for researchers.

Training in I2S: A UC Berkeley model

Bammer's book advocates strongly for training a cadre of I2S specialists, including different levels of training for: 1) leaders, 2) disciplinary specialists, 3) other integrative applied research team members, and 4) policy makers and practitioners. She recommends that leaders be adept at managing the processes and that they have a detailed understanding of the many relevant barriers and facilitators; that disciplinary experts have a good understanding of concepts and processes and specific understanding of case examples; that other team members have a general understanding of I2S; and that policy makers and practitioners have a similar appreciation of I2S and what research teams can offer.

Some commentators in this book had concerns about the feasibility of training cross-disciplinary experts, given the tenacious hold of disciplines on research. I agree with these concerns, but suggest a more optimistic path forward from my own experience. Like all universities, UC Berkeley is organised around disciplines. A notable exception is our School of Public Health, which focuses on cross-disciplinary issues, has faculty from varied disciplines and many intersectoral partnerships, as mentioned earlier.

School leaders have recognised the need to train students in high-level skills to integrate knowledge across disciplines and implement it in real-world settings. Similarly, for the past two decades, US public health leaders and national mandates have called for training of transdisciplinary scientists and researcher-practitioners.[20] Educator Ernest Boyer proposed that university education should foster a stronger link between research and its translation into action.[21] His view of an 'engaged university' that would integrate knowledge across disciplines and focus on collaborative approaches to solve important problems is well aligned with I2S goals. A major challenge has been to translate theoretical guidance into practical curricula.

In 1996, our school decided to create a Doctor of Public Health (DrPH) program that would include all the public health sub-disciplines and connect with many other disciplines on campus.[22] The program was launched in 2000 and has an explicit transdisciplinary and problem-based orientation to research,

---

20   Nash et al. (2003); Stokols (2006).
21   Boyer (1990).
22   For details, see Neuhauser et al. (2007b).

and an emphasis on translating research to action in multiple sectors. Admitted students are required to have a graduate degree in a field relevant to health (such as medicine, sociology, statistics, education, and so on), professional experience and evidence of leadership qualities. Each student cohort is selected to have a mix of disciplinary backgrounds and interests. Students are trained in cross-disciplinary areas, multi-method research, and in leadership and communication skills. Their dissertation research typically is problem based, rather than limited to testing theory. Students do a field residency to address practical health issues with stakeholder groups. The program has been very effective and DrPH graduates are successful in finding senior-level work in academia, government, community organisations, policy institutes, consulting, and often in combinations of these areas.

There are intriguing parallels between this program and skills advocated for I2S leaders and disciplinary specialists. My view is that it may be hard to train I2S specialists who do not have some kind of disciplinary home, because they need university support and a practical career path. An alternative route is to begin training I2S experts within disciplines that have strong interdisciplinary connections and a practice base. I also suggest that such training be highly problem based, rather than just focused on a skill set. My experience has been that people only learn these skills when engaged in addressing specific issues. The Berkeley DrPH program is one such promising model of I2S training.

Suggestions to Move Forward with I2S

In summary, Bammer's book takes on the very important areas of advancing integrative applied research to address complex problems and creating an I2S discipline. I appreciate that Bammer has begun with a practice orientation to develop I2S—a pragmatic approach that should ensure that this field meets researchers', practitioners' and policy makers' needs as it evolves.

I2S represents a radical change in the traditional approach to research, but one that is well supported by current scientific thinking. Overall, I like the proposed I2S framework. My main suggestion is that there is a stronger emphasis on the importance of a very close collaboration between researchers and stakeholders, and more explicit guidance about strategies to engage stakeholders. Both groups have important and, ultimately, equal roles in creating knowledge and applying it to address problems. I also recommend that all aspects of this work be as problem oriented as possible, to ground and motivate those engaged with it, and to build a 'business case' about its value.

The proposed I2S Development Drive is certainly ambitious, but warranted by the seriousness of the problem it intends to address. If such a 'Big Science' effort were not possible to fund, smaller incremental efforts would still be valuable. In fact, given the iterative nature of I2S work, it might be preferable to allow more time for reflection and refinement of this emerging field. As a next step, I suggest finding support for: 1) several meetings of people interested in I2S to discuss selected Drive issues and refine a two-year work plan; 2) synthesis of available information about I2S in several discrete areas; and 3) experimental training of I2S in a university or field setting. No matter which directions are taken to develop I2S, it is time to move ahead with this important work.

Contributed December 2011

References

Bammer, G. (2005). 'Integration and Implementation Sciences: building a new specialization'. *Ecology and Society*, 10 (2): article 6; <www.ecologyandsociety. org/vol10/iss2/art6>

Best, A., Hiatt, R. A. and Norman, C. D. (2008). 'Knowledge integration: conceptualizing communications in cancer control systems'. *Patient Education and Counseling*, 71 (3): 319–27.

Boyer, E. L. (1990). *Scholarship Reconsidered: Priorities of the professoriate*. Princeton, NJ: Carnegie Foundation for the Advancement of Teaching.

Cook, T. (1985). 'Postpositivist critical multiplism'. In: Shotland, R. and Mark, M. (eds). *Social Science and Social Policy*. Beverly Hills, CA: Sage, 25–62.

Cook, T. and Campbell, D. (1979). *Quasi-Experimentation: Design and analysis issues for field settings*. Boston, MA: Houghton Mifflin.

Green, L. W. and Glasgow, R. E. (2006). 'Evaluating the relevance, generalization, and applicability of research: issues in external validation and translation methodology'. *Evaluation and the Health Professions*, 29 (1): 126–53.

Jensen, P. S. (2003). 'Commentary: the next generation is overdue'. *Journal of the American Academy of Adolescent Psychiatry*, 42 (5): 527–30.

Kiefer, L., Frank, J., Di Ruggerio, E., Dobbins, M., Manuel, D., Gully, P. R. and Mowat, D. (2005). 'Fostering evidence-based decision-making in Canada: examining the need for a Canadian population and public health evidence centre and research network'. *Canadian Journal of Public Health*, 96 (3): I1– I19.

Nash, J. M., Collins, B. N., Loughlin, S. E., Solbrig, M., Harvey, R., Krishnan-Sarin, S. et al. (2003). 'Training the transdisciplinary scientist: a general framework applied to tobacco behavior'. *Nicotine and Tobacco Research*, 5 (Supplement 1): S41–S53.

National Institutes of Health. (2005). *Overview of the NIH Roadmap*. Bethesda, MD: National Institutes of Health; <http://commonfund.nih.gov/aboutroadmap.aspx> (accessed 15 January 2013).

Neuhauser, L. (2010). 'Creating and implementing large-scale parenting education programs: bridging research, decision-making and practice'. In: Bammer, G. with, Michaux, A. and Sanson, A. (eds). *Bridging the 'Know–Do' Gap: Knowledge brokering to improve child wellbeing*. Canberra: ANU E Press; <http://epress.anu.edu.au/knowledge_citation.html>

Neuhauser, L., Constantine, W. L., Constantine, N. A., Sokal-Gutierrez, K., Obarski, S. K., Clayton, L., Desai, M., Sumner, G. and Syme, S. L. (2007a). 'Promoting prenatal and early childhood health: evaluation of a statewide materials-based intervention for parents'. *American Journal of Public Health*, 97 (10): 813–19.

Neuhauser, L., Richardson, D., Mackenzie, S. and Minkler, M. (2007b). 'Advancing transdisciplinary and translational research practice: issues and models of doctoral education in public health'. *Journal of Research Practice*, 3 (2): article M19; <http://jrp.icaap.org/index.php/jrp/article/view/103/97> (accessed 9 August 2012).

Neuhauser, L., Rothschild, B., Graham, C., Ivey, S. and Konishi, S. (2009). 'Participatory design of mass health communication in three languages for seniors and people with disabilities on Medicaid'. *American Journal of Public Health*, 99 (December): 2188–95.

Simon, H. (1996). *The Sciences of the Artificial*. Third Edition. Cambridge, MA: MIT Press.

Stokols, D. (2000). 'Social ecology and behavioral medicine: implications for training, practice, and policy'. *Behavioral Medicine*, 26: 129–38.

Stokols, D. (2006). 'Toward a science of transdisciplinary research'. *American Journal of Community Psychology*, 38: 63–77.

Stokols, D., Harvey, R., Gress, J., Fuqua, J. and Phillips, K. (2005). 'In vivo studies of transdisciplinary scientific collaboration: lessons learned and implications for active living research'. *American Journal of Preventive Medicine*, 28 (Supplement 2): 202–13.

Sussman, S., Valente, T. W., Rohrbach, L. A., Skara, S. and Pentz, M. A. (2006). 'Translation in the health professions: converting science into action'. *Evaluation and the Health Professions*, 29 (1): 7–32.

World Health Organisation (WHO). (2004). *World Report on Knowledge for Better Health*. Geneva: World Health Organisation; <http://www.who.int/rpc/wr2004> (accessed 9 August 2012).

Brief Biography

Linda Neuhauser DrPH is Clinical Professor of Community Health and Human Development at the University of California, Berkeley School of Public Health. Her research, teaching and practice are focused on using participatory approaches to translate research findings into improved health interventions that are relevant to people's needs and social contexts. She is principal investigator of the UC Berkeley Health Research for Action Center that works with diverse groups to research a broad range of health issues and to 'co-create' effective solutions. She helped design the current UC Berkeley Doctor of Health Program that trains students in integrative applied research. She was previously a US health officer in West and Central Africa.

Made in the USA
San Bernardino, CA
24 May 2019